...ptides
as Antigens

LABORATORY TECHNIQUES IN BIOCHEMISTRY AND MOLECULAR BIOLOGY

Edited by

P.C. van der Vliet — *Department for Physiological Chemistry, University of Utrecht, Utrecht, Netherlands*

Volume 28

ELSEVIER

AMSTERDAM – LAUSANNE – NEW YORK – OXFORD – SHANNON – SINGAPORE – TOKYO

SYNTHETIC PEPTIDES
AS ANTIGENS

M. H. V. Van Regenmortel
S. Muller

UPR 9021 Immunochimie des Peptides & Virus
I.B.M.C., CNRS, 15 rue René Descartes
67084 Strasbourg Cedex, France

1999
ELSEVIER
AMSTERDAM – LAUSANNE – NEW YORK – OXFORD – SHANNON – SINGAPORE – TOKYO

ELSEVIER SCIENCE B.V.
Sara Burgerhartstraat 25
P.O. Box 211, 1000 AE Amsterdam, The Netherlands

First edition 1999

Library of Congress Cataloging in Publication Data
A catalog record from the Library of Congress has been applied for.

British Library Cataloguing in Publication Data
A catalogue record from the British Library has been applied for.

ISBN: 0-444-82175-9 (library edition)
ISBN: 0-444-82176-7 (pocket edition)
ISBN: 0-7204-4200-1 (series)

Transferred to digital printing 2006

Printed and bound by CPI Antony Rowe, Eastbourne

Acknowledgements

We are grateful to the many colleagues who read parts of the book and suggested various improvements. We are particularly indebted to Fred Brown, Kieran F. Geoghegan, Patricia L. Domen, Francis Schuber, David A. Isenberg, Christiane Stussi-Garaud, for helpful suggestions. We also thank Suzanne Wencker and Nathalie Uhlmann for very efficient secretarial help.

Acknowledgments

We are grateful to the many colleagues who read parts of the book and suggested various improvements. We are particularly indebted to Phil Brown, Byron R Googlegan, Patrick G Donnan, Francis Sanchez, David A Isenberg, Christine Slessi-Green, for helpful suggestions. We also thank Suzanne Worsley and Belinda Osborne for very efficient secretarial help.

List of abbreviations

Ab	antibody
ABH	azido benzoyl hydrazide
Ag	antigen
AIDS	acquired immune deficiency syndrome
AMV	alfalfa mosaic virus
APC	antigen-presenting cell
APG	*p*-azidophenylglyoxal monohydrate
BB Gly (Lys)	benzoylbenzoyl glycine (lysine)
BDB	bisdiazobenzidine
Boc	*tert*-butyloxycarbonyl
BP	bullous pemphigoid
BSA	bovine serum albumin
CaMV	cauliflower mosaic virus
cDNA	complementary DNA
CDR	complementarity determining region
CFA	complete Freund's adjuvant
CIE	counter-immunoelectrophoresis
CPG	control pore glass
CPV	canine parvovirus
CS	circumsporozoite
CTL	cytotoxic T lymphocyte
DMA	dimethyl adipimidate
DMF	dimethyl formamide
DMP	dimethyl pimelimidate
DMS	dimethyl suberimidate
DNP	2,4-dinitrophenol
DPPE	dipalmitoyl phosphatidylethanolamine
DTPB	dimethyl 3,3′-dithiobisproprionimidate

EBIZ	N-ethylbenzisoxazolium fluoborate
ECL	enhanced chemiluminescence
EDC	1-ethyl-3-(3-dimethylamino propyl) carbodiimide hydrochloride
EDTA	ethylenediaminetetraacetic acid
ELISA	enzyme-linked immunosorbent assay
Fab	fragment of antibody containing one binding site
FITC	fluorescein isothiocyanate
Fc	crystallizable fragment
FMDV	foot-and-mouth disease virus
Fmoc	9-fluorenylmethyloxycarbonyl
FPLC	fast protein liquid chromatography
GFLV	grapevine fanleaf virus
gp	glycoprotein
HA	haemagglutinin
HBV	hepatitis B Virus
HBsAg	hepatitis B surface antigen
HEL	hen-egg lysozyme
Hepes	N-2-hydroxyethylpiperazine-N'-2 ethanesulfonic acid
HF	hydrogen fluoride
HIV	human immunodeficiency virus
HLA	human leucocyte antigen
HPLC	high-performance liquid chromatography
HSV	herpes simplex virus
HTLV	human T cell leukemia virus
IBCF	isobutylchloroformate
id	intradermal
IFA	incomplete Freund's adjuvant
im	intramuscular
ip	intraperitoneal
IPTG	isopropyl-β-D galactopyranoside
K_a	equilibrium association constant
k_a	kinetic association constant
k_d	kinetic dissociation constant
kD	kilodalton
KLH	keyhole limpet haemocyanin
LDH	lactate dehydrogenase

LH-RH	luteinizing hormone-releasing hormone
mAb, Mab	monoclonal antibody
MAP	multiple antigen peptide
MBS	m-maleimidobenzoyl N-hydroxysuccinimide ester
MCDI	1-cyclohexyl-3-(2-morpholinyl-4-ethyl) carbodiimide methyl-p-toluene sulfonate
MCS	6-maleimidocaproic acyl N-hydroxysuccinimide ester
MCTD	mixed connective tissue disease
MDP	muramyl dipeptide
Me	methyl
MEV	mink enteritis virus
MHC	major histocompatibility complex
MHS	6-(N-maleimido)-n hexanoate
Mo-MuLV	Moloney leukemia virus
Mo-MuSV	Moloney murine sarcoma virus
MPB-PE	N-(4-(p-maleimidophenyl) butyryl) phosphatidylethanolamine
MPL	monophosphoryl lipid A
Mr	molecular ratio
MV	measles virus
NHS-	N-hydroxysuccinimide
OD	optical density
OVA	ovalbumin
PAGE	polyacrylamide gel electrophoresis
PARP	poly(ADP ribose polymer)ase
P_3C	tripalmitoyl-s-glycerylcysteine
PBS	phosphate-buffered saline
PBS-T	phosphate buffered saline containing Tween
PC	phosphatidylcholine
PCNA	proliferating cell nuclear antigen
PDEA	2-(2-pyridinyldithiol)ethaneamine hydrochloride
PE	phosphatidyl ethanolamine
p.f.u.	plaque-forming units
PG	phosphatidyl glycerol
PLGA	poly(lactic-coglyolic)acid
pMHC	peptide-MHC complex
pSS	primary Sjögren's syndrome
RA	rheumatoid arthritis

RAS	Ribi adjuvant system
REV	reverse phase evaporation vesicle
RIA	radioimmunoassay
RNP	ribonucleoprotein particle
RU	resonance unit
sc	subcutaneous
SD	standard deviation
SDS	sodium dodecyl sulfate
SIAB	N-succinimidyl(4-iodoacetyl)aminobenzoate
SLE	systemic lupus erythematosus
SMCC	succinimidyl 4-(N-maleimidomethyl) cyclohexane 1 carboxylate
SMPB	succinimidyl 4-(p-maleimidophenyl) butyrate
SMPT	succinimidyl oxycarbonyl-α-methyl-α (2 pyridyldithio)-toluene
SOC	sequential oligopeptide carrier
SPDP	N-succinimidyl 3-(2-pyridyldithio) propionate
SPR	surface plasmon resonance
SS	Sjögren's syndrome
SSV	simian sarcoma virus
SUV	small unilamellar vesicle
SV 40	simian virus 40
TASP	template-assembled synthetic proteins (peptides)
TBS	tris-buffered saline
TCR	T-cell receptor
TDM	trehalose dimycolate
TLC	thin-layer chromatography
TMV	tobacco mosaic virus
TMVP	tobacco mosaic virus protein
Tris	tris(hydroxymethyl) aminomethane
TSH	human thyroprotein
TT	tetanus toxoid
VSV	vesicular stomatitis virus
VP	viral protein

Contents

Chapter 3.   *Immunization with peptides* 133
S. Muller

CHAPTER 1

Molecular dissection of protein antigens and the prediction of epitopes

1.1. Introduction

Interest in the immunological properties of synthetic peptides stems mainly from the fact that peptides can be used to mimic the antigenic sites of proteins. Since most antigens of biological interest are proteins, one of the major goals of molecular immunology has been to elucidate the antigenic structure of proteins. The development by Merrifield (1963) of the solid-phase method of peptide synthesis made it much easier to obtain short fragments of a protein by synthesis rather than by enzymatic or chemical cleavage of the protein. Natural fragments obtained by cleavage of a protein must be separated from each other, and since the level of purity required for immunological studies is extremely high, this is often no mean task. Indeed, if a fragment of a protein devoid of antigenicity is contaminated by a small amount of a highly reactive antigenic fragment derived from the same molecule, this may lead to the erroneous conclusion that the major, inactive peptide component is antigenic. Such misinterpretations are eliminated when synthetic fragments are used to locate antigenicity in proteins.

In an earlier version of this book (Van Regenmortel et al., 1988), a chapter was included which reviewed for the non-specialist the laboratory methods used in solid-phase peptide synthesis. In the intervening years, numerous texts have appeared which can be consulted for guidance on the procedures of peptide synthesis (Fields,

1997; Grant, 1992; Lloyd-Williams et al., 1997; Pennington and Dunn, 1994).

The molecular dissection of protein antigens has been undertaken, not only to increase our understanding of immunological specificity, but also because such knowledge makes it possible to manipulate the immune system and leads to many useful practical applications in molecular biology, biochemistry and microbiology. For instance, increasing knowledge of the location of antigenic sites in toxins, viruses and parasites has led to many attempts to develop new synthetic peptide vaccines (Arnon, 1987; Arnon and Van Regenmortel 1992; Francis, 1994; Nicholson, 1994b; Van Regenmortel and Neurath, 1990). It was found, for instance, that protective immunity could be elicited against foot-and-mouth disease, influenza, hepatitis B and cholera by immunizing animals with synthetic peptides (see Chapter 8, this volume). Synthetic peptides are also increasingly replacing intact proteins as reagents for the diagnosis of viral and autoimmune diseases (see Chapters 6 and 7).

Another major application of synthetic peptides relies on their ability to elicit antipeptide antibodies that cross-react with the corresponding complete protein. Such antibodies have been found to be extremely useful reagents for isolating and characterizing gene products (Boersma et al., 1993; Lerner, 1984; Walter, 1986). Because of advances in gene cloning and sequencing, the information on protein sequences is nowadays nearly always derived from nucleotide sequence analysis. In many cases, the protein is not available in sufficient quantity for conventional chemical studies, or its presence in the cell may even be in doubt. By synthesizing a peptide fragment of the putative protein inferred from nucleic acid sequencing and raising antibodies against it, it is possible to isolate and characterize the protein using appropriate immunoassays (see Chapter 5).

For many years the antigenic properties of proteins were defined only in terms of B-cell epitopes recognized by antibodies and B-cell receptors. Once it was established that antigens were also specifically recognized by T cells, a second type of epitope known as a

T-cell epitope was defined which corresponds to linear fragments of the antigen capable of interacting with T-cell receptors. In the absence of further qualification, the term 'epitope' is used to denote a B-cell epitope, and this convention will be used in the present text. Sections 1.2–1.6 of this chapter discuss B-cell epitopes, while Section 1.7 is devoted to T-cell epitopes.

1.2. Definition of antigenicity and the concept of epitope

The antigenic reactivity of a protein refers to its capacity to bind specifically to the functional binding sites or paratopes of certain immunoglobulin (Ig) molecules. When such a binding is observed experimentally, the particular Ig becomes known as an antibody specific for the protein.

Immunoglobulin molecules are heterodimers consisting of four polypeptide chains linked by disulphide bridges (Nezlin, 1994). There are two identical heavy (H) chains of 450–600 amino acid residues and two light (L) chains of about 220 residues. The sequence of the N-terminal domain of both H and L chains differs in antibodies of different specificity and are called variable (V) regions, while the remaining domains in each chain are invariant and are called constant (C) regions. Within each V region, three segments exhibit sequence hypervariability and form the complementarity determining region (CDR) of the Ig. The most common type of Ig is known as IgG and contains a H chain called γ. Immunoglobulins can be cleaved at the middle of their H chains by various proteases (Nezlin, 1994). Papain cleaves γ-chains at the N-terminal side of the disulphide bridges that keep the H chains together, thereby generating two fragment antigen binding (Fab) fragments and one fragment crystallizable (Fc) fragment. Each Fab fragment contains at its tip one of the two identical combining sites (or paratopes) of the Ig constituted by the three CDRs of the H chain and the three CDRs of the L chain (Fig 1.1). The CDR loops vary not only in sequence but also in the length from one antibody

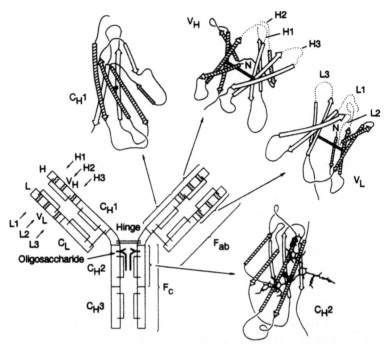

Fig. 1.1. Schematic representation of an antibody molecule (human subclass IgG 1). The homologous domains within the H and L chains are indicated, as well as the hypervariable segments within the V regions. Inter- and intrachain disulphide bridges are indicated by solid lines. The folding of the polypeptide chain within individual domains is also shown: the arrows represent strands of β-sheets, the solid bars are the intradomain disulphide bridges, and the homologous four-stranded sheets of each domain are cross-hatched. The location of the hypervariable loop regions (H1-3, L1-3) may be seen within the V domains. An N-linked oligosaccharide chain covers part of the four-stranded face of each CH2 domain. (From Sutton, 1993, with permission.)

to the next (Lesk and Tramontano, 1993). Each paratope is capable of binding specifically to an area of about 28×28 Å of its complementary antigen.

The portion of the antigen that is recognized by the paratope of the antibody constitutes an antigenic determinant or epitope of the antigen. The size of the antigen surface in contact with each antibody molecule covers an area of about 800 $Å^2$ which corresponds to an antibody footprint. The entire accessible surface of a protein antigen consists of a large number of overlapping epitopes (Benjamin et al., 1984) and the same residues may be involved in a number of different epitopes built up from individual atomic groups that interact in a unique manner with different paratopes (Malby et al., 1994; McCoy et al., 1997). As illustrated in Fig. 1.2, the orientation of the CDR loops with respect to the epitope may vary for different paratopes (Lescar et al., 1995). This figure also shows that the same antigenic area can be recognized by two paratopes that possess no sequence similarity. The converse situation also exists since the same antibody may recognize two epitopes (usually termed 'mimotopes') devoid of any sequence similarity (Geysen et al., 1987).

It is important to realize that the recognition between epitope and paratope does not take place at the level of whole residues but at the level of individual atoms. The reason why peptides showing little sequence similarity sometimes cross-react with the same antibody is because only a minority of the atoms of any residue actually participate in the interaction. As illustrated schematically in Fig. 1.3, similar atomic groups present in different residues may interact with the same atoms of the paratope. In addition, different atomic groups in the residues of two cross-reacting peptides may also interact with different individual atoms in the paratope. This leads to antigenic cross-reactivities between peptides that would not be expected to occur if whole residues were viewed as the units of recognition (Berzofsky, 1985; Jerne, 1960).

In the same way that the antibody nature of an Ig is identified only when its complementary antigen has been recognized, the epitope nature of a set of amino acids in a protein can be established only by finding an Ig capable of binding to it (Van Regenmortel, 1989). Both epitopes and paratopes are thus relational entities defined by their mutual complementarity. Furthermore, since the occurrence of a binding reaction is required for identifying the in-

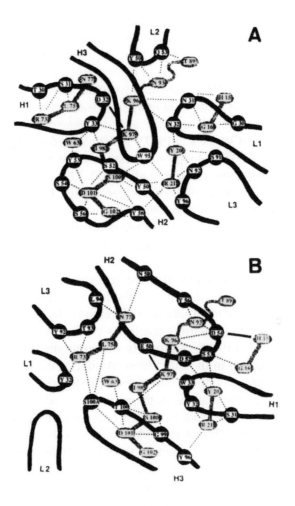

Fig. 1.2. Schematic view of the intermolecular contacts (dotted lines) showing the relative orientation of the CDRs of two monoclonal antibodies (Mabs) binding to the same antigenic site of lysozyme. Note the absence of any sequence similarity in the two sets of CDRs. (A) Mab F9–13.7; (B) Mab HyHEL-10. The lysozyme polypeptide chain is represented in light grey and the CDRs in black. Salt bridges with antibody residues E50, D52, D54 and D32 are indicated by thick lines. (Adapted from Lescar et al., 1995, with permission.)

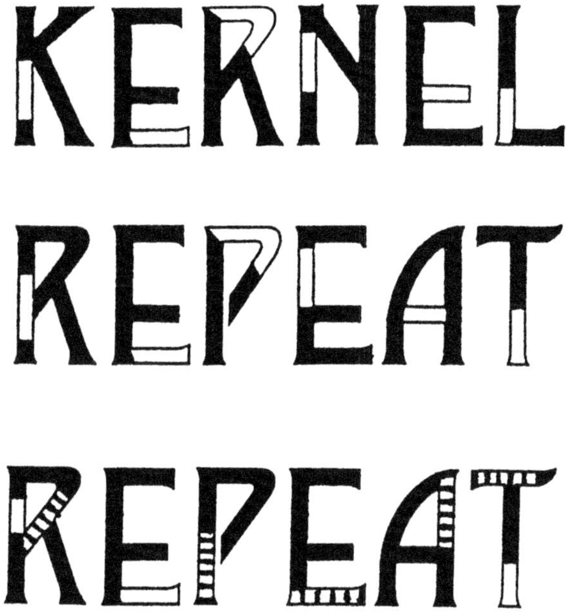

KERNEL

REPEAT

REPEAT

Fig. 1.3. Schematic illustration showing how the antigenic cross-reactivity between two dissimilar peptide sequences represented by their one-letter amino acid
symbols could arise because the same atomic groups (white areas) within each
residue interact with atomic groups of the antibody. It is also possible for different
atomic groups (hatched areas) of the cross-reactive peptide to interact with other
individual atoms within the antibody binding pocket. Such cross-reactivities would
not be expected when whole residues are viewed as the units of recognition.

teracting partners, it is the functional activity during the binding
process that makes it possible to define each of the two partners. In other words, the concept of epitope is dependent on the
process of binding to a complementary partner, and cannot be defined by a structure identifiable before the interaction has taken
place. Studies of antigen-antibody interactions at the molecular
level have shown that attempts to describe epitopes as static structures independently of the process of binding cannot give a full
account of antigenic recognition. Early crystallographic studies of

antigen-antibody complexes led to the conclusion that the inter-acting surfaces of the two reactants are not altered by the process of binding (Mariuzza et al., 1987). However, subsequent crystal-lographic analysis showed that binding often involves a significant amount of induced fit or mutual adaptation of the two partners (Bhat et al., 1990; Fischmann et al., 1991; Rini et al., 1992; Wilson et al., 1994).

In spite of the major contribution provided by structural analy-sis to our understanding of immunological interactions, antigenic specificity cannot be fully described only in terms of three-dimensional structures, since it is necessary to incorporate the fourth dimension of time inherent in all binding activity mea-surements (Greenspan, 1992; Van Regenmortel, 1989, 1996). The concept of structure is actually derived from the selective attention given to the visual representation of an object at a specific time. The structure of an epitope is thus only a visual time slice in a dynamic process of interaction.

An epitope is not an intrinsic structural feature of a protein exist-ing independently of its paratope partner, but it is a relational entity recognizable only through the complementary paratope. The source and origin of the antibody used to identify a particular protein epi-tope are irrelevant. Usually, the antibody is obtained from an animal immunized with the protein in question, but it could also originate from an animal immunized with a related antigen possessing either the same or a cross-reacting epitope. The antibody could even be derived from a nonimmunized animal (Dighiero et al., 1985) or from an animal for which the immunizing stimulus is unknown. For instance, antibodies derived from autoimmune mice have been found to recognize epitopes in DNA and in histones (Muller and Van Regenmortel, 1993).

Some authors are reluctant to define epitopes only in terms of their antigenic reactivity, i.e. their ability to bind to paratopes, for they consider that the concept of epitope also involves the property known as immunogenicity. Immunogenicity refers to the ability of a protein to induce an immune response and depends on host factors such as the Ig gene repertoire, self-tolerance, and various regulatory mechanisms (Sercarz and Berzofsky, 1987). Atassi (1984), for instance, has argued that the regions in myoglobin consisting of residues 1–6 and 121–127 are not epitopes of the protein, because he could not find any antibodies recognizing these peptides in the antimyoglobin sera he examined. The fact that peptides 1–6 and 121–127, when injected as free or conjugated peptides, were capable of inducing antibodies that recognized the myoglobin molecule was not taken as a sufficient criterion for considering them as myoglobin epitopes (Atassi and Young, 1985). According to Atassi (1984), therefore, an epitope refers to a region of a protein that is recognized by antibodies and lymphocytes receptors during the immune response when the whole protein is used as an immunogen. Such a viewpoint, which makes the existence of epitopes in a protein dependent on immunogenetic and immunoregulatory mechanisms of the immunized host, will not be followed in the present text. A different viewpoint will be adhered to, namely, that epitopes need not possess both antigenic reactivity and immunogenicity at all times and under all conditions. When the two properties are dissociated, there is no difficulty in admitting that a self-antigen that is nonimmunogenic in the tolerant autologous animal nevertheless possesses epitopes. It is, indeed, customary to distinguish between the antigenic reactivity and the immunogenicity of proteins, and it seems equally important to apply the same distinction to epitopes. In practice, this means for instance, that a region of a protein that does not appear to be immunogenic when the whole protein is used for immunization may be given the status of epitope when it is found to bind to antibodies induced by a peptide fragment of the protein. It should be noted that a protein epitope may appear to be nonimmunogenic simply because it is not immunodominant when the complete protein molecule is injected in a particular animal. Since the phenomenon of immunodominance is poorly understood, the definition of epitope adopted here circumvents the difficulties that would arise if one were to use the relative strength of immune responses as a criterion for the recognition of epitopes.

Another difficulty in defining epitopes arises from the fact that the antigenic reactivity of a protein is not the same in the native and denatured forms of the molecule. It is thus important to specify whether, or not, the epitopes being studied pertain to the native protein. This problem has become particularly relevant because of the popularity of solid-phase immunoassays (see Chapter 4). When proteins are adsorbed to a layer of plastic in such assays, they tend to undergo some physical distortion or denaturation and, in many cases, the epitopes corresponding to the native state are not preserved (Darst et al., 1988; Friguet et al., 1984; Jemmerson, 1987; Kennel, 1982; Mierendorf and Dimond, 1983; Soderquist and Walton, 1980). In order to ascertain whether, or not, antibodies elicited by peptides derived from a given protein truly recognize the 'native' form of the protein, it is necessary to test these antibodies in a liquid-phase type of assay that preserves the original conformation of the protein antigen (Spangler, 1991).

1.3. Types of epitopes

It is customary to divide epitopes into a number of conceptual categories that are not easily distinguished experimentally. Most commonly, epitopes are classified as either continuous or discontinuous (Atassi and Smith, 1978), depending on whether the residues involved in the epitope are contiguous in the polypeptide chain, or not (Fig. 1.4). This classification has mostly replaced the earlier distinction between sequential (or linear) and conformational epitopes (Sela, 1969). A peptide was said to correspond to a conformational epitope if it adopts in solution a conformation similar to that present in the corresponding region of the native protein. Antibodies to conformational epitopes were considered to be specific for this conformation and unable to recognize the corresponding unfolded peptide. On the other hand, antibodies to sequential epitopes were expected to bind to unfolded polypeptides which had not retained the original conformation present in the native protein. It should

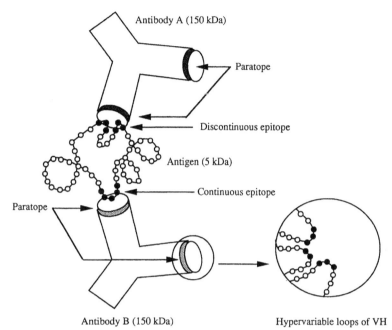

Fig. 1.4. Schematic representation of two antibodies reacting with a continuous and a discontinuous epitope of a protein antigen. If the individual loops of a discontinuous epitope are able to bind to the antibody on their own, they may be given the status of continuous epitope. The insert shows the three CDR loops of an antibody VH chain that contribute to the paratope. If some of these loops are able to bind to the antigen on their own, they may be considered continuous paratopes.

be stressed that antibodies that bind to a sequential epitope nevertheless recognize a certain conformation in the peptide, but one that is different from the native protein conformation. Thus, sequential epitopes should not be equated with conformation-independent epitopes.

The label 'continuous epitope' is given to any short, linear peptide fragment of the antigen capable of binding to antibodies raised against the intact protein. Because the peptide fragment does not usually retain the conformation present in the folded protein and mostly represents only a portion of more complex epitope, it tends to react only weakly with the antiprotein antibodies.

The second type of epitope, known as 'discontinuous epitope', is believed to represent the vast majority of epitopes present in proteins. Discontinuous epitopes are made up of residues that are not contiguous in the sequence, but are brought into spatial proximity by the folding of the polypeptide chain (Fig. 1.4). When the protein is fragmented into a number of peptides, the residues originating from the distant parts of the sequence that made up the discontinuous epitope are scattered, and each constitutive component is usually no longer recognized by the antibody. As a rule, antibodies to discontinuous epitopes will recognize the antigen only if the protein molecule is intact and its native conformation preserved. There are exceptions, however, and an antibody raised against a discontinuous epitope may sometimes react with a short linear stretch of residues present within the discontinuous structure. If the tertiary structure of the protein is unknown, such an antibody may then be considered to be directed to a continuous epitope. The extent to which continuous epitopes identified by antibody binding to short peptides actually represent subregions of more complex discontinuous epitopes is difficult to ascertain. In general, it is concluded that an antibody is directed to a discontinuous epitope if it fails to react with any linear peptide fragment of the antigen molecule.

Although this classification is widely used, the borderline between continuous and discontinuous epitopes is rather fuzzy as is frequently the case with boundaries in conceptual dichotomies (McNeill and Freiberger, 1993; Van Regenmortel, 1998a). Discontinuous epitopes usually contain several continuous stretches of a few contiguous residues and conversely, so-called 'continuous epitopes' often contain a number of indifferent residues that are not implicated in the binding interaction and make the epitope discontinuous in a functional sense.

The same problem of definition arises with paratopes. Since paratopes are constituted of six CDR loops, they are clearly discontinuous structures. However, it has been shown in recent years that peptides corresponding to certain individual CDR sequences are capable of binding the antigen with the same specificity as the intact antibody, albeit with lower affinity (Laune et al., 1997). This situation is analogous to what is observed with continuous epitopes. Such CDR peptides that are capable of binding the antigen can be viewed as continuous paratopes (Van Regenmortel, 1998b).

It should be stressed that most studies aimed at unravelling the nature of protein antigenicity have actually focused on the phenomenon of cross-reactive antigenicity between proteins and short peptides. As a result, our knowledge of protein epitopes mainly concerns adulterated, incomplete epitopes that have retained only part of their identity after fragmentation of the protein.

Some authors have challenged the view that native proteins possess continuous epitopes recognized by antiprotein antibodies. (Laver et al., 1990) suggested that all so-called 'continuous epitopes' represent unfoldons, i.e. unfolded regions of the protein antigen that cross-react only with antibodies specific for the denatured protein. Such antibodies may be present in antiprotein sera, because some of the molecules used for immunization were denatured either before or after injection of the animal (Jemmerson, 1987; Lando and Reichlin, 1982; Scibienski, 1973). In reciprocal assays that use antibodies raised to peptides, it is also possible that the antibodies recognize the protein because the antigen preparation used in the assay contained some denatured molecules. Some support for the interpretation that all cross-reactions between peptides and proteins are due to antibodies to unfoldons is derived from the fact that these cross-reactivities are often detected in solid-phase immunoassays in which the immobilized protein antigen is at least partly denatured (Darst et al., 1988; Spangler, 1991). However, a compelling argument against the generality of the unfoldon interpretation lies in the observation that antisera raised to peptides are often capable of neutralizing the biological activity associated with the native state of proteins. It is well known, for instance, that immunization with short linear peptides can lead to the formation of antibodies that neutralize virus infectivity (Anderer and Schlumberger, 1965b; Bittle et al., 1982; Emini et al., 1985; Smyth et al., 1990). Such findings imply that the antipeptide antibodies probably recognize the native state of the viral protein present in infectious virus particles. However, the existence of a genuine cross-reactivity between peptide and viral protein does not mean that the peptide exactly reproduces the structure of the epitope present in the infectious virus particle. All that is needed is a sufficient degree of epitope resemblance to allow antibody cross-reactivity. Although it may be only a small fraction of the total immune response against a peptide that shows this cross-reactivity, such antibodies are important in the development of synthetic vaccines (Arnon and Van Regenmortel, 1992; Nicholson, 1994b) and diagnostic reagents (Boersma et al., 1993).

When a short synthetic peptide obtained from a combinatorial library is found to bind to an antiprotein antibody, and the same peptide sequence is present in the protein immunogen used to raise the antibody, the peptide is considered to be a continuous epitope of the protein. On the other hand, if the sequence of the antigenically active peptide is not present in the immunogen, the peptide is said to correspond to a mimotope, i.e. a structure that is believed to mimic a discontinuous epitope of the protein. The term 'mimotope' was coined by Geysen et al. (1986) and was originally defined as a peptide capable of binding to the paratope of an antibody but unrelated in sequence to the epitope used to induce the antibody. In its current usage, the term 'mimotope' is used more broadly and applied to any mimic of an epitope. Since it is possible to mimic a continuous epitope with a mimotope peptide showing little sequence similarity with the original epitope, the distinction between mimotopes that mimic continuous and discontinuous epitopes is as fuzzy as the distinction between the two types of epitopes themselves (Van Regenmortel, 1998a). However, the value of the mimotope concept is not diminished because of the vagueness of its structural definition, since the term is used mainly for referring to the immunological reactivity of peptides, rather than to their structure. In order to qualify as a mimotope, a peptide must also be capable of eliciting antibodies that recognize the epitope being mimicked. This requirement stems from the fact that a single Ig molecule may harbour a considerable number of partly overlapping or nonoverlapping paratopes, each one capable of binding to related or unrelated epitopes. Each individual paratope is made up of atoms from not more than 15–20 residues, which implies that about two-thirds of the 50 or so CDR residues of the antibody do not participate directly in the interaction with the complementary epitope. These noninteracting residues are potentially capable of binding to other epitopes that bear no structural resemblance to the first epitope. This phenomenon gives rise to antibody multispecificity and explains why the relation between an antibody and its antigen is never of an exclusive nature.

For instance, a single Ig molecule could harbour two totally independent subsites representing two paratopes for unrelated epitopes. Such a situation has been described in the case of an Ig that was capable of binding phosphorylcholine and α-D-galactopyranoside concomitantly at two separate paratope subsites (Bhattacharjee and Glaudemans, 1978). A more frequent finding is that the different subsites partly overlap, in which case binding to one epitope prevents a second epitope from being accommodated at a nearby location. Therefore, when a peptide is labelled as a mimotope of epitope A solely on the basis of its capacity to bind to an anti-A antibody, it cannot be excluded that the so-called 'mimotope' in fact binds to a different subsite from the one that interacts with epitope A. This is why it is essential to establish that the putative mimotope is also capable of inducing antibodies that cross-react with epitope A. Only if this is the case can it be said that the antigenically active peptide is a true mimotope of epitope A (Hirabayashi et al., 1996).

In addition to mimotopes, two further categories of epitopes can be distinguished that are particularly relevant in the analysis of viral antigenicity: the so-called 'cryptotopes' and 'neotopes'. Cryptotopes are hidden epitopes that become expressed only after fragmentation, depolymerization or denaturation of the antigen (Jerne, 1960). In viral capsids, cryptotopes are found, for instance, on the surfaces of subunits that are turned inward and become buried after polymerization (Van Regenmortel, 1966, 1992a). The existence of cryptotopes is also responsible for the fact that many antibodies raised by immunization with denatured proteins do not react with the corresponding native molecule.

Another important category of viral epitopes are neotopes. These epitopes are specific for the quaternary structure of proteins and are thus absent in the constituent monomeric subunits of viral capsids (Neurath and Rubin, 1971; Van Regenmortel, 1966, 1992a). Neotopes arise as a result of conformational changes in the monomer induced by intersubunit bonds, or by the juxtaposition of residues from neighbouring subunits (Saunal and Van Regenmortel, 1995a).

Regarding the number of epitopes likely to be found on a protein molecule, it is now accepted that the entire surface of the protein harbours numerous overlapping epitopes (Benjamin et al., 1984). This viewpoint, which arose from the results of epitope mapping using monoclonal antibodies (Mabs), has superseded the earlier belief that proteins possess only a few immunodominant epitopes with discrete boundaries. The view expounded by Atassi (1984) that proteins possess only a few epitopes was based on the belief that Mabs give a distorted picture of the number of epitopes because they emphasize minor epitopes that may not be easily detectable with polyclonal antisera. However, it is now generally accepted that the range of specificities observed with a panel of Mabs is similar to that in a polyclonal antiserum raised against the same antigen (Quesniaux et al., 1990).

Since epitopes can only be identified operationally by virtue of their relational nexus with complementary paratopes, the number of epitopes in a protein can be equated with the number of different Mabs that can be raised against it. In the case of insulin, for instance, this number was estimated to be around 100 (Schroer et al., 1983). Antigenic diversity is thus defined in terms of the size of the immunological repertoire of the immunized host. In effect, analysis of the antigen is thereby replaced by an analysis of the complementary antibody tool used in the study.

Mapping with Mabs often leads to the identification of clusters of overlapping epitopes at the surface of a protein antigen. Such clusters are usually said to constitute an antigenic site, although the boundaries of such sites are not clearly defined (Van Regenmortel 1998a).

1.4. Methods used for localizing epitopes

The various methods that have been used for delineating epitopes are listed in Table 1.1. From the preceding discussion, it should be clear that the delineation of epitopes cannot be reduced to only a structural description of which residues of the antigen are in contact with residues of the antibody once a stable immune complex has been formed (Van Regenmortel, 1998a).

It must also be emphasized that it is not a trivial matter to establish which residues are contact residues contributing to the structure of an epitope. Different definitions of what constitutes a contact have been used (Getzoff et al., 1988). Contact residues have been said to be residues within Van der Waals contact, residues buried to a certain radius probe sphere or residues with their side chains interacting directly. The ambiguity lies partly in the fact that the protein building blocks, i.e. individual amino acids, that embody the genetic message do not correspond to the units of recognition operative at the level of epitope-paratope interfaces. Interactions between individual atoms rather than between amino acid residues represent the appropriate level of analysis (Fig. 1.3). This was clearly illustrated, for instance, in a study of cyclosporin-Fab complexes which utilized hundreds of analogues modified at single atomic positions for constructing an epitope map of cyclosporin at the atomic level (Rauffer et al., 1994; Vix et al., 1993).

As discussed above, the concept of epitope as a static structure cannot fully account for the dynamic process of antigen-antibody interaction. Epitopes are entities endowed with a specific activity and questions concerning which factors affect the binding reac-

TABLE 1.1

Methods used for localizing epitopes in proteins

Method	No. of residues in epitope	Criterion for residue allocation
Crystallographic analysis of antigen-antibody complexes	15–22	Contact in epitope paratope interface
Synthetic peptides as antigenic probes in binding studies a. Free peptides b. Peptides adsorbed to solid phase c. Peptides conjugated to a carrier d. Peptides attached to support used for synthesis	5–8	Cross-reactive binding with antiprotein antibodies
Identification of critical residues in peptides by systematic replacement of residues	3–5	Decrease in cross-reactive binding
Peptides sequences inserted in recombinant proteins	5–8	Cross-reactive binding with antiprotein antibodies
Binding of antipeptide antibodies to protein	5–8	Induction of cross-reactive antibodies
Binding of antiprotein antibodies to chemically modified or mutated proteins	3–5	Decrease in binding compared to unmodified protein
Protection of antibody-bound residues of epitope to chemical attack	5–10	Chemical reactivity of individual residues
Competitive topographic mapping	Only relative position of epitope is defined	Not applicable

tion can only be answered by performing binding experiments and looking for structural correlates to functional activity. Structural and functional approaches to the study of antigenicity, in fact, correspond to asking different types of questions about the nature of epitopes (Van Regenmortel, 1989, 1995). Both approaches are needed and lead to complementary information about two facets of the epitope concept: its static structure and its dynamic activity. Asking what a binding site looks like in three-dimensional space and asking what it does in terms of interaction are two separate questions that cannot be answered simultaneously to provide a single picture of antigenic reality. It should come as no surprise, therefore, that structural and functional methods of antigenic analysis lead to different perceptions of the nature of epitopes.

1.4.1. Crystallographic analysis of antigen-antibody complexes

X-ray crystallographic studies of complexes of several protein antigens with Fab fragments have provided detailed knowledge of the molecular basis of antigen-antibody recognition (Colman, 1988; Davies et al., 1990; Mariuzza and Poljak, 1993; Padlan, 1994, 1996). More than 20 epitopes have been characterized by this method (Table 1.2) including six Fabs complexed with lysozyme, two with influenza virus neuraminidase and four with anti-idiotipic antibodies. An area of about 700–900 $Å^2$ of the protein surface, comprising between 15 and 22 amino acid residues, is usually found to be in contact with about the same number of residues of the antibody. All epitopes characterized by crystallography so far are discontinuous and made up of residues from between two and five separate stretches of the antigen polypeptide chain. The various paratopes comprised residues originating from four, five or all six of the CDRs of the antibody, as well as from some invariant framework residues. In the case of peptide-antibody complexes, the surface contact areas are usually smaller than those observed for complexes between intact protein and antibody. The conformation of peptides

TABLE 1.2

Crystal structures of antigen-antibody complexes

Antigen	Mab	Reference
Hen-egg lysozyme	D1.3, Fab D1.3,	Amit et al. (1986),
	Fv D1.3	Bhat et al. (1994),
		Fischmann et al. (1991)
	HyHEL-5	Sheriff et al. (1987)
	HyHEL-10	Chitarra et al. (1993),
	D11.15	Padlan et al. (1989)
	D44-1	Braden et al. (1994)
Pheasant lysozyme	Fv D11.15	Chitarra et al. (1993)
Guinea-fowl lysozyme	Fab F9.13.7	Lescar et al. (1995)
Bobwhite quail lysozyme	HyHEL-5	Chacko et al. (1996)
Turkey lysozyme	D1.3	Braden et al. (1996)
Influenza virus	NC 41	Tulip et al. (1992a),
neuraminidase N 9		Tulip et al. (1992b)
Neuraminidase N 9	Fab NC 10	Malby et al. (1994)
Influenza Virus	Fab HC 19	Bizebard et al. (1995)
X-3 I haemagglutinin		
E. coli protein HPr	Fab Jel 42	Prasad et al. (1993)
Fab D1.3	Fab E225	Bentley et al. (1990)
Fab 730.1.4	Fab 409.5.3	Ban et al. (1994, 1995)
Fab Ys T 9.1	Fab T 91 AJ5	Evans et al. (1994),
		Rose et al. (1993)
Fv D1.3	FE 5.2	Fields et al. (1995)
Various peptides of 8–20		Altschuh et al. (1992),
residues		Churchill et al. (1994),
(myohaemerythrin,		Ghiara et al. (1994),
influenza, haemagglutinin,		Rini et al. (1992),
cyclosporin, HIV,		Rini et al. (1993),
rhinovirus, poliovirus)		Shoham (1993),
		Stanfield et al. (1990),
		Tormo et al. (1994),
		Wien et al. (1995)

bound to antibodies often differs significantly from that of the peptide free in solution, or from the conformation of the corresponding region in the cognate protein.

The binding forces that contribute to the energy of interaction of protein-antibody complexes are listed in Table 1.3. The binding is mediated by many intermolecular hydrogen bonds and by a small number of salt bridges. A large number of Van der Waals contact points are also present in all epitope-paratope interfaces. Unfortunately, the static picture derived from a structural analysis of the interface does not provide information on the relative contribution of the different types of interaction to the energetics of the binding reaction. Since, a tenfold increase in binding affinity corresponds to a free-energy change of only 1.4 kcal/mol (5.8 kJ/mol) at 25°C, typical antibody affinity constants of $K = 10^7 M^{-1}$ to $10^9 M^{-1}$ correspond to a free-energy change of 9.8 and 12.6 kcal/mol, respectively. This means that the entire range of antigen-antibody interactions encompass no more than a few kcal of free-energy change. Since an electrostatic interaction and a hydrogen bond contribute about 5 and 0.5–1.5 kcal of binding energy, respectively, it follows that very small modifications in the antigen will be capable of significantly affecting the binding energy and the affinity of an interaction (Van Oss, 1994).

It should also be noted that many available crystal structures of immune complexes have been determined to a resolution of only about 3.0 Å, which is insufficient to reveal the precise nature of the atomic interactions. In a study of the lysozyme-D1.3 antibody complex at an improved resolution of 1.8 Å, it was found that 48 water molecules were present at the antigen-antibody interface (Bhat et al., 1994). A considerable number of water molecules have also been found at the interface in several other antigen-antibody complexes (Chacko et al., 1995; Malby et al., 1994). The presence of many water molecules at the interface is at odds with the earlier generalization, drawn from data obtained at lower resolution, that water is extruded from epitope- paratope interfaces (Davies et al., 1990). The residual interstitial water molecules between epitope

TABLE 1.3

Binding forces contributing to the energy of interaction of antigen-antibody complexes

Antigen	Antibodies	No. of Van der Waals contacts[a]	No. of hydrogen bonds	No. of salt bridges	References
Lysozyme	D1.3	75	15	0	Amit et al. (1986)
	HyHEL-5	74	10	3	Sheriff et al. (1987)
	HyHEL-10	111	14	1	Padlan et al. (1989)
Neuraminidase	NC41	108	23	1	Tulip et al. (1989)
D1.3	E225	100	9	1	Bentley et al. (1990)

[a] These represent molecular contact points and do not necessarily involve so-called van der Waals bonds.

and paratope represent the water of hydration that surrounds all protein molecules (Van Oss, 1995). These water molecules are not expelled from the interface during the interaction because of the imperfect complementarity between the two surfaces, and they contribute hydrogen bonds to the antigen-antibody interaction (Chacko et al., 1995; Goldbaum et al., 1996; Schwartz et al., 1995). The extent to which these water molecules contribute to the binding energetics is difficult to quantify (Ladbury, 1996). The presence of residual water at the interface agrees with the fact that the packing density at antigen-antibody interfaces is less tight than previously thought (Tulip et al., 1992a). The degree of steric fit between epitope and paratope is considerably less than in the interior of protein molecules and this leads to a rather imperfect complementarity between the two partners. This loose fit also facilitates the occurrence of cross-reactivity and so-called 'heterospecific binding'. Studies with Mabs have clearly established that antibodies are not only polyspecific (Lane and Koprowski, 1982) but also heterospecific, i.e. they are often capable of binding more strongly to other antigens than to the one against which they were raised (Harper et al., 1987; Mäkelä, 1965; Underwood, 1985; Van Regenmortel, 1982). Heterospecific binding appears to be a universal feature of antibodies but is seldom noticed simply because the cross-reactivity tests that could demonstrate the phenomenon are not performed. In view of the polyspecific and heterospecific nature of antibodies, it is futile to turn the delineation of epitopes into a search for the 'true' antigenic structure to which a paratope is supposed to fit perfectly. Cross-reactive fit rather than absolute fit is the rule underlying epitope-paratope interactions. A detailed review of the molecular basis of antigenic cross-reactivity has been published (Roberts et al., 1993).

An interesting example of cross-reactivity is provided by the crystallographic study of the binding of two Fabs (F9.13.7 and HyHEL-10) to guinea fowl and hen-egg lysozyme, respectively (Lescar et al., 1995). Twelve out of 13 lysozyme residues in contact with the F9.13.7 paratope were also found to interact with the HyHEL-10 paratope, in spite of the absence of any amino acid sequence homology in the CDRs of the two antibodies. Although the same 12 residues of the antigen interact with the two antibodies, the two Mabs bind the antigen in different orientations (Fig 1.2). The two epitopes are clearly different in spite of atomic contributions from the same amino acid residues. This study also confirmed that side-chain mobility of epitope residues contributes to the steric and electrostatic complementarity observed with differently shaped paratopes (Malby et al., 1994; Wilson and Stanfield, 1993). In spite of the absence of any structural or sequence similarity in the two paratopes, a high level of functional mimicry leading to similar affinity constants was present. This study illustrates the importance of differentiating between structural and functional characterization of binding sites (Van Regenmortel, 1989).

The ability of certain antibodies to recognize both the native protein and short peptide fragments of the same protein has many applications in molecular biology and medicine (see Chapters 5–8). In order to understand the structural basis of this type of cross-reactivity, attempts have been made to establish whether, or not, the conformation of the peptide in the antibody-peptide complex is the same as in the corresponding region of the intact protein. Two typical studies are those of the Fab-peptide complexes corresponding to a 19-residue peptide of myohaemerythrin (residues 69–87), and a 36-residue peptide of influenza virus haemagglutinin (Wilson and Stanfield, 1993; Wilson et al., 1991). Structure determination of the Fab-myohaemerythrin peptide complex indicated that residues 69–75 of the peptide interacted with the paratope, but that the conformation of the peptide bound to the Fab was very different from its conformation in native myohaemerythrin. The peptide had a type II β-turn conformation (residues 71–74) when bound to the antibody, but had a preponderantly helical conformation in the protein. The Mab B13–I2 used in this study was obtained by immunization with the 69–87 peptide conjugate and, although there is no information on the conformation of the region 69–75 in the conjugated peptide, it is likely to be different from the helical conformation present in the protein. It was initially claimed that Mab B13–I2 reacted with native myohaemerythrin (Fieser et al., 1987; Stanfield et al., 1990), but in a subsequent study the antibody was shown to react only with myohaemerythrin immobilized on a solid-phase, and not with the protein in a solution-phase assay (Spangler, 1991). Only a crystallographic analysis of the complex of myohaemerythrin with antibody B13–I2 would be able to establish if this antibody is actually capable of recognizing the helical configuration of the region 69–75 in the protein, although the evidence so far indicates that this is unlikely. This study of myohaemerythrin illustrates the importance of performing carefully controlled binding assays if structural data are to be interpreted correctly.

The Fab-haemagglutinin peptide complex analyzed corresponds to a nonapeptide epitope (residues 100–108) of influenza haemagglutinin (Schulze-Gahmen et al., 1988). Comparison of the Fab structure in free and complexed form showed that a major rearrangement in the H3 CDR loop occurred following antigen binding (Rini et al., 1992). This was the first clear demonstration that induced fit contributes to antigen-antibody recognition. The structure of the bound peptide was also different from that of the corresponding region in the cognate protein, a finding also observed in other peptide-antibody complexes (Churchill et al., 1994; Schulze-Gahmen et al., 1993). In most of the reported crystal structures of antibodies in their free and bound forms, some conformational rearrangements have been observed in the complexed antibody structure compared to the uncomplexed state (Davies and Cohen, 1996). These include reorientations in the quaternary association of the variable antibody domains, with rotations ranging from 3° to 16° (Stanfield et al., 1993; Tormo et al., 1994), as well as displacements of 4–10 Å in CDR residues, especially in the CDR 3 of the H chain (Bizebard et al., 1995; Wilson and Stanfield, 1994). Since many of the potential hydrogen bond partners are present on the mobile surface side chains of the antigen and antibody, the complementarity observed in the complex may not be predictable from the structure of the free molecules before induced fit and mutual adaptation have taken place. This flexibility, together with our inability to account for the role of water molecules in the binding, is responsible for the fact that attempts at antigen-antibody docking and binding energy predictions have had little success so far (Carneiro and Stewart, 1994; Van Regenmortel, 1995)

Two competing explanatory models have been used for many years to describe the mechanism of antigen-antibody recognition— the lock-and-key and induced fit models. According to the lock-and-key model, the two partners interact as rigid bodies and the recognition depends on very precise steric and chemical complementarity without any deformation in either of the two partners (Lancet et al., 1994). This model is in line with the view that the location of epitopes results from the static surface accessibility of certain regions of the protein antigen (Novotny et al., 1987). The alternative induced fit model borrows a terminology that was initially coined to describe the emergent enzymatic activity resulting from the induction of an activated state (Koshland et al., 1966). In immunochemistry, 'induced fit' refers to the occurrence of conformational rearrangements of main and side-chain atoms in one or both reactants which allows them to improve their complementarity and form more stable complexes. Strictly speaking, the term 'induced fit' implies that the binding reaction brings about the conformational change, and it may be inappropriate to apply the term to a situation where one of the partners selects one of several pre-existing conformational states of the other reactant. However, it is difficult to distinguish a true induction mechanism from a selection process since the end result in the complex is the same (Crumpton, 1986). One observation favouring the true induction mechanism, rather than the selection of pre-existing conformational states, is the variety of different crystal structures of the same unliganded antibody molecule that can be observed compared to the antigen bound structure (Stanfield and Wilson, 1994). Most crystallographic studies of antigen-antibody complexes show the presence of at least some degree of induced fit, and it seems, therefore, that the static lock-and-key analogy is a less satisfactory model for representing immunochemical interactions (Miyazaki et al., 1997).

1.4.2. Binding studies with analogues and mutagenized molecules

This method consists of studying the antigenic cross-reactivity between related proteins possessing known amino acid substitutions and gives unambiguous information only when Mabs are used as probes and the tertiary structure of the proteins is known (Benjamin et al., 1984; Hannum and Margoliash, 1985; Van Regenmortel, 1984). The method is based on the assumption that if the substitution leads to a change in antibody binding, the mutated residue is likely to be directly involved in the structure of an epitope. Although this assumption is valid in many cases (Hornbeck and Wilson, 1984), especially when the substitution occurs in a highly accessible surface residue, it is well known that the reactivity of epitopes can also be altered by conformational changes induced by substitutions occurring elsewhere in the protein (Blondel et al., 1986; Collawn et al., 1988; Hurrell et al., 1977; Ibrahimi et al., 1979; Milton et al., 1980). Since the number of available substitutions in a series of homologous proteins is always limited, and the substitutions inside an epitope need not necessarily always affect antibody binding, this approach cannot lead to the identification of all the residues in the epitope.

Immunological comparison between the members of several families of homologous proteins have demonstrated that there is a good correlation between degree of sequence difference and degree of antigenic difference (Champion et al., 1975; Prager et al., 1978; Van Regenmortel, 1986). From the extent of correlation, it has been inferred that about 80% of the substitutions that have accumulated during the evolution of monomeric globular proteins are antigenically detectable (White et al., 1978). Such a finding is in keeping with the view that internal substitutions may influence the reactivity of epitopes located at the surface of the protein. A particularly striking example concerns a mutant of tobacco mosaic virus protein (TMVP) in which a substitution occurs at residue 107 in the polypeptide chain, i.e. at a distance of 5 nm away from the outer viral surface. This exchange was found to alter the binding of antibody to the virus (Al Moudallal et al., 1982), presumably by long-range transmission of a conformational change through the closely packed α-helix located in residues 114–134 of the protein.

Changes in paratope specificity have been observed after the introduction of substitutions outside of CDR residues directly in contact with the antigen (Callebaut et al., 1996; Lavoie et al., 1992). In recent years, antigenic variants generated by site-directed chemical modifications (Cooper and Paterson, 1987; Oertle et al., 1989), or by site-directed mutagenesis (Benjamin and Perdue, 1996; Smith and Benjamin, 1991; Smith et al., 1991), have been increasingly used in this type of study. Alanine- and homologue-scanning mutagenesis have been used successfully to map a variety of epitopes (Cunningham and Wells, 1989; Jin et al., 1992; Wells, 1991). Mutations to alanine are used because it is the least disruptive way of removing an interaction beyond the β-carbon, without imposing disruptive or productive interactions (Jin and Wells, 1994)

Recently, biosensor instruments based on surface plasmon resonance have become increasingly used for measuring the change in binding affinity and kinetics that result from single residue substitutions (Jin and Wells, 1994; Kelley, 1996). Such studies have shown that only 3–5 residues of the epitope defined on a structural basis contribute significantly to the binding energy. This makes it possible to define a so-called 'energetic epitope' which is much smaller than the structural epitope which usually entails about 20 residues.

Activity measurements confirmed that the level of binding affinity normally encountered in antigen-antibody interactions (Ka values of 10^7–10^9 M^{-1}) can be reached provided there is an intimate contact between a few residues of the epitope and paratope. This conclusion agrees with the observation that increasing the size of epitopes above a molecular weight (MW) of 400–500 (equivalent to about 4 amino acid residues) does not lead to higher binding affinities of antigen-antibody interactions. When all published Ka values of Mabs to small haptens were plotted against the MW of the hapten, the Ka values reached a maximum of about 10^{10} M^{-1} when the MW reached a value of 450 (Chappey et al., 1994; Morel-Montero and Delaage, 1994).

In the case of protein antigens, antibody affinity constants also rarely exceed the value 10^{10} M^{-1}, probably because of the difficulty of achieving a very high degree of steric and chemical fit over protein surfaces as large as 700–900 Å^2. In general, the shape complementarity of antigen-antibody interfaces is poorer than that of other protein ligand interfaces, which explains the maintenance of water molecules at the interface (Bhat et al., 1994). These solvent molecules which are not expelled during the interaction fill the many cavities that are present at the interface.

In their classic studies of the antigenic structure of myoglobin, Atassi and collaborators (1975, 1977b) analyzed how chemical modifications at 23 residue locations in the sequence of myoglobin influenced the antigenic reactivity of the protein. In the case of snake toxins, epitopes were located by measuring the change in affinity of antitoxin Mabs for chemical derivatives of the toxin modified at single residue locations (Boulain et al., 1982; Menez et al., 1992). Fine mapping of the epitopes of cyclosporin was achieved by measuring the effect of single atomic modifications on the ELISA reactivity and binding affinity of a large panel of monoclonal antibodies (Quesniaux et al., 1987b; Rauffer et al., 1994).

Instead of inferring the position of epitopes from the antigenic differences observed between naturally occurring protein variants, the same can be achieved by selecting antigenic mutants by means of Mabs. A classic example of this approach is the determination of the antigenic map of influenza virus haemagglutinin (Caton et al., 1982; Gerhard and Webster, 1978; Wilson et al., 1981). By growing the virus in the presence of neutralizing Mabs, nonneutralizable virus mutants were selected which were found to have single amino acid substitutions in the haemagglutinin. By locating these substitutions in the known three-dimensional structure of the protein, several clusters of exchanges at the surface of the molecule were identified as likely epitopes. This approach has been used extensively to map the epitopes of viruses (Richards and Konigsberg, 1973; Talmage, 1959; Van Regenmortel, 1984; Van Regenmortel and Neurath, 1990).

1.4.3. Binding studies with peptide fragments

Most of our knowledge concerning the approximate location of epitopes in proteins has been obtained by studying the antigenic cross-reactivity between the intact molecule and peptide fragments. These studies were possible because the precision of fit between paratope and epitope is not absolute. As a result our knowledge of protein antigenicity concerns mainly cross-reactive antigenicity.

Since the relationship between the two immunological partners is never of an exclusive nature, the relationship is sometimes described as promiscuous or degenerate. Although it has been known for a long time that an individual epitope can be recognized by a variety of different paratopes, it is a surprising feature of the history of immunology that the reciprocal situation has become accepted much more slowly. The fact that an antibody is polyspecific, i.e. able to react with a variety of more or less closely related epitopes was in fact surmised many years ago (Cameron and Erlanger, 1977; Richards and Konigsberg, 1973; Talmage, 1959). One of the most common methods used for localizing protein epitopes consists of identifying which peptide fragments of the antigen are able to cross-react with antibodies raised against the intact protein. Any linear peptide that is capable of binding to the protein antibodies is said to contain a continuous epitope. Frequently, peptides of decreasing size are tested and the smallest peptide that retains a measurable level of antigenic reactivity is given the status of epitope (Benjamini, 1977). The degree of antigenic cross-reactivity observed with short peptides tends to be very low, with the exception of peptides corresponding to chain termini (Absolom and Van Regenmortel, 1977; Altschuh et al., 1983; Anderer, 1963; Walter et al., 1980). The strong antigenicity of terminal segments of proteins is linked to the fact that these regions are frequently surface-oriented (Thornton and Sibanda, 1983) and more mobile than internal sections of the polypeptide chain (Tainer et al., 1984, 1985; Westhof et al., 1984). There is no general consensus about the minimum number of residues necessary to give rise to the process of immunological recognition. In the case of TMVP, it was shown that even a single, highly accessible C-terminal residue could be recognized with a reasonable degree of specificity by antibodies (Anderer and Schlumberger, 1966a). This should come as no surprise in view of the existence of antibodies capable of recognizing a structure as small as dinitrophenol (Eisen and Siskind, 1964). In general, however, the minimum size of an antigenic peptide is 5–8 residues. Increasing the length of peptides does not always lead to a higher level of cross-reactivity, since longer peptides may adopt a conformation different from that present in the cognate protein (Wilson et al., 1984). It was found, for instance, that an antiserum to histone H2A, which reacted with peptide 1–15 of H2A, was unable to bind to histone fragments 1–39, 1–56 and 1–71 (Muller et al., 1986). In some cases it seems that shorter peptides fold more easily into the conformation required for binding to the antibody (Hodges et al., 1988).

The difficulties encountered when one tries to determine the exact size of an epitope can be illustrated in the case of the epitope located in the region 103–112 of TMVP. In a series of classical immunochemical studies (Benjamini, 1977; Young et al., 1967), the antigenic activity of this region was studied in direct binding assays by means of labelled synthetic peptides varying in length from dipeptide to decapeptide. Since the shortest peptide showing significant binding to TMVP antibodies was the pentapeptide 108–112, this region was identified as the epitope, although considerably more activity was present in the octapeptide 105–112 (Benjamini et al., 1968a). In subsequent work, it was shown that the entire length of the decapeptide 103–112 was needed for obtaining optimal binding to some Mabs raised against TMVP (Morrow et al., 1984). These findings illustrate the difficulty in interpreting such data since the increased antigenic activity of longer peptides may result from a direct participation of the additional residues in the epitope structure, or it may reflect the fact that longer peptides are better able to assume the conformation present in the complete molecule. It also cannot be excluded that nonspecific effects, for instance hydrophobicity, may play a role. It was found, for instance, that the antigenic activity of the pentapeptide 108–112 of TMVP was greatly enhanced by the addition of 5 alanine residues at its N-terminal end (Benjamini et al., 1968b). In studies with other peptides, it was shown that the addition of lysine residues to a short peptide fragment also increased its apparent reactivity in a nonspecific manner (Leach, 1984; Shi et al., 1984).

1.4.3.1. Synthetic peptides as antigenic probes
Because of the efficiency and convenience of solid-phase peptide
synthesis (Atherton and Sheppard, 1989; Geysen et al., 1987; Kent
and Clark-Lewis, 1985; Plaué et al., 1990), synthetic peptides have
virtually replaced natural peptide fragments as antigenic probes for
epitope mapping. After synthesis, the peptides are cleaved from the
resin and tested either as free peptides in solution, as immobilized
peptides adsorbed to a solid-phase or as peptide-carrier conjugates.
Since the conformation of the peptide may differ in different immunoassay formats, the apparent antigenicity of a peptide often
depends on the type of assay used (Muller et al., 1986). Sometimes
the free peptide in solution, when tested for its capacity to inhibit the
reaction between antibody and intact protein, is more active than the
conjugated or immobilized peptide (Altschuh and Van Regenmortel, 1982). A recent modification of the pepscan method of peptide
synthesis (Geysen et al., 1984) allows the peptides to be cleaved
from the pins used for synthesis, and this permits the rapid testing of
hundreds of free peptides (Maeji et al., 1991). A number of combinatorial approaches of peptide synthesis have been described which
make it possible to obtain millions of short peptides very rapidly
(Houghten et al., 1992, 1991; Lam et al., 1996).

   Several chemical strategies have been developed to increase the
level of conformational mimicry between peptide and intact protein.
If the peptide corresponds to a loop structure in the protein, cyclization of the peptide may lead to improved antigenic cross-reactivity
(Arnon et al., 1971; Fourquet et al., 1988; Jemmerson and Hutchinson, 1990; Muller et al., 1990b). However, cyclization per se is not
always sufficient and it may be necessary to achieve a high degree
of conformational mimicry to obtain improved reactivity (Joisson et
al., 1993; Plaué et al., 1990). Various approaches have been used to
stabilize peptides corresponding to α-helical or β-sheet structures in
the protein into the correct conformation (Gras-Masse et al., 1988;
Satterthwait et al., 1989; Vuilleumier and Mutter, 1992).

   Short peptides adsorbed to a solid-phase tend to have a significant proportion of their surface unavailable for binding to antibody,

and this may reduce their antigenic reactivity compared with free peptides in solution. Furthermore, it may be necessary to test a variety of buffers to ensure optimal adsorption of the peptide to the solid-phase (Geerligs et al., 1988). Sometimes the peptide may retain its activity only if it is prevented from drying up during the test (Norrby et al., 1987).

A peptide may be more antigenically active when it is conjugated to a carrier protein, presumably because the microenvironment at the surface of the carrier induces the peptide to adopt a more suitable conformation for antibody recognition (Al Moudallal et al., 1985). The peptide-carrier conjugate may also be more active than the unconjugated peptide adsorbed to plastic because of less steric hindrance for antibody binding. The chemical procedure used for conjugating a peptide can also influence its reactivity (Dyrberg and Oldstone, 1986; Schaaper et al., 1989). When several peptide moieties are coupled to a carrier protein, each peptide finds itself in a different local environment and this may alter its conformation and antigenic reactivity. A more homogeneous presentation of peptide moieties is achieved by coupling them to liposomes, and this type of conjugate tends to give results that are more easily interpretable (Friede et al., 1994).

Peptides can also be tested for antigenic reactivity without prior cleavage from the support used during synthesis (Chong et al., 1992; Shi et al., 1984). An efficient method for testing large numbers of peptides is the so-called 'pepscan technique' (Geysen et al., 1984, 1987). In this technique, hundreds of peptides of 6–10 residues are synthesized concurrently on polyethylene pins assembled into a polyethylene holder with the format and spacing of a microtitre plate. This allows the peptides to be tested by ELISA while they remain attached to the pins. After each test the pins can be freed of bound antibody by sonication and retested with different antibody preparations at least 30 times. It is customary to analyze the antigenic reactivity of sets of all possible overlapping peptides of a protein, starting from the N-terminus down to the C-terminus.

The high concentration of peptide on the pins favours bivalent binding and slow dissociation of antibody, and this facilitates the detection of very low levels of cross-reactivity with antiprotein antibodies. As a result, unexpected cross-reactions arising from the presence in unrelated proteins of identical short sequences of 2 or 3 residues may sometimes be detected (Geysen et al., 1986; Trifilieff et al., 1991). The specificity of pepscan reactions can be verified by analyzing the ability of free peptides or cognate protein to inhibit the reaction between antibodies and pin-bound peptides.

The pepscan technique is commonly used for analyzing the contribution of individual amino acids to the antigenic activity of a peptide (Rodda and Tribbick, 1996). This is achieved by synthesizing peptide replacement sets in which each residue of the peptide is replaced, in turn, by the other 19 possible amino acids (Geysen et al., 1988). When all the analogues are tested, some critical residues are found to be essential for binding, since they cannot be replaced by any residue without impairing antigenic reactivity. Other residues can be replaced by any of the amino acids, without affecting binding (Getzoff et al., 1988; Geysen, 1985). In the latter case, it is possible that only main-chain atoms of the residue interact with the antibody.

Another approach of epitope delineation using synthetic peptides consists in synthesizing so-called 'mimotopes' (Geysen et al., 1986). The mimotope approach disregards the sequence of the protein under study and analyzes the ability of peptides of increasing size to bind to antiprotein antibodies. Starting with the 400 possible dipeptides obtainable with the 20 common amino acids, the dipeptide possessing the highest binding activity is selected and lengthened on either side with the residues that produce the greatest increment in antigenic reactivity. In this way, hexapeptides can be constructed which possess considerable binding capacity for a particular antiprotein antibody. Such peptides, which are called 'mimotopes', do not usually reproduce the sequence of the protein epitope that induced the antibody, although they must possess certain features of the epitope in order to bind (Geysen et al., 1986).

One drawback of this approach is that it may lead to the accumulation of nonspecific binding effects caused, for instance, by hydrophobic and electrostatic interactions (Benjamini et al., 1968b; Leach, 1984). In recent years, a number of mimotopes reacting with antiprotein antibodies have been obtained capable of inducing antibodies that recognized the antigenic structure being mimicked (Delmastro et al., 1997; Hirabayashi et al., 1996).

1.4.3.2. Peptide sequences inserted in recombinant proteins

Advances in genetic engineering make it relatively easy to insert a foreign peptide sequence in a vector protein, or to fuse the peptide sequence at the N- or C-terminus of the vector. Recombinant genes can be expressed in bacterial, insect or mammalian cells, from which the recombinant protein can be extracted and purified. Since the foreign peptide is introduced in the recombinant protein by genetic association, the construction is a highly reproducible entity.

Methods used for expressing foreign antigens as recombinant proteins have been reviewed by Hofnung and Charbit (1993) Some bacterial vector proteins such as β-galactosidase (Benito and Villaverde, 1994; Broekhuijsen et al., 1987), or the δ gt11 bacteriophage system (Mehra et al., 1986) are expressed only in the cytoplasm, whereas others, such as the maltose-binding protein, are secreted through the cytoplasmic membrane into the periplasm or the medium (Benito and Van Regenmortel, 1998). It is also possible to express foreign peptides at the surface of bacteria using proteins such as LamB of Escherichia coli (Hofnung, 1991). Short peptide sequences of poliovirus (Van der Werf et al., 1990) hepatitis virus B (Charbit et al., 1987), and foot-and-mouth disease virus (Agterberg et al., 1990; Ruppert et al., 1994) expressed in recombinant proteins were able to induce antibodies that reacted with virus particles.

Other proteins, such as the core antigen of hepatitis B virus or the polymerase of phage MS2 have also been used as vector proteins in E. coli (Clarke et al., 1987; Francis et al., 1990; Nicosia et al., 1987).

Methods for mapping viral epitopes by means of expression vectors have been reviewed by Lenstra et al. (1990).

It is also possible to express libraries of peptides on the surface of filamentous phage particles (Daniels and Lane, 1996; Scott, 1992; Zwick et al., 1998). Random oligonucleotides are inserted into phages (one oligonucleotide per phage), and the resultant peptide is expressed within the filament protein on the phage surface. Phages that express a peptide epitope are screened with the antibody of interest (Christian et al., 1992) and the peptide sequence can be determined after amplifying the DNA from the selected phage by polymerase chain reaction. The peptide can be fused to the N-terminus of protein pIII of which there are about five copies at one extremity of the phage (Cwirla et al., 1990; Devlin et al., 1990; Scott and Smith, 1990; Stephen and Lane, 1992), or to the N-terminus of protein pVIII, which is present in about 2700 copies along the particle (Greenwood et al., 1991).

1.4.4. Binding studies with antipeptide antibodies

In this approach, peptides are used for immunizing animals and the resulting antipeptide antibodies are tested for their capacity to cross-react with the intact protein. A positive cross-reaction is taken as evidence that the peptide approximates to an epitope of the protein.

Although it has been claimed in the past (Green et al., 1982; Lerner, 1982, 1984; Luka et al., 1983; Niman et al., 1983) that immunization with peptides leads to a high frequency of induction of antibodies capable of recognizing the *native* protein, this is no longer believed to be true. It seems that such claims arose because it was not realized that the antipeptide antibodies actually reacted with protein molecules that had become denatured by adsorption to plastic during the solid-phase immunoassay (Darst et al., 1988; Jemmerson, 1987; Kennel, 1982; Soderquist and Walton, 1980; Spangler, 1991). In order to demonstrate that antipeptide antibodies are capable of reacting with a truly native protein, the test should be performed by a liquid-phase immunoassay that does not alter the conformation of the antigen (Spangler, 1991).

The contention that antibodies against a highly disordered state (the peptide) are usually capable of recognizing the highly ordered state (the native protein), whereas the reverse is not necessarily true, has been called the 'order-disorder paradox' (Dyson et al., 1988). In an attempt to resolve this apparent contradiction, it was suggested that the peptide takes on a preferred conformation in solution that becomes stabilized either at the surface of the carrier protein, or when the peptide binds to the B-cell receptor during immune stimulation. However, it is unclear why a similar induction of the correct peptide conformation does not occur when the peptide interacts with antibodies raised against the protein. On the other hand, the paradox simply vanishes if one accepts that the extent of cross-reactivity between peptides and native protein is always limited, irrespective of whether antiprotein or antipeptide antibodies are tested (Jemmerson and Blankenfeld, 1989).

Methods used to produce antipeptide antisera have been described in several reviews (Boersma et al., 1993; Walter, 1986) (see Chapter 3). For peptides shorter than about 15 residues, it is customary to use peptide-carrier conjugates for immunization (Briand et al., 1985; Friede et al., 1993a; Soutar and Palfreyman, 1986). It is impossible to predict which method of conjugation will give the best results (Bahraoui et al., 1987; Boersma et al., 1993; Dyrberg and Oldstone, 1986; Mariani et al., 1987; Schaaper et al., 1989), and several coupling procedures should be tested. Branched peptides known as multiple antigen peptides (MAP), were developed by Tam (1988) to enhance the immunogenicity of peptides. The MAPs, which consist of a polylysine core onto which the peptide of interest in synthesized, avoid the formation of antibodies to a carrier protein (McLean et al., 1991; Tam, 1988). However, MAPs do not always lead to the formation of antibodies cross-reactive with the intact protein (Briand et al., 1992b).

1.4.5. Differential sensitivity of free and bound epitopes to chemical attack or amide exchange

Binding of a Mab to its antigen will usually prevent contact residues of the epitope from reacting with a particular enzyme or chemical reagent. The differential rate of proteolysis of certain peptide bonds within an epitope when it is free or bound to a Mab has been used to characterize, for instance, discontinuous epitopes of cytochrome c (Jemmerson and Paterson, 1986). By comparing the degree of protection from reaction with acetic anhydride of 18 lysine and 7 threonine side chains in free and antibody-bound cytochrome c, certain residues could be assigned to a discontinuous epitope of the protein (Burnens et al., 1987). Subsequently, the same technique was used to further characterize four discontinuous epitopes of the same protein (Oertle et al., 1989).

The ability of deuterium to exchange with amide protons in a protein is greatly decreased for the residues of an epitope buried in the antibody combining site (Paterson, 1992). The effect of antibody binding on the exchange kinetics of amide hydrogens can be determined by two-dimensional NMR, and this approach has been used to identify certain residues in discontinuous epitopes of cytochrome c (Paterson et al., 1990; Saito and Paterson, 1996). The same technique has been applied to an epitope-paratope pair for which the crystal structure of the complex was previously determined by X-ray crystallography (Benjamin et al., 1992). Changes in the amide exchange rates were observed for some residues that were remote from the epitope defined by structural analysis. Such effects were attributed to a reduction in fluctuations of the protein, resulting from the binding interaction. These findings indicate that long-range changes may occur in proteins by the formation of protein-antibody complexes, and imply that the assignment of residues to an epitope on the basis of amide exchanges may sometimes be unreliable (Benjamin et al., 1992).

1.4.6. Competitive topographic mapping

Competitive binding assays with pairs of Mabs are used to determine the relative position of epitopes on the surface of a protein. In such assays, two epitopes will be recognized as different only if they are far enough apart to allow simultaneous binding of the two Mabs. However, steric hindrance may prevent Mabs directed against distinct but neighbouring epitopes from binding simultaneously to the antigen surface (Daiss and Scalice, 1994).

By testing all possible pairs of Mabs in double-antibody binding assays., each antibody can be assigned to particular reaction patterns relative to other Mabs. This makes it possible to construct two-dimensional 'surface-like' maps that mimic the distribution of epitopes on the surface of the antigen. The ability of pairs of Mabs to bind concurrently to the antigen is usually measured by ELISA, and this requires labelling one of the two Mabs for instance with biotin.

Recently, a biosensor technique based on surface plasmon resonance was shown to possess many advantages over ELISA for the purpose of topographic epitope mapping (Daiss and Scalice, 1994; Fägerstam et al., 1990; Malmqvist, 1996). This technique is further discussed in Chapter 4.

1.5. The antigenic structure of model proteins

1.5.1. Myoglobin

Sperm-whale myoglobin is a protein composed of a single polypeptide chain comprising 153 residues folded in a highly helical compact structure. Its antigenic properties have been extensively studied (Atassi, 1977b, 1984; Crumpton, 1974). Following initial investigations by Crumpton and collaborators, Atassi (1975) delineated the position of five continuous epitopes by means of inhibition experiments with synthetic peptides and claimed that these five regions (residues 15–22, 56–62, 94–99, 113–119 and 145–151) accounted for the entire antigenic reactivity of the native myoglobin molecule. This claim was based on the findings that serial elution with the five peptides displaced 81% of the total elutable antibody from a myoglobin- Sepharose immunosorbent column (Atassi, 1975), and that the five peptides achieved 89–94% inhibition of the precipitin reaction between myoglobin and its antibodies (Atassi, 1977b). However, the significance of the inhibition data is hard to assess, as no indication was given of total radioactive counts of antigen used in the experiments. If, for instance, only a small percentage of antigen added was precipitated, the inhibition of this precipitation would be difficult to interpret in quantitative terms.

The claim that the total antigenicity of myoglobin resides in five continuous epitopes of 6–7 residues has been challenged by several other groups (Benjamin et al., 1984; Todd et al., 1982). Comparisons between several mammalian myoglobins using antibodies specific for the fragment 1–55 of myoglobin showed that the antigenicity of this fragment did not reside solely in the epitope identified by Atassi in residues 15–22 (East et al., 1980). It was found that the synthetic peptides corresponding to residues 22–55 and 72–89 of myoglobin reacted with antibovine myoglobin antibodies and thus also contained epitopes (Leach, 1983). In another study in which several hundred synthetic peptides of myoglobin were tested for reactivity when attached to a plastic support, a major epitope was localized in the region 48–55 (Rodda et al., 1986). Furthermore, synthetic peptides corresponding to residues 1–6 and 121–127 of myoglobin were shown to elicit antibodies that reacted with native myoglobin (Schmitz et al., 1983b; Young et al., 1983). Thus, these various studies bring to nine the number of continuous epitopes that have been identified in myoglobin (Table 1.4).

A number of discontinuous epitopes were also identified in myoglobin on the basis of cross-reactivity studies between mammalian myoglobin, using Mabs (Berzofsky et al., 1982; East et al., 1982). By identifying which surface residues are conserved among cross-reacting myoglobins and vary in noncross-reacting myoglobins, a number of spatially adjacent residues were implicated in the forma-

TABLE 1.4
Amino acid residues shown to be involved in epitopes of myoglobin

No.	Continuous epitopes	Reference	No.	Discontinuous epitopes	Reference
1	1–6	Schmitz et al. (1983c)	1	34 and 113	East et al. (1982)
2	15–22	Atassi (1975)	2	87 and 142	East et al. (1982)
3	48–55	Leach (1983)	3	4 and 79	Berzofsky et al. (1982)
		Rodda et al. (1986)			
4	56–62	Atassi (1975)	4	83, 144 and 145	Berzofsky et al. (1982)
5	72–89	Leach (1983)	5	140	Berzofsky et al. (1982)
6	94–99	Atassi (1975)			
7	113–119	Atassi (1975)			
8	121–127	Schmitz et al. (1983c)			
		Rodda et al. (1986)			
9	145–151	Atassi (1975)			

tion of certain epitopes. For instance, residues 4 and 79 were found to contribute to one epitope and residues 34 and 113 to another (Table 1.4). Various representations of the epitopes of myoglobin are shown in Fig. 1.5. Each model has some merit and highlights a particular feature of the epitopes. However, each model also inevitably gives a distorted view of the dynamic nature of epitopes (Van Regenmortel, 1996).

It has been argued (Atassi, 1984; Young et al., 1983) that cross-reaction studies with Mabs are likely to lead to erroneous assignments of discontinuous epitopes, because investigators allegedly tend to disregard the possibility that the substitutions alter the conformation of the protein by long-range effects and may affect epitopes elsewhere in the protein. However, this possibility seems unlikely when it can be shown that the substitutions affect several highly accessible residues brought in close proximity by the folding of the chain. In most cases, it is found that substitutions tend to affect antibody binding only at one particular site and the reaction of Mabs that bind to other sites remains unaffected. In this context, it is interesting to note that the cleavage of myoglobin into three large fragments altered the conformation of epitopes to such a degree that reactivity with all the available Mabs specific for myoglobin was abolished (Berzofsky et al., 1982). This finding demonstrates that any distant alterations brought about by amino acid substitutions are probably less detrimental to the conformational integrity of epitopes than fragmentation of the protein. Obviously, when an epitope is excised from a protein, conformational features induced by distal parts of the molecule before the cleavage occurred are lost. This means that both the fragmentation approach advocated by Atassi (1984) and studies with Mabs (Berzofsky et al., 1982), cannot establish the location of epitopes in proteins in a very precise manner. Both approaches are complementary but neither is capable of providing the detailed structural information that is obtainable by X-ray crystallography of antigen-antibody complexes.

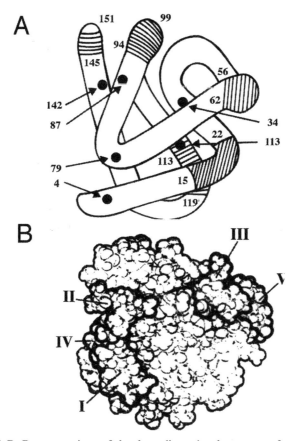

Fig. 1.5A,B. Representations of the three-dimensional structure of some of the epitopes of myoglobin. (A) Drawing of myoglobin showing the five continuous epitopes delineated by Atassi (1975) as hatched regions (peptides 15–22, 56–62, 94–99, 113–119 and 145–151). Pairs of residues indicated by arrows (4 and 79; 34 and 113; 87 and 142) refer to residues that are brought together by the folding and are part of three discontinuous epitopes recognized by separate Mabs (Berzofsky et al., 1982; reproduced with permission from Van Regenmortel, 1984). (B) Space-filling model of myoglobin showing the five continuous epitopes (I: 15–22; II: 56–62; III: 94–99; IV: 113–119; V: 145–151) delineated by Atassi (1975). Most of the surface appears to be nonantigenic (reproduced by permission from Leach, 1983).

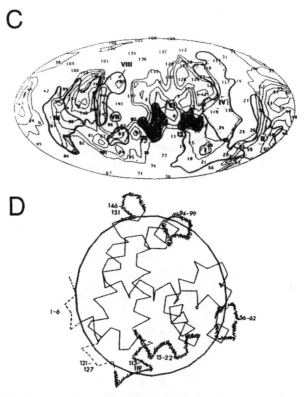

Fig. 1.5C,D. Representations of the three-dimensional structure of some of the epitopes of myoglobin. (C) Mollweide projection of the molecular surface of myoglobin with a contour interval of 8 Å. Superimposed in heavy lines are outlines of the molecular surfaces of epitopes. Sites I–V are the continuous epitopes of Atassi (1975);. site VI (darkened) corresponds to a discontinuous epitope comprising residues 4, 12 and 79. The epitopes generally coincide with major convex protrusions of the surface (reproduced with permission from Novotny et al., 1986). (D) Plot of myoglobin backbone showing the location of the five continuous epitopes (thick lines) delineated by Atassi (1975), as well as two additional accessible regions (peptides 1–6 and 121–127). The ellipsoid representation shows that epitopes are located on protruding regions of the protein (reproduced with permission from Thornton et al., 1986).

1.5.2. Lysozyme

Hen-egg white lysozyme (HEL) consists of a single polypeptide chain of 129 amino acid residues, internally cross-linked by four disulphide bonds. A large number of lysozymes of the c (chicken) type have been sequenced from bird species, and these naturally occurring variants have been very useful for defining HEL epitopes (Harper et al., 1987). The gene for HEL has been expressed in yeast and this made it possible to use site-directed mutagenesis for epitope mapping (Kam-Morgan et al., 1993). Cleavage of the disulphide bonds of HEL leads to a total loss of antigenic reactivity as measured by antibodies directed to native lysozyme. Tryptic digestion of the reduced lysozyme molecule was shown to give rise to fragments devoid of antigenic reactivity (Young and Leung, 1970).

Digestion of lysozyme with enzymes such as thermolysin, pepsin and trypsin produces antigenically active peptide fragments containing intact disulphide bonds. Some of the regions that have been extensively studied are peptide 17 (also known as the N–C fragment), which contains both the amino and carboxyl regions linked by the Cys_6–Cys_{127} disulphide bond (Fujio et al., 1959), loop I defined by Cys_{64}–Cys_{80} and loop II defined by Cys_{76}–Cys_{94} (Fujio et al., 1974). The corresponding peptide loops are labelled Ploop(I) and Ploop(II), respectively. An additional fragment, Ploop(I, II), known as peptide 8 contains both the intact Cys_{64}–Cys_{80} and Cys_{76}–Cys_{94} bridges (Fujio et al., 1971).

About 5% of antibodies to HEL have been shown to be directed to LoopI (Arnon and Sela, 1969; Maron and Bonavida, 1971) and a similar proportion was found to react with LoopII (Fujio et al., 1974). Antibodies raised to PloopI and Ploop(I–II) were able to react with HEL and the antigenic reactivity was dependent on the integrity of the disulphide bridges (Arnon and Sela, 1969; Ota et al., 1993; Seki et al., 1992). Mabs raised against PloopI also reacted with native HEL but with an affinity considerably lower than in the case of the reaction with the homologous, immunizing peptide (Darsley and Rees, 1985).

About 40% of antibodies to HEL react with peptide 17 (Fujio et al., 1968) and some Mabs to HEL were also found to react with this peptide (Kobayashi et al., 1982; Metzger et al., 1984). A continuous epitope of HEL has also been identified in the region 34–54 (Takagaki et al., 1980).

Three antigenically active peptides possessing intact disulphide bridges were obtained by Atassi et al. (1973) using trypsin digestion. Since these three peptides inhibited the precipitation reaction between lysozyme and its specific antiserum by 85–89%, it was claimed that they accounted for almost the entire antigenic activity of lysozyme (Atassi and Habeeb, 1977). Atassi and colleagues attempted to mimic the epitopes present in these three disulphide-containing peptides by a method known as 'surface-simulation synthesis'. This method attempts to reproduce certain features of the surface topography of the molecule (Lee and Atassi, 1976) using Gly residues as spacers. Three surface-simulation peptides were synthesized which together were reported to cause 95% inhibition of the reaction between HEL and specific antiserum (Atassi and Lee, 1978). However, since two of the three pairs of natural and synthetic peptides were totally dissimilar in structure, possessing, respectively, only two out of six and two out of 10 residues in common between the native and synthetic structures, it seems unlikely that both sets of peptides could account for the entire antigenic reactivity of HEL. Such a conclusion would also be at odds with the data obtained in several other studies (Arnon and Sela, 1969; Fujio et al., 1968, 1974; Grivel and Smith-Gill, 1996; Metzger et al., 1984).

Mabs raised against HEL have been used to map epitopes by functional assays using several related bird lysozymes (Harper et al., 1987; Smith-Gill et al., 1982), as well as site-directed mutants (Kam-Morgan et al., 1993; Lavoie et al., 1992). Such studies with Mabs HyHEL-5, HyHEL-10 and D1.3 led to the identification of a limited number of HEL residues that could not be substituted without affecting the reactivity of the corresponding epitopes. The structural epitopes recognized by these three Mabs have been defined by X-ray crystallography (Table 1.2), and were found to include a larger number of contact residues than the number identified in binding assays. Obviously, not all substitutions within a protein epitope affect binding equally. Some changes may be accommodated by mutual adaptation of side chains, or their influence on binding may be below reproducible detection. Furthermore, substitution of whole residues may be too crude an approach to unravel the subtleties of epitope-paratope complementarity operating at the atomic rather than the residue level.

Additional information concerning the antigenic structure of lysozyme is available in a recent review by Grivel and Smith-Gill (1996).

1.5.3. Tobacco mosaic virus protein

Tobacco mosaic virus (TMV) is a rod-shaped particle, 300 nm long, consisting of 2130 identical protein submits of 17,500 MW arranged as a helix around an RNA molecule of 2×10^6 MW. The coat protein (TMVP) of the virus contains 158 amino acid residues and was the first viral protein to be sequenced and to have its three-dimensional structure elucidated by X-ray crystallography (Bloomer and Butler, 1986; Bloomer et al., 1978).

Initial studies of TMV antigenicity concentrated on two antigenic sites, the C-terminal region corresponding to residues 153–158 of the coat protein (Anderer, 1963) and the disordered loop region corresponding to residues 93–113 (Benjamini et al., 1965, 1964; Young et al., 1966). Subsequently, a total of 10 continuous epitopes (Table 1.5) were identified in the protein by testing the antigenic reactivity of peptides by radioimmunoassay (Benjamini, 1977), inhibition of complement fixation (Milton and Van Regenmortel, 1979) and enzyme immunoassay (Altschuh and Van Regenmortel, 1982).

The seven, 7–10 residue long continuous epitopes of TMVP were found to correspond to regions of the viral protein, which were

TABLE 1.5

Continuous epitopes of TMVP

Position in sequence	Detected with: Polyclonal antisera	Monoclonal antibodies	Correlated with Segmental mobility[a]	References
1–10	+		+	Altschuh et al. (1983)
19–32	+			Al Moudallal et al. (1985)
34–39	+		+	Altschuh et al. (1983)
55–61	+		+	Altschuh and Van Regenmortel (1982)
62–68	+		+	Milton and Van Regenmortel (1979)
80–90	+	+	+	Al Moudallal et al. (1985)
105–112	+	+	+	Benjamini (1977)
115–132	+	+		Al Moudallal et al. 1985
134–146	+	+		Al Moudallal et al. (1985)
153–156	+	+	+	Anderer (1963)

[a] Data from Westhof et al. (1984).

shown by X-ray crystallography to possess a high segmental mobility (Westhof et al., 1984). This correlation between antigenicity and mobility along the peptide chain has also been found in other proteins (Tainer et al., 1984; Westhof et al., 1984), and has been used to develop algorithms for predicting the location of continuous epitopes in proteins (Karplus and Schulz, 1985). The correlation arises because flexible regions in proteins tend to correspond either to N- and C-terminal segments (Thornton and Sibanda, 1983), or to surface loops that are more likely to mimic the conformation of peptides in solution than regions of constrained secondary structure. Antibodies specific for the helices in TMVP have also been obtained but these were detected only when longer, structured peptides were used in the immunoassays (Al Moudallal et al., 1985; Van Regenmortel, 1986).

Studies with Mabs have demonstrated the presence of many discontinuous epitopes in TMVP. In one study with 30 Mabs raised against dissociated viral protein, more than 80% of the Mabs were unable to recognize any of the 18 synthetic peptides which together span the entire TMVP polypeptide chain (Al Moudallal et al., 1985). These antibodies are therefore likely to be specific for discontinuous epitopes. Several discontinuous epitopes were identified at the surface of virus particles by analyzing the ability of Mabs prepared against intact virions to cross-react with viral mutants, with other tobamoviruses and with dissociated viral submits (Altschuh et al., 1985). Using computer-generated images of the surface residues of TMVP, it was possible to identify two clusters of residues (66, 67, 140–143; and 1, 3, 4, 9, 150, 152, 153, respectively) that are part of discontinuous epitopes.

It has been known since the early 1950s that the antigenic properties of intact TMV particles are different from those of dissociated coat protein submits (Jeener et al., 1954; Takahashi and Ishii, 1952). The terms 'neotope', 'cryptotope' and 'metatope' were subsequently introduced to distinguish between the epitopes found on virions and dissociated subunits (Van Regenmortel, 1966). Once anti-TMV Mabs had been obtained, it became easier to distinguish these various types of epitopes and to map them on the surface of the viral antigen (Dore et al., 1988, 1990; Saunal and Van Regenmortel, 1995a). Immunoelectron microscopy using gold-labelled antibodies was used to visualize the location of neotopes and metatopes on TMV particles. Data obtained by electron microscopy and ELISA could be compared by experimenting on electron microscope grids deposited at the bottom of microtitre wells. The assay was carried out in one well with the usual ELISA reagents while in a duplicate well, the reacting antigen was visualized by replacing the enzyme-labelled antibodies by gold-labelled Mabs, followed by examination of the grids in the electron microscope (Dore et al., 1988).

Most Mabs raised against TMVP were found to be specific for metatopes and were located at one of the two extremities of viral rods. By partly uncovering the 5' end of the RNA in virus particles by the action of 6 M urea before the immunoassay, it could be shown that these metatopes were located at the end of the virion containing the 5' end of the RNA (Dore et al., 1990). Since this is the extremity of viral rods that becomes disassembled first during the infection process (Wilson et al., 1984), it is not entirely surprising that these antimetatope Mabs were able to block the disassembly of virions and the translation of viral RNA (Saunal and Van Regenmortel, 1995a; Saunal et al., 1993).

Two-site binding assays with Mabs were used to determine the relative position of epitopes on surfaces A and E of the TMVP subunit. By determining the binding stoichiometry with a biosensor instrument (Saunal and Van Regenmortel, 1995b), it was easy to ascertain if Mabs bind to only one extremity of TMV particles, or along the entire length of virions (Fig. 1.6). The precise location of several epitopes on TMVP surfaces A and E was determined from pairwise interaction data by assuming that the combining sites of the antibodies cover a surface of 600 Å^2 in a circular footprint (Braden et al., 1995). The resulting epitope map shown in Fig. 1.7 provides some insight in the mechanism by which certain anti-TMV antibodies are capable of inhibiting the disassembly of TMV by ribosomes. Since Mabs 25P, 151P, 167P, 181P and 188P which possessed the

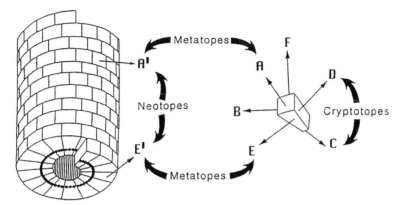

Fig. 1.6. Schematic representation of the coat protein subunits of TMV in monomeric form and in the virus particle. Neotopes are found on surfaces A′ and E′. Metatopes are found on surfaces A, A′, E and E′. Cryptotopes are found on surfaces B, C, D and E. The type of epitope on surface F has not been defined. The E′ extremity of the virion contains the 5′ end of the RNA.

strongest inhibitory capacity bind to the region of surface E that is known to interact with the viral RNA, it was concluded that the inhibitory Mabs act by sterically preventing the interaction between RNA and ribosomes (Saunal and Van Regenmortel, 1995a).

When biosensors were used to analyze the reaction, it was found that when a monomeric TMVP molecule was captured by certain antimetatope Mabs, it underwent a conformational change which then allowed it to be recognized by an antineotope Mab (Dubs et al., 1992; Saunal and Van Regenmortel, 1995a). The induction of a neotope conformation in monomeric viral subunits following binding of the subunit to a first antibody probably mimics at least partly the conformational change that occurs in the subunits when they assemble into virions. However, not all antineotope Mabs become capable of recognizing dissociated TMVP after it has reacted with a first antimetatope antibody. In such cases, the antineotope antibodies probably recognize an epitope formed by the juxtaposition of residues from two neighbouring subunits. Additional information

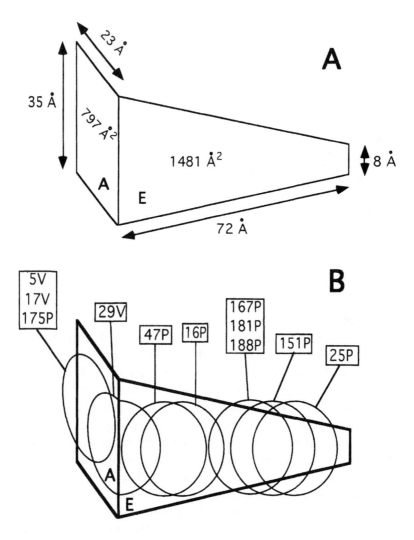

Fig. 1.7. (A) Schematic model of surfaces A and E of the TMVP subunit. (B) Schematic epitope maps constructed from pairwise interaction data with Mabs, using biosensor technology. Mabs 25P, 151P and 181P strongly inhibit the disassembly of the virus by blocking the interaction of the viral RNA with ribosomes (from Saunal and Van Regenmortel, 1995a, reprinted with permission).

on the antigenic properties of TMV can be obtained in a recent review (Van Regenmortel, 1999a).

1.6. Antigenicity prediction

1.6.1. General principles

The accumulated knowledge of the antigenic structure of several well-characterized proteins has given rise to the expectation that it may be possible to find empirical rules for predicting the position of epitopes in proteins. When the three-dimensional structure of a protein is known, it is a simple matter to identify the most accessible residues and to predict that these will be part of the protein epitopes. In fact, a good correlation has been found to exist between the parts of a protein that protrude and the experimentally determined antigenic regions of proteins (Novotny et al., 1986; Thornton et al., 1986). However, such an approach obviously is of little use for predicting the continuous epitopes of proteins of unknown three-dimensional structure. For the vast majority of proteins known today, the only available structural information concerns their amino acid sequences which are deduced from the nucleotide sequence of the corresponding gene. In this case, antigenicity prediction involves the identification of the segments in the sequence that are expected to bind to antibodies raised to the intact protein. The corresponding peptides which represent continuous epitopes can then be synthesized in order to raise antipeptide antibodies that are expected to recognize the parent protein (Friede et al., 1994; Walter, 1986).

Although only a small fraction of the total immune response against a protein is usually responsible for the observed cross-reaction between the intact protein and peptide fragments, this limited cross-reactivity is of considerable practical significance (Van Regenmortel, 1992b). It is now widely appreciated that antibodies to continuous epitopes are useful immunochemical reagents for isolating and characterizing gene products (Lerner, 1984; Walter, 1986) and in diagnostic immunoassays (Joisson et al., 1992; Leinikki et al., 1993; Maruyama et al., 1992).

It is important to realize that prediction methods based on the analysis of linear sequences cannot provide information on the location of discontinuous epitopes. In the absence of tertiary structure information, it is not possible to identify or predict which residues along a linear sequence contribute to a particular discontinuous epitope. Hopp (1993) has claimed that his hydrophilicity prediction method is applicable to discontinuous epitopes but such a claim overlooks the fact that is is meaningless to predict antigenicity in individual, noncontiguous residues along a peptide chain. In order to predict the actual location of a discontinuous epitope, it is necessary to establish which particular set of noncontiguous residues come together to collectively form such an epitope (Van Regenmortel and Pellequer, 1994).

Since epitopes need to be accessible at the antigen surface in order to be recognized by B-cell receptors or by antibodies, several methods of antigenicity prediction have been developed which in some way rely on predicted accessibility. Hopp and Woods (1981), for instance, postulated that since epitopes must be accessible to the solvent, they should correspond to regions of the protein that are particularly hydrophilic and contain most of the charged residues. Studies with a few well-characterized proteins have, indeed, shown that parameters such as hydrophilicity, accessibility and flexibility of short segments of the polypeptide chain tend to be correlated with the location of continuous epitopes (Hopp, 1986; Pellequer et al., 1991).

Prediction calculations are based on propensity scales for each of the 20 amino acids which reflect different physicochemical parameters that have been associated with antigenicity. The following five properties have been used for developing propensity scales (Pellequer et al., 1994).

Hydrophilicity or inverted hydrophobicity. These are the most widely used scales. In hydrophobicity scales, the more hydrophobic amino acids have the highest positive values while the more hydrophilic ones have the highest negative values. An inverted hydrophobicity scale corresponds to a hydrophobicity scale in which values are multiplied by 1.

About a dozen different scales of hydrophilicity or hydrophobicity have been derived from measurements of partition coefficients of amino acids between two noninteracting isotropic phases as well as by several other methods (Pellequer et al., 1994). The most commonly used scales are those of Hopp and Woods (1981), Kyte and Doolittle (1982) and Parker et al. (1986).

Accessibility. Accessibility scales are based on the measurement of surface accessibility of each amino acid in a series of globular proteins of known three-dimensional structure (Hopp, 1984b). The results can be expressed, for instance, as the proportion of residues that have 95% of their atoms buried (Chothia, 1976).

Flexibility. The flexibility scale of Karplus and Schulz (1985) is based on values of the temperature B factors of the α-carbons of 31 proteins of known tertiary structure. Another accessibility scale has been developed by Ragone et al. (1989).

Antigenicity. The antigenicity scale developed by Welling et al. (1985) is based on the relative frequency with which different amino acids are found in the continuous epitopes of a few proteins of known antigenic structure.

Secondary structure. These scales are based on the predictions of certain elements of secondary structure such as turns or helices derived from statistical analysis of proteins of known structure (Hopp, 1986; Krchnak et al., 1989; Pellequer et al., 1993). The core of proteins usually contains a combination of helices and sheets which are hydrophobic. Since the core is mostly devoid of water molecules, the formation of intramolecular hydrogen bonds is favoured. In contrast, turns and loops are situated on the surface of the protein in contact with solvent and they are thus both accessible and hydrophilic (Rose et al., 1985b). In addition, loops tend to be flexible which is also a property associated with antigenicity (Westhof et al., 1984). The two most commonly used algorithms for predicting secondary structure are those of Chou and Fasman (1978) and Garnier et al. (1978). The success rate of these two algorithms has been found to be only 55–70% (Kabsch and Sander, 1983; Rooman and Wodak, 1988).

In order to compare the prediction results obtained with different scales it is necessary to normalize the scales. This is usually done within the values +3 and –3 which correspond to the range of values of the first hydrophilicity scale used for antigenicity prediction (Hopp and Woods, 1981). Different normalized scales that have been used to construct antigenicity prediction profiles are listed in Table 1.6. When these scales are used to construct prediction profiles, the scale value for each amino acid is not assigned to the corresponding position in the sequence. Instead, a so-called 'window' is used that allows a certain segment of the protein to be analyzed. A window of 5 residues is suitable for locating turns while a window of 7 residues is most commonly used for predicting continuous epitopes. Values taken from the propensity scale are introduced for each amino acid of the window and the arithmetical mean is then calculated and assigned to the centre of the window. The window is then shifted by 1 residue and the process is repeated. Each mean value is placed on a graph where the abscissa represents the protein sequence and the ordinate the average propensity value of the window. In order to eliminate excessive fluctuations in the profiles, it is customary to use a smoothing procedure. One smoothing approach consists of assigning a certain weight to each position in the window by which the value of each residue will be multiplied before averaging. Karplus and Schulz (1985), for instance, assigned the following weights to each of the seven positions of the window in order to emphasize the central value: 0.25; 0.50; 0.75; 1.0; 0.75;

TABLE 1.6

Normalized scales for 20 common amino acids used to construct antigenicity prediction profiles. (The published original values of the scales have been normalized between +3 and 3 by the PREDITOP program, except in the case of scale 21, which was left unchanged)

References	Arg	Asp	Glu	Lys	Ser	Asn	Gln	Gly	Pro	Thr	Ala	His	Cys	Met	Val	Ile	Leu	Tyr	Phe	Trp
Inverted hydrophobicity scales																				
(1)	3.00	2.30	2.30	2.60	0.50	2.30	2.30	0.30	1.10	0.50	1.20	2.10	1.70	1.30	2.80	3.00	2.50	0.90	1.90	0.60
(2)	3.00	1.82	1.37	0.86	0.04	0.46	0.31	0.40	0.59	0.13	0.70	0.62	0.85	1.21	1.00	1.15	1.12	0.07	1.42	1.00
(3)	1.22	2.14	1.04	1.60	1.74	1.53	1.17	0.47	1.59	1.25	0.10	0.75	1.85	1.60	3.00	2.95	2.14	0.57	1.19	1.11
(4)	0.12	2.63	1.49	2.05	1.13	0.95	1.69	0.83	1.27	1.45	0.55	0.39	1.61	2.14	2.26	2.16	3.00	0.34	2.14	0.29
(5)	1.10	1.50	1.50	3.00	0.80	1.30	1.50	0.10	1.10	0.20	0.40	1.00	3.00	2.10	2.30	2.50	1.90	0.70	2.50	2.10
(6)	0.92	2.04	1.90	1.04	0.86	1.43	1.42	1.04	0.76	0.43	0.62	0.60	0.26	1.59	1.42	1.95	1.90	2.60	3.00	0.78
(7)	0.40	2.99	1.33	2.58	1.34	2.10	1.27	1.11	2.08	1.32	0.42	0.60	1.56	2.47	2.41	2.74	3.00	1.65	2.75	0.22
(8)	3.00	2.14	1.87	2.03	0.54	0.94	0.74	0.65	0.32	0.70	0.81	0.44	0.92	1.30	1.08	1.22	1.14	3.18	1.39	0.89
Hydrophilicity scales																				
(9)	3.00	3.00	3.00	3.00	0.30	0.20	0.20	0.00	0.00	0.40	0.50	0.50	1.00	1.30	1.50	1.80	1.80	2.30	2.50	3.40
(10)	0.87	2.46	1.86	1.28	1.50	1.64	1.37	1.28	0.30	1.15	0.03	0.30	0.11	1.41	1.27	2.45	2.78	0.78	2.78	3.00
Accessibility scales																				
(11)	2.10	0.30	0.60	3.00	0.80	0.10	0.60	1.70	0.30	0.60	1.70	0.80	3.00	1.90	2.30	2.60	2.10	0.10	2.10	1.70
(12)	3.00	1.60	1.30	2.80	0.90	1.90	2.40	0.60	1.30	0.80	0.80	1.40	2.00	1.00	2.40	3.00	1.50	1.60	2.00	0.40
(13)	1.75	0.95	0.11	0.68	1.84	0.58	0.32	2.98	0.78	1.04	2.11	0.54	1.18	0.66	0.35	0.59	0.56	1.81	1.80	3.00
(14)	0.30	2.10	0.50	1.40	1.80	2.30	0.20	3.00	2.60	0.10	0.50	0.40	2.60	1.80	1.70	2.50	2.50	2.00	2.70	3.00
Flexibility scales																				
(15)	0.20	0.30	1.20	1.10	3.00	1.70	2.90	2.30	0.20	0.62	0.10	1.60	2.10	2.50	1.60	1.10	2.00	2.10	2.90	3.00
(16)	0.88	1.39	0.28	0.05	1.92	0.96	0.17	2.57	1.12	1.22	1.76	0.13	0.55	1.08	0.56	1.50	1.18	1.70	1.96	3.00
Antigenicity scale																				
(17)	0.80	0.90	0.30	2.10	0.10	0.30	0.20	1.30	0.10	0.10	1.30	3.00	0.70	3.00	0.20	2.20	1.00	0.40	0.90	0.70
Turn scales																				
(18)	0.21	2.47	1.32	0.09	2.31	3.00	0.06	3.00	2.78	0.16	1.74	0.21	1.04	2.06	2.59	2.75	2.11	0.78	2.06	0.16
(19)	1.01	1.50	2.35	0.46	1.26	2.05	0.17	2.79	1.75	0.12	2.50	0.17	2.15	2.40	3.00	3.00	2.80	1.40	0.91	1.75
(20)	0.22	1.43	0.11	0.02	1.15	1.02	0.08	2.15	3.00	0.27	0.56	0.85	0.44	1.69	1.50	1.38	1.16	0.30	1.13	0.60
(21)	0.95	0.81	0.84	0.97	0.65	0.78	0.84	0.48	0.75	0.70	0.49	0.66	0.26	0.48	0.36	0.34	0.40	0.76	0.42	0.51

(1) Kyte and Doolittle (1982), (2) Von Heijne (1981), (3) Manavalan and Ponnuswamy (1978), (4) Cornette et al. (1987), (5) Rose et al. (1985a), (6) Sweet and Eisenberg (1983), (7) Engelman et al. (1986), (8) Zimmerman et al. (1968), (9) Hopp and Woods (1981), (10) Parker et al. (1986), (11) Janin et al. (1978), (12) Chothia (1976), (13) Chothia (1984), (14) Karplus and Schultz (1985), (15) Ragone et al. (1989), (16) Welling et al. (1985), (17) Welling et al. (1985), (18) Chou and Fasman (1978), (19) Garnier et al. (1978), (20) Garnier et al. (1978a), (21) Levitt (1976a), (21) Emini et al. (1985).

0.50; and 0.25. Another type of smoothing based on the proce-
dure used in the University of Wisconsin Genetics Computer Group
(UWGCG) programs (Devereux el al., 1984) has been applied by
Jameson and Wolf (1988).

The PREDITOP program developed by Pellequer and Westhof
(1993) smooths the window by a Gaussian function which empha-
sizes the centre of the window and decreases the importance of the
neighbours. The function is,

$$F(x) = \frac{1}{\sigma\sqrt{2\pi}}\exp\left(-\frac{(x_i - x_j)^2}{2\sigma^2}\right)$$

where x_i is the point to be smoothed with i varying from 1 to the
window length, and x_j is the mean of the window (Van Regenmortel
and Daney de Marcillac, 1988). The best smoothing is achieved
by using the value of $\sigma = 2$. Each value within the window is
multiplied by the corresponding value of the Gaussian function.

In the PREDITOP program, the calculations of each successive
window creates a file in ASCII form, in which the centres of all
the shifted windows are written, one per line. The first line of the
result file is filled by the length of the protein and the last two lines
correspond to the mean and standard variation around the mean of
all values. The PREDITOP program then calculates and displays a
protein profile using the sequence of the protein and one of several
propensity scales. The PREDITOP program can be obtained on re-
quest from the authors (Pellequer and Westhof, 1993; Pellequer et
al., 1993, 1994).

1.6.2. Review of propensity scales

Some of the most commonly used scales are described below.

1.6.2.1. Hydrophilicity scale of Hopp and Woods (1981)
Hopp and Woods (1981) were the first to establish a link between
hydrophilicity and the location of epitopes at the surface of proteins.

An example of an hydrophilicity plot is shown in Fig 1.8. They constructed a scale of the hydrophilicity of the 20 amino acids based on solvent parameters assigned to amino acids by Levitt (1978). Some of scale values of Levitt were modified since this improved the level of correct predictions. The four charged residues (Asp, Glu, Lys and Arg) were given the maximum value of 3.0 and the value for proline was increased from −1.4 to 0. In the profiles constructed with this scale, not all hydrophilicity peaks correspond to epitopes and all known epitopes of a protein are not necessarily located in the most hydrophilic regions (Hopp and Woods, 1983). The quality of the predictions was assessed by counting the number of known epitopes in 12 proteins located correctly (C) in peaks, or wrongly (W) outside peaks. The ratio C/C + W was taken as the percentage of correct prediction. This method of assessing prediction efficacy ignores the peaks situated in regions where no epitopes have been identified by mapping studies and leads to a spuriously high rate of successful predictions (Hopp, 1993; Van Regenmortel and Pellequer, 1994). Problems encountered in the assessment of the comparative efficacy of different prediction scales are discussed in Section 1.6.3.

1.6.2.2. Hydropathy scale of Kyte and Doolittle (1982)
Kyte and Doolittle (1982) devised a scale for predicting which residues are located on the outside of a protein. This hydropathy scale was based on two types of correlated interactions: the access of hydrophilic side chains to the aqueous solvent and the minimization of the contact between hydrophobic side chains and water. The authors measured amino acid partition coefficients between water and a noninteracting isotropic phase and calculated the free-energy change. These values together with the solvent accessibility values of amino acids determined by Chothia (1976) were used to construct the hydropathy scale. Some of the values for individual amino acids were adjusted somewhat arbitrarily. For instance, the value for Arg was the lowest and was set at −4.5 because the highest value in the scale was +4.5.

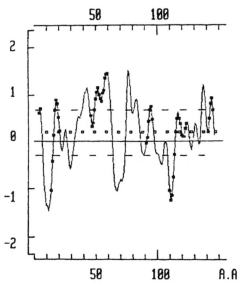

Fig. 1.8. Hydrophilicity profile of myoglobin calculated with the scale of Hopp and Woods (1981) using the smoothing procedure of Van Regenmortel and Daney de Marcillac (1988). The black squares correspond to amino acids known to be part of continuous epitopes of myoglobin (see Table 1.4). The white squares represent the average value of the hydrophilicity parameter over the entire sequence and the two horizontal broken lines correspond to ±0.7 SD from the mean. The plot is traced from the 4th residue on wards and until the (n 3)th residue.

1.6.2.3. Hydrophilicity scale of Parker et al. (1986)

Parker et al. (1986) constructed a hydrophilicity scale based on peptide retention times observed during high-performance liquid chromatography on a reversed-phase column. The scale consisted of retention times normalized from +10 to −10 and the peptides were of the type: acetyl-Gly-X-X-(Leu)-(Lys)$_2$-amide where X represents the studied amino acid. The scale also incorporated values for increased hydrophilicity caused by the presence of charged groups at the C- and N-termini of protein sequences. The value +9.7 was added to the N-terminal residue and the value +14.3 to the

C-terminal residue. The scale was used to construct hydrophilicity profiles using a window of 7 residues.

Parker et al. (1986) also constructed composite surface prediction profiles by combining their own hydrophilicity profile with the surface accessibility profile of Janin (1979) and the flexibility profile of Karplus and Schulz (1985). From each profile, the highest peaks were given the value of 100 and the mean value was put at 0. Any residues with a profile value greater than 25% above the mean value were defined as surface sites. The three plots were then superimposed to give a composite profile value. A 50% cut-off line in the composite profile was taken as threshold for the prediction of antigenic residues. (A program for generating composite profiles is available for the IBM-PC or Macintosh computer from the Biochemistry Department, University of Alberta, Edmonton, Canada T6G 2H7.)

1.6.2.4. Acrophilicity scale of Hopp (1984b)
Hopp (1984b) developed the acrophilicity scale by measuring the relative degree of exposure of amino acids in 49 proteins of known structure. He used stereo-paired α-carbon drawings and identified the amino acids located in each protein protrusion. The scale was obtained by measuring the distance between the centre of the protein and each amino acid in protruding regions. The acrophilicity scale contains the same residues with positive values as the Hopp and Woods (1981) scale, but higher values were attributed to residues that are frequently found at the surface of proteins (glycine, proline, asparagine and aspartic acid).

1.6.2.5. Flexibility scale of Karplus and Schulz (1985)
Following two reports (Tainer et al., 1984; Westhof et al., 1984) which described a link between segmental mobility and antigenicity, Karplus and Schulz (1985) developed a method for predicting the flexibility of protein segments. The method is based on the known temperature B factors of the α-carbons of 31 proteins of known structure. The amino acids were found to be separated into

two classes comprising 10 flexible and 10 rigid residues. The rigid residues (Ala, Leu, His, Val, Tyr, Ile, Phe, Cys, Trp and Met possessed average values lower than 1. Three scales for the amino acids, called BNORM0, BNORM1 and BNORM2, were derived which correspond to different degree of rigidity in the neighbouring residues. BNORM0 is the scale that applies when none of the two neighbouring residues is rigid. BNORM1 is the scale used when one of the two neighbouring residues is rigid and BNORM2 when both neighbouring residues are rigid. The profile, therefore, takes into account the flexible nature of a stretch of residues and not only the propensity of single residues.

1.6.2.6. Antigenicity scale of Welling et al. (1985)

Welling et al. (1985) constructed an antigenicity scale based on the statistical analysis of the 606 amino acids found in 69 continuous epitopes of 20 proteins. Each amino acid was characterized by its frequency of appearance in antigenic regions. The scale values were obtained by dividing the frequency of appearance of an antigenic residue by the frequency of each amino acid found in the National Biomedical Research Foundation protein data base (Dayhoff, 1978).

1.6.2.7. Antigenicity index of Jameson and Wolf (1988)

Jameson and Wolf (1988) developed an algorithm that combined different profiles representing different aspects of protein architecture. Two scales of secondary structure (Chou and Fasman, 1974; Garnier et al., 1978) were used as well as scales of hydrophilicity (Kyte and Doolittle, 1982), accessibility (Emini et al., 1985) and flexibility (Karplus and Schulz, 1985). After giving each parameter a certain weight, the sum of the five curves was computed which gave rise to a so-called 'antigenic index'. The weights were chosen so that 40% of the index was derived from the secondary structure component. The accessibility and flexibility parameters were each given a weight of 15% and the remaining 30% were allocated to inverted hydrophobicity. The choice of weights was arbitrary and it is possible that a different combination could improve the prediction success of the antigenic index.

1.6.2.8. Turn scales of Pellequer et al. (1993)

It has been known for many years that epitopes are often located in turns (Dyson et al., 1985; Rose et al., 1985b; Schulze-Gahmen et al., 1985), and this has led to the use of turns for antigenicity prediction (Jameson and Wolf, 1988; Krchnak et al., 1989). Pellequer et al. (1993) developed new turn scales based on the occurrence of amino acids at each of the four positions of a turn using a three-dimensional database of 87 proteins. Only β-turns consisting of 4 residues were considered (Richardson, 1981) and the turn identification was based on the hydrogen bond pattern between the residue i and $i + 3$ (Kabsch and Sander, 1983). Three classes of turns were identified: the nonspecific '33' turn, the hairpin 'EE' turn and the 3_{10} helical turn labelled '10' turn. For each of the scales, the four positions in the turn were handled separately by calculating four profiles corresponding to be first, second, third and fourth position of a turn (Pellequer and Westhof, 1993). The final value assigned to each residue in the sequence was obtained by adding (ADDITIO procedure) or multiplying (MULTIPLI procedure) the four files, using the PREDITOP package (Pellequer and Westhof, 1993). The level of correct antigenicity prediction obtained with these turn scales was about 70%, which is higher than the levels achieved with other prediction algorithms. The major difference compared to other methods is that a much smaller number of antigenicity peaks are predicted, on the average about two peaks per prediction per protein (see Fig. 1.9). By eliminating incorrect predictions, the investigator who wants to identify regions that give rise to antipeptide antibodies cross-reactive with a protein avoids the synthesis of what are likely to be ineffective peptides.

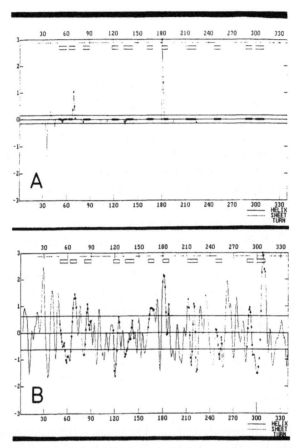

Fig. 1.9. Antigenicity prediction profiles of renin constructed with: (A) the TURN33 scale of Pellequer and Westhof (1993); and (B) the turn scale of Levitt (1978). The two plain lines around the mean correspond to ±0.7 SD. Rectangles at the top of the profiles correspond to the known epitopes of renin with the circles drawn on the curves corresponding these residues. The secondary structure is shown above the rectangles. The plain line corresponds to a helix, a dashed line to a sheet and a dotted line to a turn. In (A), only 3 peaks are obtained by the MULTIPLY procedure, leading to a correct prediction of 83%. In (B), 21 peaks were obtained leading to a correct prediction of 42%. The PREDITOP method of Pellequer and Westhof (1993) predicts a small number of antigenicity regions with a high level of confidence (from Pellequer et al., 1993; reprinted with permission).

1.6.3. Comparative efficacies of different prediction scales

A number of different approaches have been used to measure the efficacy of antigenicity prediction achieved with different scales. A simple method is to compare the position of the peaks in the profile with the position of known epitopes in the protein. Hopp (1993, 1986) and Callebaut et al. (1996) for instance assessed the quality of the prediction by counting the number of known epitopes located in peaks (C) and outside peaks (W). The ratio C/C + W was taken as the percentage of correct prediction. This approach is unsatisfactory because it does not take into account the number of incorrect predictions. Wrong predictions correspond to peaks located in regions where no epitopes have been identified by comprehensive mapping studies (Van Regenmortel and Pellequer, 1994). This requires, of course, that an extensive search for epitopes of the protein has been carried out. However, Hopp (1993) took the view that such peaks do not correspond to wrong predictions because they lie in regions of unknown antigenicity. In their analysis of prediction efficacy, Hopp and Woods (1981) considered that if the largest hydrophilicity peak was located in a known epitope and no valley coincided with an epitope, the prediction was 100% correct. They also allowed for an overlap of ± 2 residues in the localization of the highest peak, since each value did not correspond to a single residue but to an average.

Depending on the criteria of prediction efficacy that are used, different assessments of the comparative value of different methods are obtained. Parker et al. (1986) have taken into account only peaks higher than a certain threshold, while Getzoff et al. (1988) used a statistical method based on the random draw of certain values (Monte Carlo method). In this last method, none of the three prediction scales that were tested predicted better than random. When eight scales were compared by χ^2 statistical analysis (Van Regenmortel and Daney de Marcillac, 1988) none of the methods were found to achieve a high level of correct prediction.

In their analysis of prediction efficacy, Pellequer et al. (1991) counted amino acids located inside and outside known epitopes using a threshold of 0.7 times the standard deviation around the mean and only including amino acids about this threshold. Profiles of the type shown in Fig. 1.8 are used in these comparisons. Predicted residues located in known epitopes are assigned to class A while predicted residues outside any known epitope are assigned to class C. The ratio A/A + C expresses the prediction accuracy and takes into account the incorrect predictions by counting residues located outside any known epitope. This ratio is more precise than the C/C + W ratio of Hopp (1986) since it considers predicted residues instead of predicted peaks.

Table 1.7 presents the results of a comparison of 12 propensity scales applied to 14 well-studied proteins containing a total of 85 identified epitopes (Pellequer et al., 1994). The individual epitopes used in this study are listed in Pellequer et al. (1993).

The various hydrophobicity and hydrophilicity scales and the accessibility scales gave similar results, leading to 52–61% correct predictions (Table 1.7). The lowest level of correct prediction was obtained with the scale of Welling et al. (1985), which agreed with the rating of different methods reported earlier (Van Regenmortel and Daney de Marcillac, 1988). The most successful scales were the TURN33 and TURNEE scales which led to 70% correct prediction. The success of this turn prediction method is due to the fact that it attempts to predict only a limited number of epitopes but with a high probability of success (Pellequer et al., 1994).

Some authors have reported high scores of successful antigenicity prediction (Hopp, 1993, 1986; Weijer et al., 1986), but this results from the use of unreliable criteria of prediction efficacy. The fact that most prediction methods in current use achieve only a very modest success rate may seem surprising, in view of the considerable popularity of some of these methods. However, the low success rate of antigenicity prediction is not unexpected, since it mirrors fairly closely the limited success achieved in predicting tertiary structure from sequence data. The correlation between amino acid type and secondary structure element is poor, as illustrated by the fact that proteins with only 20–30% overall sequence identity can

TABLE 1.7

Comparative value of 12 antigenicity prediction scales applied to 14 proteins of known antigenic structures (Pellequer et al., 1994)

	Correctly predicted residues[a]	Wrongly predicted residues[a]	Ratio[b]	Percentage correct prediction[c]
Inverted hydrophobicity scale of Kyte and Doolittle (1982)	333	238	1.40	58
Inverted hydrophobicity scale of Rose et al. (1985a)	312	235	1.33	57
Hydrophilicity scale of Hopp and Woods (1981)	271	243	1.11	53
Hydrophilicity scale of Parker et al. (1986)	311	206	1.51	60
Accessibility scale of Chothia (1976)	289	228	1.27	56
Acrophilicity scale of Hopp (1984b)	317	215	1.47	60
Flexibility scale of Karplus and Schulz (1985)	385	383	1.01	50
Antigenicity scale of Welling et al. (1985)	232	294	0.79	44
Scale for turns of Chou and Fasman (1978)	302	186	1.62	62
Scale for turns of Levitt (1976b)	311	198	1.57	61
Scale for turns (TURNEE) of Pellequer et al. (1993)	77	33	2.33	70
Scale for turns (TURN33) of Pellequer et al. (1993)	27	12	2.25	69

[a] The columns correctly and wrongly predicted correspond to the number of correctly and wrongly predicted amino acids, respectively, above the cut-off level (+0.7 × SE).
[b] Ratio of correctly/wrongly predicted amino acids.
[c] Ratio (correctly predicted/(correctly predicted + wrongly predicted)) expressed as a percentage of correct prediction.

possess identical tertiary foldings (Neidhart et al., 1990). Further-more, identical short peptide sequences in unrelated proteins can have different conformations (Wilson et al., 1985). Clearly, meth-ods based on a uni-dimensional analysis do not cope very well with the three-dimensional nature of epitopes and it is of course unrealistic to try to reduce the complexity of discontinuous, con-formational epitopes to simple, linear peptide models (Hopp, 1994; Van Regenmortel and Pellequer, 1994).

Even if the analysis is restricted to the epitopes of a protein that can justifiably be labelled as continuous, there is another major limitation to high prediction scores. It is well known that some residues in a continuous epitope can usually be replaced by many or even all of the 19 amino acids without affecting the antigenic activity (Geysen et al., 1988). Mutagenesis experiments with the intact protein lead to the identification of the same nonessential, replaceable residues in the epitope (Alexander et al., 1992). Such indifferent, replaceable residues are probably not contact residues interacting with the antibody, although it cannot be excluded that their backbone atoms interact with the antibody. This has impor-tant implications for antigenicity prediction. When hydrophilicity or other propensity values of individual amino acids are averaged over a 7-residue window, the value that is inserted at each indif-ferent, replaceable position corresponds to the residue that happens by chance to occupy that position. Since any of the other 19 pos-sible values could have been inserted there to describe an epitope of equal antigenic activity, it is inevitable that considerable noise is introduced in the average value of the window. Therefore, an-other reason for the low level of correct antigenicity prediction is the presence in most continuous epitopes of indifferent residues not directly implicated in the binding interaction (Van Regenmortel and Pellequer, 1994).

1.7. T-cell epitopes

1.7.1. Nature of T-cell epitopes

For many years the antigenic properties of proteins were defined only in terms of B-cell epitopes recognized by antibodies and B-cell receptors. Once it was established that antigens are also recognized specifically by T cells, a second type of epitope known as T-cell epitope was defined which corresponds to linear fragments of the antigen that interact with T-cell receptors (TCRs). Whereas, B-cell receptors interact directly with intact antigen and recognize its three-dimensional structure, TCRs only recognize peptide fragments derived from the intracellular processing of the antigen and bound to major histocompatibility complex (MHC) molecules. MRC molecules are membrane glycoproteins, present at the surface of antigen-presenting cells (APC), which bind peptides generated by the cellular processing machinery and present them to TCR molecules. A T-cell epitope will thus be identified only if three conditions are met:

(1) an appropriate fragment must be generated by the intracellular processing of the antigen;

(2) a suitable MHC molecule must be present, bind the fragment and present it at the cell surface;

(3) a T cell with the appropriate TCR capable of recognizing the peptide-MHC antigen complex must be present.

Under normal in vivo conditions, the recognition of T-cell epitopes occurs at the interface between two cells, a T cell and an APC, and it involves a trimolecular complex consisting of a T-cell receptor, a peptide fragment and an MHC molecule. The TCR-peptide-MHC recognition triggers a cascade of intercellular signals which lead to the synthesis of various lymphokines that stimulate antibody-producing B cells or cytotoxic T lymphocytes. In general, the immune system will be capable of producing specific antibodies only if a T-cell epitope providing T cell help is administered together with the B-cell epitope immunogen (Zegers and Boersma, 1995).

The MHC molecules are divided into two classes, MHC classes I and II, that have similar overall structures. MHC class I molecules consist of a polymorphic 43 kD transmembrane glycoprotein (α-chain) which is noncovalently linked to a 12 kD microglobulin molecule. MHC class II molecules consist of two noncovalently associated polymorphic transmembrane glycoproteins, a 34 kD α-chain and a 29 kD β-chain. The structure of MHC classes I and II molecules has been determined by X-ray crystallography by Björkman et al. (1987) and Brown et al. (1993), respectively. In the human, MHC molecules are called 'human leukocyte antigen' (HLA) molecules.

Class I molecules are found on most cells, while class II molecules occur on macrophages and on B cells. In humans, over 100 different class I and class II molecules have been identified, although only three to six of these structural isoforms are expressed on the cells of any particular individual. Since each individual expresses only a small number of different MHC molecules, each isoform must be capable of binding to a very large number of distinct peptide antigens in order to enable the immune system to respond specifically to a wide variety of challenges. Each MHC molecule is capable of retaining a large variety of different peptides on the cell surface, long enough for T-cell recognition to occur. It is remarkable that a very restricted set of MHC molecules is capable of binding in a degenerate manner to thousands of different peptides with an affinity of the order of 10^7 M^{1} (Sette et al., 1994). This low specificity of peptide binding permits the presentation of virtually any T-cell epitope to the appropriate, highly specific TCR. Most-cells express 10^5–10^6 MHC mol/cell and the majority of these molecules contain bound peptides that are derived from the degradation of normal cellular proteins. These peptides can be eluted from the MHC molecules by acid extraction and it is possible to determine their sequence by Edman degradation analysis and mass spectrometry (Joyce and Nathenson, 1994). Over 2000 distinct peptides present at 100–4000 copies per cell have been identified in extracts from different classes I and II isoforms (Engelhard, 1994a, b).

Peptides that associate with class I molecules are usually generated from proteins synthesized in the cell cytoplasm, whereas peptides that associate with class II molecules originate from externally added proteins and are usually produced in the endosomal or lysosomal compartment. MHC class I molecules present endogenously derived peptides to cytotoxic T cells that express the accessory molecule CD8. A virus-infected cell for instance will present a peptide derived from a viral protein in association with class I molecules and this will target the infected cell for killing by the CTL. In contrast, MHC class II molecules present exogenously derived peptides to helper T cells that predominantly express the CD4 accessory molecule. A cell which picks up antigen from the extracellular environment will present a peptide in association with class II molecules, and this will lead to the recruitment of T helper cells.

Since peptides that are given the status of T-cell epitope are capable of binding both to an MHC molecule and to a TCR, it is possible to distinguish two separate functional sites on the peptide. The residues that interact with the MHC molecule have been called an agretope (Schwartz, 1985) while the residues that interact with the TCR actually form the so-called 'epitope'. However, the situation is further complicated by the fact that the TCR simultaneously recognizes residues of the peptide and residues of the bound MHC molecules. The T-cell epitope portion of the peptide, therefore, has no functional identity of its own, since its binding capacity is achieved only through the additional contribution of MHC residues whose position in space may also depend on the primary peptide-MHC (pMHC) interaction. The crystal structures of two TCR-pMHC complexes have shown that contacts between TCR and MHC are about three times more numerous than between the TCR and the peptide (Garboczi et al., 1996; Garcia et al., 1996).

1.7.2. The peptide-binding groove of MHC class I and II molecules

Although they differ in their domain organization both MHC molecules possess a similar peptide binding groove, the walls of which are formed by two α-helices and the floor by eight β-pleated strands. The polymorphic residues that line the binding groove determine the binding specificity of the MHC-peptide interaction. Crystallographic studies of human and mouse class I molecules have shown that the binding groove in these molecules is closed at both ends so that it can only accommodate peptides of defined length, usually 8–9 residues (Fremont et al., 1992; Silver et al., 1992). The amino- and carboxy-terminal ends of the peptide interact with conserved residues in two pockets of the binding groove, termed A and F, respectively. This gives rise to a common orientation of peptides in the binding site, with the amino terminal end in pocket A. The peptides are held in a largely extended conformation and binding of the peptide main chain is clustered at the two termini by a network of hydrogen bonds (see Fig. 1.10). The peptide carboxy-terminal residue is either an aliphatic hydrocarbon which then interacts with the Phe or Tyr residue present at position 116 of the complementary class I molecule, or it is a positively charged residue in which case it interacts with a class I molecule that has Asp at position 116. The most common length of peptides bound to class I is 9 residues, but longer peptides can be accommodated by bulging in the centre of the peptide (Guo et al., 1992).

The second common structural feature present in most peptides associated with class I molecules is the residue at position 2 (P2) which binds in the B pocket of the groove (Engelhard, 1994b). In the absence of strong selectivity at P2, there is usually a marked selectivity for residue 5 which interacts with the C pocket. Side chains at P2 and P5 are known as anchor side chains (Saper et al., 1991). The location of pockets A to F of a class I binding groove and the orientation of chains P1–P9 of a bound peptide in such a groove are illustrated in Fig. 1.11. The side chains at P1, P2, P3, P6, P7 and P9 fit into pockets A, B, D, C, E and F, respectively.

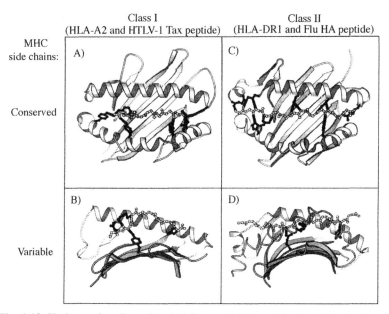

Fig. 1.10. Hydrogen bonding of a viral Tax peptide bound in the cleft of a class I MHC molecule and of an influenza haemagglutin (HA) peptide bound in the cleft of a class II MHC molecule. (A) and (B): HLA – A2 (grey) and human T-lymphotropic 1 (HTLV–1) Tax peptide (white). (C) and (D): HLA-DR1 (grey) and influenza HA peptide (white). Hydrogen bonds are shown in black (A and C): top view of the peptide-binding cleft showing hydrogen bonds made to peptide by conserved MHC side chain and, for HLA-DR1, main chain atoms. (B and C): side view of the peptide-binding cleft, showing hydrogen bonds made to peptides by variable MHC side chains. The $\alpha 2$-helix has been omitted from (B) and is rendered as a thin coil in (D) (from Madden, 1995; reprinted with permission).

The side chains at P1, P4 and P5 of the peptide protrude toward the solvent and can be recognized by the TCR (Matsumura et al., 1992). Whereas class I molecules bind peptides of a fairly uniform length, class II molecules which have a binding groove that is open at both ends are capable of binding peptides ranging in length from 10 to more than 30 residues. The conserved residues of class II molecules that interact with the main chain atoms of the bound peptide are distributed along the entire length of the groove (Stern et al.,

1994). The peptide termini play only a secondary role in binding whereas the amide and carbonyl groups along the peptide main chain interact with MHC side chains. This produces a relatively sequence-independent (i.e. side-chain independent) binding of the peptide. The extensive contacts with the peptide main chain impose a clear polarity on the orientation of the bound peptide. If the orientation of the bound peptide were reversed, most of the MHC binding interactions with the peptide main chain would be disrupted. Furthermore, since in class I molecules the N- to C-terminal orientation of bound peptides is dictated by conserved hydrogen bonds involving the peptide termini, it appears that the orientation of bound peptides is powerfully conserved in both classes I and II molecules (Madden, 1995). Sequences of peptides that have been shown to bind to MHC classes I and II molecules have been listed by Engelhard (1994a) and Stevanovic and Rammensee (1996).

1.7.3. T-cell receptor binding of peptide-MHC complexes

The binding of peptides to MHC molecules is the prerequisite for the antigen-specific T-cell recognition that regulates cellular interactions in the immune system. TCR molecules are disulfide-linked heterodimers composed of α and β (or γ and δ) chains consisting of V and C regions homologous to those of antibodies (Bentley et al., 1995). The crystal structure of two TCR-pMHC complexes has been established (Garboczi et al., 1996; Garcia et al., 1996, 1998). Loops homologous to the CDRs of Igs are present at the surface of the V region and form the antigen-binding site. This site interacts with side chains of the T-cell epitope that are prominently exposed at the surface of the pMHC complex and are known as 'flag' side chains (Madden, 1995). The upward-pointing orientation of peptide 'flag' side chains such as P1 and P4 is conserved in many pMHC complexes (Matsumura et al., 1992), suggesting that these residues are responsible for the specificity of recognition between the peptide and the TCR. Other peptide side chains make contact with both

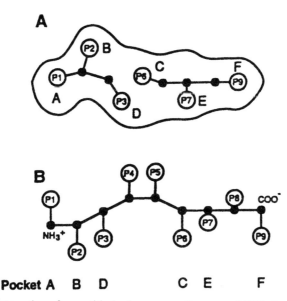

Fig. 1.11. Interaction of a peptide in the groove of a mouse MHC class I molecule. (A) The locations of pockets in the groove are shown by A, B, C, D, E and
F. Closed circles represent the backbone Cα and open circles represent the side
chains (P1–P9) of the peptide, respectively. The side chains at P1, P2, P3, P6, P7
and P9 fit into pockets A, B, D, C, E and F, respectively. (B) The side chains at P1,
P4 and P5 of the peptide protrude toward the solvent and, hence, can be recognized
by the TCR. The side chains at P2, P3, P6 and P9 face into the groove and are
unavailable for TCR recognition. The amino and carboxyl groups of the peptide
interact with the residues lining pockets A and F, respectively. The structures of
pockets A and F are well conserved among many class I molecules, but those of
pockets B to E differ from one class I molecule to another with respect to size and
chemical nature (from Matsumura et al., 1992; reprinted with permission).

the MHC molecule and the TCR (Fremont et al., 1992; Silver et
al., 1992; Stern et al., 1994). The binding of antigenic peptides may
also lead to conformational changes in MHC molecules and this
may contribute to the antigenic uniqueness of the resulting complex. There is considerable plasticity between the pMHC and TCR
interacting surfaces (Garcia et al., 1998). The large conformational
change in the framework of the TCR which accompanies pMHC

binding and the mechanism of the signal transduction that initiates
T-cell activation are not yet fully understood.

Reported values of the affinity of the TCR for its pMHC ligand
are rather low, which seems at odds with the high sensitivity and
specificity of T-cell binding. However, as argued by Karjalainen
(1994) it is possible that the high TCR concentration (10^{-5} M) in
the space between T cell and APC in the conjugate is sufficient to
drive the binding event.

Studies with T-cell epitopes presenting single amino acid substitutions have shown that when the affinity of the interaction between
the TCR and pMHC complexes is below a certain threshold, the
interaction results in antagonism instead of stimulation (Sette et al.,
1994). The fact that antigen analogs can act as powerful inhibitors
of T-cell activation suggests that it may be possible to develop peptides that will function as TCR competitive antagonists or partial
agonists. Such peptides may be able to modulate the type of undesirable immune responses present in allergy, graft rejection and
autoimmunity (Alexander et al., 1993). The potential use of peptides for modulating autoimmune diseases has been reviewed by
Gerritse (1995) and Zhang and Raus (1995).

1.7.4. Prediction of T-cell epitopes

in view of the ternary nature of pMHC-TCR interactions, the prediction of T-cell epitopes is even more difficult than that of B-cell
epitopes. As discussed in Section 1.7.2, the peptide-MHC interaction is highly promiscuous and each individual possesses only a
very small number of the more than 100 possible MHC classes I and
II molecules. Most T-cell epitope prediction methods only consider
the initial recognition step between peptide and MHC molecule and
do not address the issue of which residues actually interact with the
TCR.

The first attempts at predicting T-cell epitopes were made by the
groups of Berzofsky and Humphreys (Cornette et al., 1987; Stille

et al., 1987) who found that there was a correlation between T-cell presentation and the propensity of the corresponding peptide to take a helical conformation. It was initially believed that peptides with a helical structure might be able to fit in the groove of MHC molecules. When it was found that peptides bound to MHC molecules were always in an extended conformation, it was suggested that the correlation with helicity was due to the fact that helical coiling protected the peptide from proteolysis and facilitated its transfer to the MHC.

One algorithm for predicting amphipathic helices was based on the mean helical hydrophobic moment (Margalit et al., 1987) while another one used the strip-of-helix hydrophobicity index (Elliot et al., 1987). Another approach for predicting T-cell epitopes relied on the presence in the antigen sequence of motifs or patterns of 4 or 5 residues with specific chemical properties (Rothbard and Taylor, 1988). In the 4 residue motif, for instance, successive residues were charged or glycine, hydrophobic, hydrophobic, polar or glycine. Computer programs for locating such motifs in proteins are available (Kutubuddin et al., 1991). Several other motifs have been identified (Nicholson, 1994a) but none of them leads to high levels of successful prediction of CTL epitopes. The prediction of epitopes for MHC class II molecules is even less successful, as the binding motifs are even more degenerate than MHC class I motifs.

Recently, an empirical approach to epitope prediction has been developed which utilizes peptide binding assays to compare the affinities of peptides where each sequence position is sequentially mutated to all possible amino acids (Hammer et al., 1994; Reay et al., 1994). The information obtained in this way is used in a computer program which scans proteins for candidate T-cell epitopes. Another recently described method uses data from pool sequence analysis of peptides eluted form MHC class II molecules (Davenport et al., 1995). This empirical method is based on peptides that have been naturally processed and provides useful information without requiring the synthesis of large numbers of peptides.

Several reviews describing in detail the various approaches used for predicting T-cell epitopes are available (De Groot et al., 1997; Lu et al., 1992; Nicholson, 1994a).

CHAPTER 2

Peptide-carrier conjugation

S. MULLER

2.1. Introduction

Most authors agree that in order to produce antibodies against small peptides of molecular ratio (M_r) 700–1500, it is necessary to enhance their immunogenicity by coupling them to protein carriers (see Butler and Beiser, 1973). Furthermore, when short peptides are used as the immobilized antigen in solid-phase immunoassays, it is either necessary to modify the peptide (Loomans et al., 1997), or use peptide-carrier conjugates, since peptides of 6–15 residues generally do not bind satisfactorily to plastic surfaces.

The different coupling procedures that have been used to prepare peptide-carrier conjugates are listed in Table 2.1. In many instances, the chemistry of these conjugation reactions has not yet been elucidated. The aim of this chapter is to describe the different techniques in such a way that the investigator is able to choose the most appropriate procedure for his particular peptide. The choice of conjugation procedure is important since the antigenic activity of a peptide may be drastically affected by different coupling procedures (Briand et al., 1992b). The coupling of small molecules to carriers has many applications outside immunology (Pique et al., 1978; Talamo et al., 1968; Widder and Green, 1985). Several comprehensive reviews dealing with chemical modifications of proteins can be consulted to obtain information on the types of chemical intermolecular bridges that can be introduced into proteins (Atassi, 1977a; Boersma et al., 1993; Erlanger, 1980; Feeney et al., 1982; Glazer et al., 1975; Han et al., 1984; Hermanson, 1996; Kiefer,

1979; Means and Feeney, 1995; Peters and Richards, 1977; Rongen et al., 1997; Thorell and Larson, 1978).

Most procedures for preparing peptide-protein conjugates are based on the use of symmetrical or asymmetrical bifunctional reagents which either become incorporated into the final conjugate or activate certain reactive sites of the carrier protein molecule for subsequent linkage with the peptide. During the coupling reaction inter- but also intramolecular bridging can take place. Several factors such as protein concentration, ratio of coupling agent to protein, ionic strength and pH govern the kind of linkage obtained in the final product. For example, at low concentration of reactants, unwanted intramolecular linking reactions often predominate.

Although a wide range of coupling reagents has been reported in the literature, nearly all of them react primarily with the ε-amino group of lysine and the nucleophilic thiol of cysteine and only secondarily with the imidazole group of histidine and the phenolic hydroxyl group of tyrosine (Tables 2.1, 2.2). Only a few compounds such as bisimido esters are group-specific protein reagents.

2.2. Choice of carrier

Carrier molecules are chosen on the basis of criteria such as availability of reactive sites, size, solubility, immunogenicity, commercial availability and cost. The most commonly used carriers are listed in Table 2.3. One of the most important parameters that determines the suitability of a particular carrier molecule is the solubility of the final conjugate, since this may influence the accessibility of antigenic sites. When using the same coupling agent and peptide, some carriers may give insoluble conjugates while others give rise to soluble conjugates. Certain carriers are preferable when the peptide-carrier ratio is to be determined by amino acid analysis. Keyhole limpet haemocyanin (KLH), for instance, is not appropriate in this case since it has a high molecular weight and commercial preparations usually contain many impurities. In our laboratory, we

TABLE 2.1

Principal reagents used for peptide-protein conjugation[a]

Coupling agents	Modified amino acid		References
	Primary reactions	Secondary reactions	
Glutaraldehyde	ε-NH$_2$, α-NH$_2$, SH-Cys	Tyr, His	Habeeb and Hiramoto (1968)
Bisimido esters (DMA, DMS …)	α-NH$_2$, ε-NH$_2$Lys	Negligible	Means and Feeney (1971)
BDB	Tyr, SH-Cys, His, ε-NH$_2$Lys	Trp, Arg	Glazer et al. (1975)
Carbodiimides (EDC, MCDI…)	α-NH$_2$, ε-NH$_2$Lys α-COOH, Glu, Asp	Tyr, Cys	Goodfriend et al. (1964)
MBS	Cys-SH, NH$_2$ bridges	n.o.	Kitagawa and Aikawa (1976)
SPDP, MCS	Cys-SH, NH$_2$ bridges	n.o.	Carlsson et al. (1978); Lee et al. (1980)
Imido esters (2-iminothiolane)	Cys-SH, NH$_2$ bridges	n.o.	King et al. (1978)
IBCF	–COOH, NH$_2$ bridges	n.o.	Thorell and Larson (1978)
Toluene diisocyanate	α-NH$_2$, ε-NH$_2$Lys	n.o.	Talamo et al. (1968)
p-nitrobenzoyl chloride	Tyr, His, SH-Cys, ε-NH$_2$Lys	Trp, Arg	Anderer and Schlumberger (1965b)
p-amino phenyl acetic acid	α-NH$_2$, ε-NH$_2$Lys	His, Tyr	Spirer et al. (1977)
Cystamine dihydrochloride	SH-Cys	n.o.	Gilliland and Collier (1980)
EBIZ	α-NH$_2$, ε-NH$_2$Lys, –COOH	n.o.	Likhite and Sehon (1967)
Periodate oxidation	N-terminal Ser and Thr	Cys	Geoghegan and Stroh (1992); Zhang and Tam (1996)

[a] For abbreviations, see text, and list, p. vii.
n.o. = Not observed.

TABLE 2.2

Functional groups in proteins used in peptide-carrier conjugation

α-amino groups

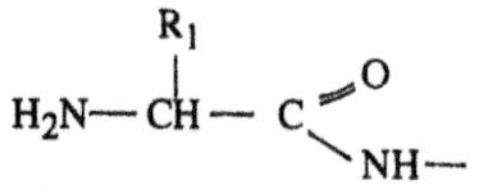

$$H_2N-\overset{\overset{\displaystyle R_1}{|}}{C}H-C\overset{\nearrow O}{\searrow}_{NH-}$$

ε-amino groups of lysine residues

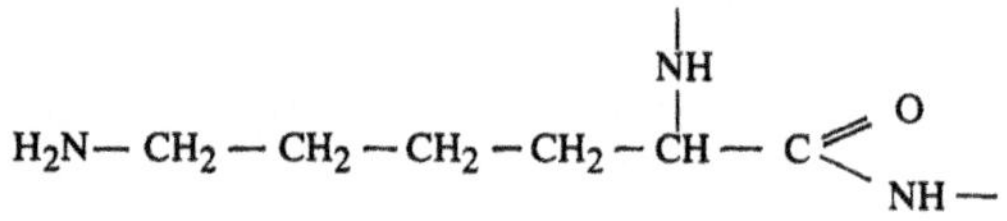

$$H_2N-CH_2-CH_2-CH_2-CH_2-\overset{\overset{\displaystyle NH}{|}}{C}H-C\overset{\nearrow O}{\searrow}_{NH-}$$

sulfhydryl groups of cysteine residues

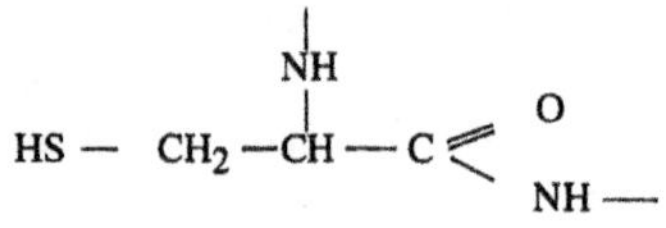

$$HS-CH_2-\overset{\overset{\displaystyle NH}{|}}{C}H-C\overset{\nearrow O}{\searrow}_{NH-}$$

phenolic hydroxyl groups of tyrosine residues

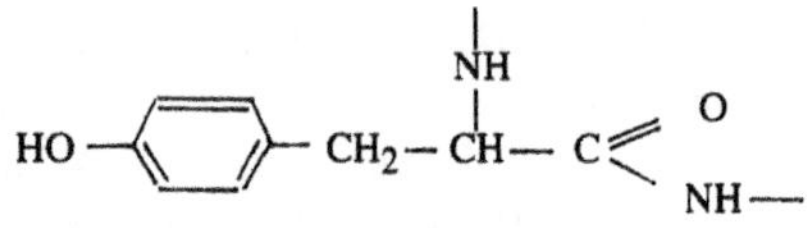

$$HO-\langle\bigcirc\rangle-CH_2-\overset{\overset{\displaystyle NH}{|}}{C}H-C\overset{\nearrow O}{\searrow}_{NH-}$$

imidazole groups of histidine residues

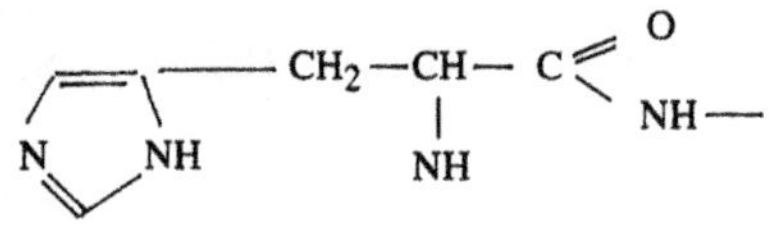

$$CH_2-\overset{|}{C}H-C\overset{\nearrow O}{\searrow}_{NH-}$$
$$\overset{}{\underset{NH}{|}}$$

α-carboxyl groups

$$-HN-\overset{\overset{\displaystyle}{|}}{C}H-COOH$$
$$\underset{Rn}{|}$$

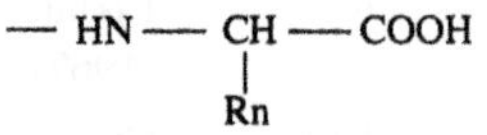

guanidino groups of arginine

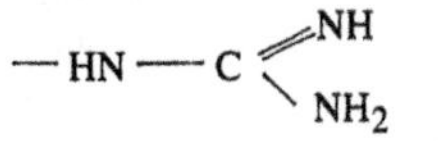

$$-HN-C\overset{\nearrow NH}{\searrow}_{NH_2}$$

currently use bovine serum albumin (BSA) for preparing peptide conjugates intended for use as antigens, and ovalbumin for preparing conjugates to be used for immunization. When this combination of carriers is used, BSA can be included as blocking agent in immunoassays without interference by the antiovalbumin antibodies present in the antipeptide-carrier antiserum.

Apart from presenting the peptide in a polyvalent fashion, the carrier can also exert an effect on the structure of the associated peptide and hence on its immunogenicity and antigenicity (Bahraoui et al., 1986b; Friede et al., 1994; Mariani et al., 1987). According to the point of attachment of the peptide to the carrier and the electrostatic and hydrophobic environment of this site, peptides can adopt different structures. In this regard, the use of liposomes as carrier of peptides presents several advantages over the protein constructs in that the surface of the liposome being uniform, it is probable that carrier effects on the structure of the peptide will be uniform (Friede et al., 1993c, 1994).

2.3. Optimal peptide density on carrier protein

Although it is possible to cover the surface of large carriers such as KLH with as many as 200–500 peptide molecules, this is seldom necessary and may even be detrimental for certain studies. It was found, for instance, that in the case of DNP-BSA conjugates, a small number (in the range 5–20) of DNP ligands per mol of carrier was sufficient for obtaining a good anti-DNP immune response whereas higher levels of substitution induced a tolerance effect (Desaymard and Howard, 1975; Klaus and Cross, 1974). A ratio of 5–20 mol of peptide per mol of carrier was found to be suitable for conjugates used either as immunogen or as antigen (Muller et al., 1986).

TABLE 2.3

Principal carriers used for coupling peptides

Carriers[a]	Usual abbrev.	M_r, kD	Number of groups				References[d]
			ε-NH₂ (Lys)	-SH (Cys)	phenol (Tyr)	imidazole (His)	
Bovine serum albumin	BSA	67	59[b]	35	19	17	(1)
Ovalbumin	OVA	43	20	6	10	7	(2)
Myoglobin	–	17	19	0	3	12	(1)
Tetanus toxoid	TT	150	106	10	81	14	(3)
Keyhole limpet haemocyanin[c]	KLH	>8000	6.9	1.7	7.0	8.7	(4)

[a] Other carriers have also been used such as thyroglobulin (669 kD), diphtheria toxoid, rabbit serum albumin, bovine or mouse γ-globulin (150 kD), poly (L-lysine) (15–300 kD), poly (L-glutamic acid) (15–100 kD), dipalmityl lysine, ficoll (40 kD) (Boyle et al., 1983; Fok et al., 1982; Hopp, 1984a; Lee et al., 1980; Talamo et al., 1968; Wheat et al., 1985).

[b] Only 30–35 of the 59 lysine residues of BSA are accessible.

[c] For KLH, the amino acid composition is expressed in g amino acid/100 g.

[d] References: (1) Dayhoff (1976); (2) Nisbet et al. (1981); (3) Bizzini et al. (1970); (4) Malley et al. (1965).

2.4. Point of attachment on peptide chain

For evident reasons, the coupling reaction should preferably not affect the configuration of amino acids that constitute the epitope. It is
important therefore, to select a coupling reagent that will crosslink
through specific groups situated preferably at either end of the
peptide and away from the presumed location of the epitope. It
is often advantageous during peptide synthesis to add a serine at
the N-terminus or a cysteine or tyrosine at the N- or C-terminus
of the peptide to serve as specific anchoring points for coupling. A
cysteine residue should also be added at either end of the peptide
when the latter is blocked by acetylation of the N-terminus or by
amidation of the C-terminus. The same type of residue should, of
course, not already be present in the antigenic sequence.

   Some authors prefer joining the peptide to the carrier via a spacer
in order to enhance the accessibility of the peptide moiety and avoid
harmful effects due to carrier proximity. A small number of glycine
or alanine residues are commonly introduced as spacers (Emini et
al., 1983; Mäkelä and Seppälä, 1986; McMillan et al., 1983).

2.5. Chemical coupling

In the following section, the properties of the most commonly used
coupling agents will be described.

2.5.1. Glutaraldehyde

2.5.1.1. Reaction mechanism
Although glutaraldehyde is the most extensively used coupling
reagent, the mechanism of reaction of glutaraldehyde with proteins is still not definitively established. Commercial preparations
of aqueous solution of 25% glutaraldehyde contain unstable derivatives of the aldehyde in the form of compounds of variable
molecular weight which easily revert to glutaraldehyde (Monsan

et al., 1975). At acidic pH (the pH of commercial solution is 3.1) glutaraldehyde is in equilibrium with its cyclic hemiacetal and polymers of the cyclic hemiacetal:

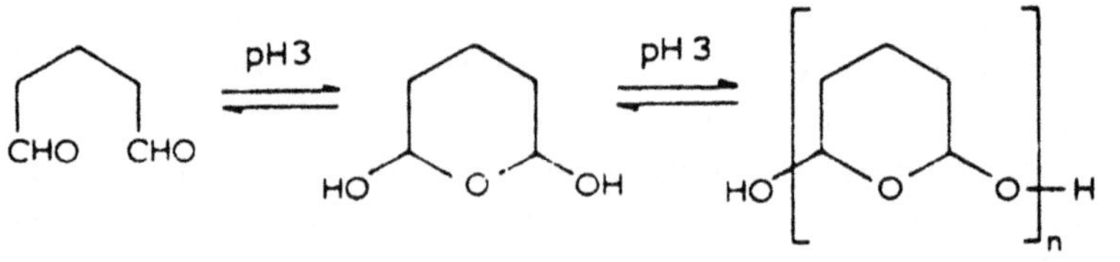

For the coupling reaction, the pH is raised to neutrality or to a slightly basic value (pH 7-8) and the dialdehyde is transformed into α, β-unsaturated aldehyde polymers:

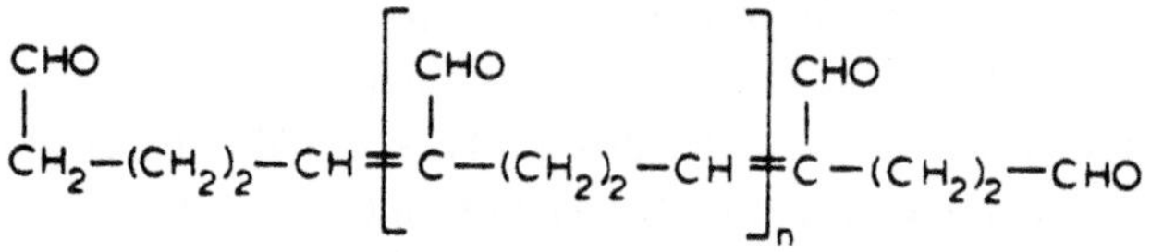

As the pH is raised, n increases until the polymer precipitates from solution (Peters and Richards, 1977).

At pH 7-8, the major reactive species (α, β-unsaturated aldehyde) appears to form a labile intermediate Schiff base with amino groups of the protein:

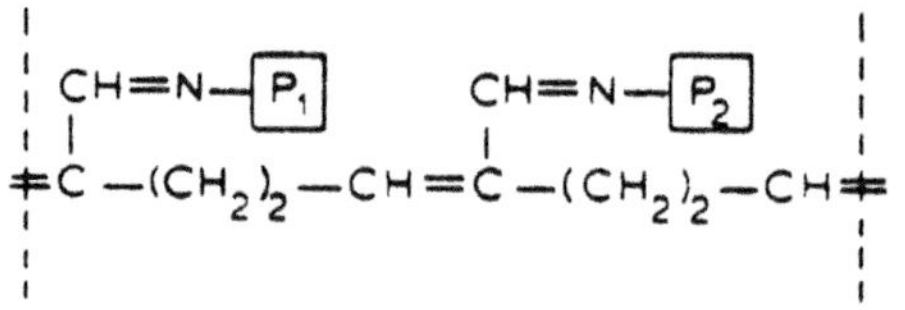

The resonance interaction of the Schiff base with the double bond is believed to lead to a stable final product. Another possible stabilization mechanism is a Michael-type addition which may occur at various sites when the local amine concentration is particularly high (Peters and Richards, 1977):

e.g.:

$$\underset{\underset{P_1}{|}}{\overset{\displaystyle CHO}{\underset{NH}{|}}}-(CH_2)_2-CH-CH-(CH_2)_2-CH-CH-\overset{\displaystyle CHO}{\underset{\underset{P_2}{|}}{\underset{NH}{|}}}$$

The reaction of glutaraldehyde with proteins involves mainly lysine residues (4 mol glutaraldehyde react per molecule of lysine; Korn et al., 1972) as well as the α-amino group and sulfhydryl group of cysteine. Secondary reactions with phenolic and imidazole groups have also been described (see Table 2.1).

2.5.1.2. Procedure (one-step method)
(a) Add peptide to a 1 mg/ml solution of carrier protein in phosphate buffered saline (PBS) pH 7.4 at a molar ratio of protein : peptide varying from 1 : 20 to 1 : 40. Cool at 4°C.
(b) Just before use, prepare a 2% (v/v) glutaraldehyde solution in water (e.g. Serva, Germany, 23114 or Fluka, Switzerland, 49626).
(c) Add dropwise an equal volume (e.g. 1 ml for 1 ml of peptide-carrier solution) of 2% glutaraldehyde solution to the protein mixture with constant stirring.
(d) After 1 h at 4°C, stop the reaction by addition of sodium borohydride (NaBH$_4$) to a final concentration of 10 mg/ml. Keep at 4°C for 1 h.
(e) dialyze against PBS (3 changes in 24 h) and store the conjugate at 4°C in presence of 0.02% sodium azide or in aliquots at – 20°C.

Note

This method is particularly adapted to peptides which do not contain internal lysine or cysteine residues. By using 0.05% glutaraldehyde instead to 1%, active conjugates have also been prepared with certain basic peptides. However, the coupling yield then drops from 70–80% to about 20% and the conjugate stability is decreased (see Section 2.9) (Briand et al., 1985).

Applications

Different coupling methods using glutaraldehyde have been successfully employed, for example with hormones (Reichlin, 1980), peptides of the large tumour antigen of simian virus 40 (Walter et al., 1980) and a (Gly)$_4$ peptide (Escribano, 1974). A procedure applicable for the conjugation of peptides with limited solubility in usual buffers has been described by Gerritse et al. (1991). In this method, peptides are dissolved in 8 M urea pH 7.0. A double-step method using glutaraldehyde with a preliminary activation of carrier and subsequent addition of peptide has also been applied by several authors (see Zegers et al., 1990).

2.5.2. Bisimido esters

2.5.2.1. Reaction mechanism

Bisimido esters are very soluble in water and react under mild conditions (pH 7–10) with a high degree of specificity with α- and ε-amino groups. The side reactions with thiol, phenolic, carboxyl, imidazolyl and guanidyl groups are negligible (Peters and Richards, 1977) (Table 2.1). The resulting amidine is stable and is resistant to total acid hydrolysis. Most of the bisimido esters are commercially available in highly purified form (Pierce, USA or Merck, Germany) (Table 2.4). The reaction of imido esters can be summarized as follows (Hartman and Wold, 1966):

TABLE 2.4

Principal bisimido esters used in coupling methods

Dimethyl adipimidate (DMA)	$Cl^-H_2^+N\!\!\diagdown\!\!C-CH_2-CH_2-CH_2-CH_2-C\!\!\diagup^{+}\!\!NH_2Cl^-$ $H_3CO\diagup$ $\diagdown OCH_3$ M_r 245.2, 8.6 Å
Dimethyl pimelimidate (DMP)	$Cl^-H_2^+N\!\!\diagdown\!\!C-CH_2-CH_2-CH_2-CH_2-CH_2-C\!\!\diagup^{+}\!\!NH_2Cl^-$ $H_3CO\diagup$ $\diagdown OCH_3$ M_r 259.2, 9.2 Å
Dimethyl suberimidate (DMS)	$Cl^-H_2^+N\!\!\diagdown\!\!C-CH_2-CH_2-CH_2-CH_2-CH_2-CH_2-C\!\!\diagup^{+}\!\!NH_2Cl^-$ $H_3CO\diagup$ $\diagdown OCH_3$ M_r 273.2, 11Å

Dimethyl 3,3'-dithiobispropionimidate (DTPB)[a]

$Cl^-H_2^+N\!\!\diagdown\!\!C-CH_2-CH_2-S-S-CH_2-CH_2-C\!\!\diagup^{+}\!\!NH_2Cl^-$
$H_3CO\diagup$ $\diagdown OCH_3$
M_r 309.3, 11.9 Å

[a] Commonly called the Wang and Richards' reagent.

2.5.2.2. Procedure used in the case of dimethyl suberimidate (one-step method)

(a) Add peptide to a 1 mg/ml solution of BSA in 0.2 M triethanolamine hydrochloride pH 8.5 (molar ratio protein : peptide = 1 : 20 to 1 : 30).

(b) Just before use, dissolve dimethyl suberimidate (DMS) in the same buffer at 0°C and within 30 sec add it to peptide-protein mixture (molar ratio DMS : peptide =3 : 1).

(c) After 3 h incubation at 22°C, the mixture is dialyzed against PBS (3 changes). The reaction needs not be stopped as the reagent is largely consumed after 3 h.

TABLE 2.5

Principal carbodiimides employed for coupling methods

diethylcarbodiimide	$C_2H_5-N=C=N-C_2H_5$	symmetrical, aliphatic
diphenylcarbodiimide	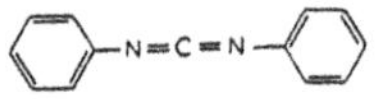	symmetrical, aromatic
ethylpropylcarbodiimide	$C_2H_5-N=C=N-C_3H_7$	asymmetrical, aliphatic
1-ethyl-3-(3-dimethylaminopropyl)-carbodiimide hydrochloride (EDC)	$C_2H_5-N=C=N-(CH_2)_3-N<^{CH_3}_{CH_3} \cdot H^+Cl^-$	asymmetrical, aliphatic
cyclohexylphenyl-carbodiimide	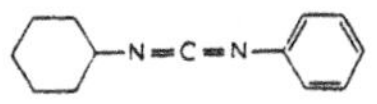	asymmetrical, aromatic
1-cyclohexyl-3-(2-morpholinyl-4-ethyl)-carbodiimide methyl-p-toluenesulfonate (MCDI)	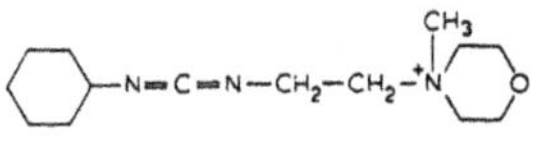 $-N=C=N-CH_2-CH_2-^+N$	asymmetrical, aliphatic

(d) Store the conjugate at 4°C in presence of 0.02% sodium azide or in aliquots at –20°C. This procedure gives a coupling efficiency around 40–70% (6–13 mol peptide per molecule of carrier).

Applications

– Chemical crosslinking reagents for protein structural studies.

– Binding of multivalent immune complexes to Fc receptors (Dower et al., 1981).

– Several other applications are listed by Han et al. (1984) and Hermanson (1996).

2.5.3. Carbodiimides

2.5.3.1. Reaction mechanism

Carbodiimides comprise a group of compounds whose general formula is $R—N = C = N—R'$ (Table 2.5). R and R' are aliphatic or aromatic groups. The mechanism of the reaction is not yet fully understood. It is postulated that an intermediate product is formed that can react through two possible pathways, the desired one being obtained at lower temperature (see pathway (a) below) by reaction between the intermediate product and amino groups (Bauminger and Wilcher, 1980; Goodfriend et al., 1964).

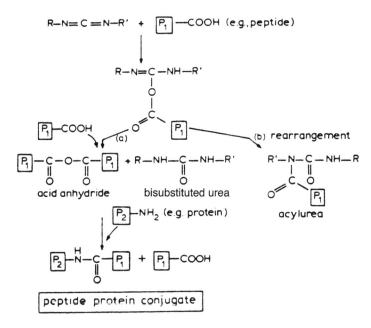

In addition to reacting with α- and ε-amino groups and carboxyl groups, carbodiimides also react with sulfhydryl and phenolic hydroxyl groups (Table 2.1). The tyrosine can be regenerated by treatment of the derivative with 0.5 M hydroxylamine pH 7 at 25°C for 5 h (Glazer et al., 1975).

2.5.3.2. Procedure (Goodfriend et al., 1964)

(a) Dissolve peptide in 1 ml of distilled water and add directly water-soluble 1-ethyl-3-(3-dimethylaminopropyl) carbodiimide (EDC) (Pierce, USA, 22980), or 1-cyclohexyl-3-(2-morpholinyl-4-ethyl) carbodiimide methyl-p-toluenesulfonate (MCDI) (Aldrich, USA, C10640-2) to a final concentration of 10 mg/ml with constant mixing. Allow to stand for 5–10 min at room temperature with gentle agitation.

(b) Add carrier protein to the mixture at final protein : peptide molar ratio of 1 : 20 to 1 : 40. Stir for 2 h at room temperature.

(c) Dialyze for 24 h at 4°C against 2–3 changes of PBS (1 l). Store at 4°C in the presence of sodium azide (0.02%), or in aliquots at –20°C.

Notes

(i) The carbodiimide should be as fresh as possible.

(ii) Using the above method, a coupling yield of 50–70% is generally obtained. According to Staros et al. (1986), the efficiency may be greatly enhanced by the addition of 5 mM N-hydroxysulfosuccinimide (sulfo-NHS, e.g. Pierce, USA, 24510 or Fluka, Switzerland, 56485).

(iii) A one-step method has also been described (Deen et al., 1990). In this procedure, N-methyl-imidazole is added in the coupling mixture to decrease the formation of acylurea adducts which lead to new antigenic determinants that are generally strongly immunogenic (Boersma et al., 1988; Briand et al., 1985; Goodfriend et al., 1964).

(iv) In order to avoid modifications of amino groups in the peptide, the latter can be pretreated with citraconic anhydride as described in Section 2.10.1. In this case, the coupling is performed at pH 8. Following the reaction with carbodiimide (step (b) of the procedure above), the citraconylated amino groups are deprotected by dialysis against 5% acetic acid. Finally, the conjugate is dialyzed against PBS as in step (c).

(v) An EDC coupling kit is available from Pierce (ref. 77101).

Applications

The method has been used successfully with hormones and peptides of cytochrome c (Likhite and Sehon, 1967), peptides of luteinizing hormone-releasing hormone (LH–RH) (Pique et al., 1978), hydroxyl-steroids and prostaglandins (Clausen, 1981), pp60^{scr} peptides of Rous sarcoma virus (Tamura et al., 1983) and peptides of influenza (Shapira et al., 1984).

2.5.4. Bisdiazobenzidine

2.5.4.1. Reaction mechanism

Bisdiazobenzidine (BDB) reacts through its diazonium functional group with the phenolic hydroxyl group of tyrosine, the imidazole group of histidine, the sulfhydryl group of cysteine and primary α- and ε-amino groups (Table 2.1). Secondary reactions involving guanidino groups of arginine and indole groups of tryptophan have also been observed.

Activated BDB is obtained by treatment of benzidine with nitrous acid (NaNO$_2$ and HCl):

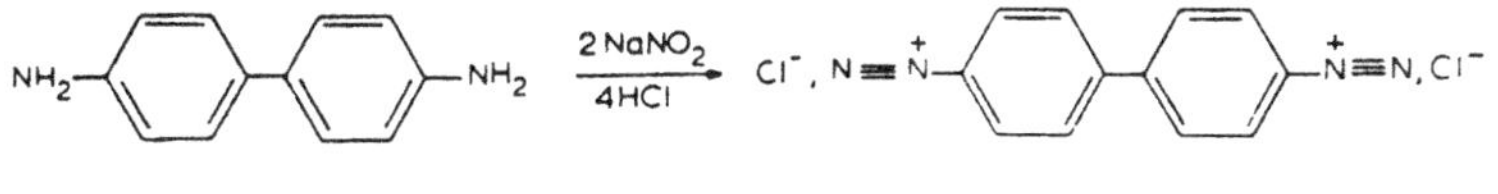

Activated BDB then reacts with different groups in protein molecules (Glazer et al., 1975). In the case of tyrosine, lysine and histidine, the products shown below are formed; reaction with SH-groups is not clearly established.

Diazo derivatives are unstable at low pH and can be stored at 0–5°C only for a short period.

2.5.4.2. Procedure (Briand et al., 1985; Tamura and Bauer, 1982)

(a) Preparation of BDB: dissolve 3.5 mg $NaNO_2$ in 1 ml of benzidine (5 mg/ml; Sigma, USA, B3383) in 0.2 M HCl at 4°C with constant agitation. Stir at 4°C for 2 h. Use precautionary measures because of the carcinogenic properties of benzidine. Aliquots can be stored at –60°C for more than 1 year.

(b) Dissolve 2.5 mg of carrier protein in 10 ml borate buffer pH 9.0 ($Na_2B_4O_{27}$ 0.16 M – NaCl 0.13 M) and add the peptide in a molar ratio protein : peptide of 1 : 30 to 1 : 40. Cool on ice.

(c) Add dropwise 0.1 ml of activated BDB to the mixture. The solution turns dark brown. Stir continuously for 2 h at 4°C. During this time adjust the pH to 9.0 with 0.5 M NaOH. The mixture will turn yellow with time.

(d) Dialyze against PBS and store at –20°C.

Notes

(i) As for carbodiimide coupling, amino groups of peptide can be blocked first by citraconylation (Section 2.10.1). In this case, coupling will occur mainly through tyrosine.

(ii) Sometimes a precipitate forms during the dialysis step at 4°C (step (d)). This can be counteracted by decreasing the time BDB is allowed to react with the peptide protein mixture (e.g. 1 h instead of 2 h); however, the coupling yield will then be decreased.

(iii) A coupling yield of 45–60% is usually obtained. Since the conjugate is very unstable at 4°C (see Section 2.9), it is important to store the conjugate at –20°C.

Applications

The method was used successfully with peptides of LH–RH (Pique et al., 1978), simian virus 40 (SV40) (Harvey et al., 1982), pp60[scr] protein (Tamura and Bauer, 1982), polio virus (Emini et al., 1983) and interferon (Russell et al., 1986).

2.5.5. m-Maleimido benzoyl-N-hydroxysuccinimide ester (MBS)

2.5.5.1. Reaction mechanism

This is the best known hetero-bifunctional reagent (Table 2.1). In neutral aqueous solution, MBS reacts first by acylation of amino groups via the active *N*-hydroxysuccinimide ester followed by formation of a thioether bond through addition of a thiol group to the double bond of the maleimide (Kitagawa and Aikawa, 1976):

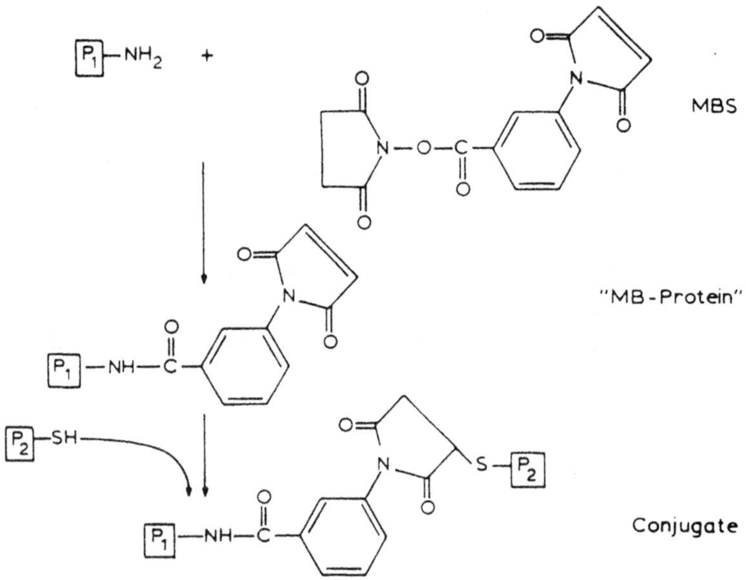

MBS

"MB-Protein"

Conjugate

The linkage proceeds via two separate reactions, thus avoiding formation of bonds between identical molecules. The method can be applied for instance to peptides that contain a cysteine residue or in which an –SH group has been introduced by thiolation. Numerous procedures for introducing thiol groups in proteins have been described (Carlsson et al., 1978; Duncan et al., 1983; Imagawa et al., 1982; Kitagawa and Aikawa, 1976; Traut et al., 1973; White, 1972). See, for example, the reaction with iminothiolane Traut's reagent (Section 2.5.7). A method for the specific introduction of thiol groups at carboxyl functions has also been described (Lin et al., 1990).

Alternatively, an additional cysteine can be incorporated during peptide synthesis or a thiol group can be introduced at the N-terminal end of the peptide during solid-phase synthesis, using the reagent 5-acetylthioglycolic acid (Presentini et al., 1986). The S-acetyl protecting group was found to be stable to HF during deprotection and cleavage of the peptide from the resin. Conjugates

could be prepared with maleimidated protein carriers by depro-
tecting the thiol group with aqueous hydroxylamine at the time of
reaction with the carrier.

2.5.5.2. Procedure (two-step method) (from Liu et al., 1979,
modified by Green et al., 1982)
  (a) Dissolve 5 mg BSA in 250 μl PBS pH 7.4 and add dropwise and
      slowly 100 μl MBS (Pierce, USA, 22310) solution (10 mg/ml)
      in dimethylformamide (DMF) (final molar ratio of protein to
      MBS of 1 : 40). Stir for 30 min at room temperature.
  (b) Remove the excess of MBS by filtration through a Sephadex G-
      25 column (14 × 0.9 cm) equilibrated with 50 mM phosphate
      buffer pH 6.0 (can be replaced by extensive dialysis during a
      few hours at 4°C). Wash the gel with the same buffer. Monitor
      by recording absorbance at 280 nm.
  (c) Pool the fractions containing activated carrier protein ('MB-
      protein') and immediately allow to react at pH 7–7.5 with
      peptide in a molar ratio peptide : protein of 30–40 : 1.
  (d) After 3 h reaction at room temperature with constant stirring,
      dialyze the mixture against PBS. Store aliquots at –20°C, or at
      4°C in presence of sodium azide (0.02%).

Notes
  (i) A coupling yield of 30–50% is usually obtained. The efficiency
      is strongly dependent on availability of thiol groups. Prelimi-
      nary trials under different pH conditions (such as PBS pH 7.5,
      acetate buffer pH 4.0) may be necessary to determine the op-
      timal conditions linked to the particular environment of –SH
      groups in a peptide (Green et al., 1982). It is recommended to
      degas all buffers to prevent oxidation of thiol groups.
 (ii) Although MBS is the best known *N*-hydroxysuccinimido es-
      ter and is widely used for peptide-protein coupling, other
      compounds of this type have also been successfully ap-
      plied in immunochemical studies (Table 2.6). For instance
      6-maleimidocaproic acyl *N*-hydroxysuccinimide ester (MCS)

has frequently been used in a one-step procedure (Clark et al., 1985; Lee et al., 1980; Lloyd Jones et al., 1989; Stevens et al., 1986; Wheat et al., 1985). Under appropriate conditions, MCS can react specifically with thiol groups on peptides. SMPB (Pierce, USA, 22315) is the extended chain length analogue of MBS. It has been used extensively for conjugating proteins and peptides to preformed liposomes (see below, Section 2.7.).

(iii) Maleimide activated protein conjugation kits are available (Sigma, USA, ref. MBK-1; Pierce, USA, Refs. 77106, 77116 and 77126).

Applications
Peptides of hepatitis B surface antigen (Lerner et al., 1981), influenza haemagglutinin (Green et al., 1982), murine cμ chain (Ghose and Karush, 1985), hormone fragments (Antoni et al., 1985), HTLV-III virus (Kennedy et al., 1986), SV40 large T antigen (Goldfarb et al., 1986) and a *ras* oncogene product (Wong et al., 1986). Several other applications are listed by Hermanson (1996).

2.5.6. N-succinimidyl 3-(2-pyridyldithio)propionate (SPDP)

2.5.6.1. Reaction mechanism
SPDP is a hetero-bifunctional reagent (Table 2.6) which, under mild conditions, reacts by its NHS-ester group with amino groups of the protein. The 2-pyridyl disulfide structure then reacts with aliphatic thiols (e.g. –SH of peptide) via a thiol-disulfide exchange reaction (shown below).

SPDP was first synthesized by Carlsson et al. (1978) and is now commercially available. The coupling reaction is efficient and proceeds rapidly at pH 5–9. The degree of substitution can be monitored spectrophotometrically. No side reaction has been described.

TABLE 2.6

Principal N-hydroxysuccinimide esters used for coupling[a]

Succinimidyl 4-(N-maleimidomethyl)cyclohexane 1-carboxylate (SMCC), M_r 334.3; 11.6 Å

m-maleimidobenzoyl N-hydroxysuccinimide ester (MBS), M_r 314.2; 9.9 Å

Succinimidyl 4-(p-maleimidophenyl)butyrate (SMPB), M_r 356.3; 14.5 Å

N-succinimidyl 3-(2-pyridyldithio)propionate (SPDP), M_r 312.4; 6.8 Å

6-maleimidocaproic acyl N-hydroxysuccinimide ester (MCS), M_r 308

Succinimidyloxycarbonyl-α-methyl-α-(2-pyridyldithio)-toluene (SMPT), M_r 388.5; 11.2 Å

N-succinimidyl (4-iodoacetyl)aminobenzoate (SIAB), M_r 402.2; 10.6 Å

[a] Most of these reagents are available as sulfo-NHS esters (Pierce, USA), which are more water soluble and can be added directly to the reaction buffer. The spacer arm-length is indicated; it has been measured after the crosslinking reaction has occurred (source: Pierce).

*2.5.6.2. Procedure (two-step method) (Granier, C., Bahraoui, E.
and Van Rietschoten, J., personal communication)*

(a) Dissolve 66 mg (1 μmol) BSA in 3 ml 100 mM phosphate
    buffer, 100 mM NaCl, pH 7.5. Add 6.5 mg SPDP (Pharmacia,
    Sweden; Pierce, USA, 21557; Boehringer Mannheim, Ger-
    many, 1112 635) suspended in 1 ml 2-propanol and allow to
    incubate during 30 min at room temperature.

(b) Collect activated BSA by filtration through a 2.5 $\times$ 100-cm
    Biogel P2 column (Rio-Rad, USA) equilibrated and washed
    in 50 mM ammonium acetate buffer, pH 8.5. Pool fractions
    (identified by monitoring at 280 nm).

(c) The number of thiopyridyl groups introduced in BSA is es-
    timated spectrophotometrically (Grassetti and Murray, 1967):
    transfer 1 ml of fractions containing modified BSA in a
    spectrophotometer cuvette and add 200 μl of 50 mM mer-
    captoethanol in 100 mM phosphate buffer, pH 7. Measure
    absorbance at 343 nm before and after addition of mercap-
    toethanol. Evaluate the quantity of thiopyridone liberated (this
    is directly proportional to introduced thiopyridyl groups) us-
    ing $A_{343nm} = 8000$ M^{-1} cm^{-1}. In standard conditions described
    above, 7–10 μmol thiopyridyl groups are generally introduced
    per μmol of BSA. If more thiopyridyl groups are introduced,
    BSA tends to precipitate.

(d) A synthetic peptide containing a cysteine residue is allowed to
    react with 8-fold excess of 2,2'-dipyridyl disulfide. The peptide
    is then purified by gel filtration as *S*-thiopyridyl derivative.

(e) Before conjugating the peptide to BSA, the cysteine thiol group
    is activated with tributyl phosphine (Merck, Germany) (Rüegg
    and Rudinger, 1977): in a glass tube, introduce 10 μmol of
    peptide dissolved in 1 ml 0.1 M Tris, pH 8 and 10 μmol of
    tributyl phosphine in 1 ml 2-propanol. Keep the mixture during
    20 h under stirring in the dark. Tris buffer and propanol must
    be saturated with nitrogen and the reaction must be carried out
    under nitrogen atmosphere.

(f) Add deprotected peptide to 10 ml activated BSA solution (7–10 μmol thiopyridyl groups) in 0.1 M Tris, pH 8. Stir during 1 h. The efficiency of coupling can be controlled by measuring the amount of thiopyridone liberated during this incubation.

(g) Stop the reaction by freezing. Lyophilize and redissolve in 2 ml of 50 mM ammonium acetate buffer, pH 8.5. Apply to a Bio-Gel P2 column for filtration and wash in the same buffer. Collect fractions that absorb at 280 nm. Pool and store at –20°C until use. Under these conditions the coupling efficiency is usually 5–6 mol of peptide per molecule of BSA.

Applications

- Peptides of calmodulin (Van Eldick et al., 1983), scorpion toxin (Bahraoui et al., 1986a), thymosin $\alpha 1$ (Incefy et al., 1986) and foot-and-mouth disease virus (Di Marchi et al., 1986).

- For a comparison of four bifunctional reagents (MHS, SMCC, MBS and SPDP) for coupling test peptides to proteins, see Peeters et al. (1989).

- Further information is available in the booklet 'SPDP, hetero-bifunctional reagent', published by Pharmacia, Sweden. Commercial kits for direct peptide coupling are available. For example lmject® maleimide activated carrier proteins (Pierce, USA) are made using sulfo-SMCC and are particularly convenient to conjugate sulfhydryl containing peptides to carrier proteins (product references 77105, 77115 and 77125, for kits containing activated KLH, BSA and ovalbumin, respectively).

2.5.7. Imido esters: 2-iminothiolane or 2-iminotetrahydrothiophene

2.5.7.1. Reaction mechanism

Unlike most imido esters, 2-iminothiolane is very stable in solution at acidic and neutral pH. This compound, also known as Traut's reagent, reacts first with primary amino groups in the presence of 4,4'-dithiodipyridine leading to an average of 1–8 thiols or 4-dithiopyridyl groups per molecule of protein. The final conjugate contains an intramolecular disulfide bond. The reaction scheme can be simplified as follows (from King et al., 1978):

The required thiol group in P2 can also be introduced as described in Section 2.5.5.1.

2.5.7.2. Procedure (one-step method)

The following method is a modification from that of Kings et al. (1978):

(a) Dissolve 1 mg BSA in 0.45 ml borate buffer 25 mM, pH 9, and add successively 0.1 ml 4,4'-dithiodipyridine (Sigma, USA, D8136) at 2.2 mg/ml in acetonitrile (CH_3CN) and 0.45 ml 20 mM 2-iminothiolane (Sigma, USA, 16256) in borate buffer, pH 9, or phosphate buffer, pH 8.1. Stir for 2 h at room temperature. Note that precipitation is often observed.

(b) For introducing sulfhydryl groups in the peptide, dissolve peptide (in a molar ratio carrier : peptide of 1 : 40) in 0.5 ml 25 mM borate buffer, pH 9, and add 2-iminothiolane in a 200 molar excess compared to α-NH$_2$ groups contained in the peptide. Stir for 2 h at room temperature.

(c) Mix activated BSA and thiolated peptide and add 0.5 ml phosphate buffer containing 4 mM EDTA, pH 8; leave to react overnight at room temperature keeping the reaction vessel under nitrogen.

(d) Apply to a Sephadex G100 column (60×1.2 cm) equilibrated in PBS, pH 7.4, and wash with the same buffer. Collect fractions that absorb at 280 nm. The first peak corresponds to conjugated (and unconjugated) BSA. Pool and store at 4°C or –20°C. The coupling efficiency is usually 6–10 mol of peptide per molecule BSA.

Notes

(i) Prepare stock solution of 2-iminothiolane just before use.

(ii) The extent of BSA substitution may be estimated before peptide coupling by the spectrophotometric method described by Van Eldick and Lukas (1986).

Applications
Calmodulin peptides (Van Eldick et al., 1983).

2.5.8. Hydrazone formation following periodate oxidation of N-terminal serine or threonine residues

2.5.8.1. Reaction mechanism
Periodate very rapidly oxidizes N-terminal serine or threonine residues, converting either of these to an α-N-glyoxylyl group (C=CH–CO-protein). So rapid is this reaction at pH 7.0 that it can be accomplished selectively when a protein with N-terminal serine or threonine is treated with a low molar ratio (e.g. 5 : 1) of periodate,

even though periodate is also capable of oxidizing several other amino acid side chains. Proteins containing free thiols should not be used, however, as these groups may react rapidly with periodate. Glycoproteins may also present difficulties.

Oxidation at the N-terminus generates an aldehyde which is the only such group in the protein. The unique reactivity of this function can then be used to make it the target for a second reaction in which a modifying group is coupled to the protein. A number of applications have been described, including the formation of both hydrazone (Gaertner et al., 1992; Geoghegan et al., 1993; Geoghegan and Stroh, 1992) and oxime (Vilaseca et al., 1993) adducts. It is important to remember that the hydrazone bond, while relatively stable, is potentially subject to reversal by hydrolysis. This occurs more readily at lower pH, and the best stability is obtained at pH 6–8. In certain cases, the hydrazone can be stabilized by reduction with cyanoborohydride (Gaertner et al., 1992).

The method gives exceptionally homogeneous bioconjugates. For peptide-carrier conjugation, condensation of an N-terminally oxidized protein with a peptide containing a hydrazide function at its C-terminus may be an especially interesting option (Rose et al., 1991). A recently described adapter molecule that permits the attachment of multiple drug or other molecules to the carrier also offers new potential in this regard (Vilaseca et al., 1993).

2.5.8.2. Procedure (two-step method) (primarily from Geoghegan and Stroh (1992); refer also to the other papers cited above)
(a) Dissolve the protein with N-terminal serine or threonine in 0.05 M sodium phosphate pH 7.0, chill to 0°C and add a 5-fold molar excess of $NaIO_4$. Allow the reaction to proceed for 30 min, and then remove the periodate while also buffer-exchanging the protein by gel filtration into 0.05 M sodium acetate pH 4.5 (e.g. Sephadex G-25 in Fast Desalting Column HR 10/10 for Pharmacia FPLC, or disposable PD-10 column (Pharmacia)). If possible, check that the N-terminus has been oxidized by isoelectric focussing or automated Edman degradation. If ox-

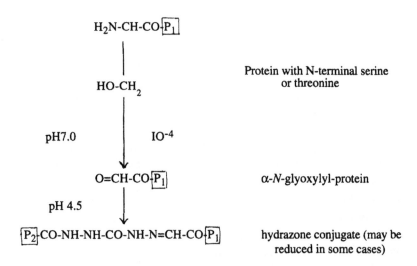

idation is not complete, try a 10-fold excess of periodate; if still not effective, consider what interfering periodate-reactive species may be present.

(b) Concentrate the α-N-glyoxylyl-protein using a Centricon (Amicon, USA) to the greatest possible extent, then allow it to react at room temperature with a hydrazide reagent at 10–20 mM concentration. In some cases, this may require the addition of some organic solvent to make the reagent soluble. If the protein is present at >1 mM concentration, reaction may be complete in 1–2 h. If it is present at 0.05–1 mM, it may be better to allow the reaction to proceed overnight. Examples of reagents used to date are Lucifer Yellow CH and biotin-X-hydrazide (Molecular Probes, USA). Estimate the progress of coupling by HPLC or electrophoresis, checking for a change in relative mass or the incorporation of a recognizable functional entity such as biotin or an antigen. Mass spectrometry is the most reliable method. Complete the procedure by removing excess reagent.

(c) When using conjugates prepared in this manner, be aware of the possibility that the hydrazone linkage will be cleaved by hydrolysis. The equilibrium extent of hydrolysis increases with dilution, and dissociation becomes a significant risk at concentrations of <1 μM even at pH 6–8. Check on the extent of this whenever possible.

Notes (Geoghegan, K.F. 1994, personal communication)

(i) Use no membrane devices that contain glycerol when preparing the protein for the first step, as glycerol will compete for the periodate. Periodate oxidation of N-terminal serine or threonine is very fast and reliable in the absence of interfering compounds. Failure to obtain it using a 5- to 10-fold molar excess of periodate over protein indicates the presence of such interference.

(ii) The rationale for using isoelectric focussing to check on the oxidation is that the positively charged native N-terminus should have been changed to a neutral group. This method is useful for smaller proteins in which loss of a single charge significantly alters the isoelectric point (Geoghegan and Stroh, 1992). When Edman sequencing is used, full oxidation causes a large drop in the signal from the N-terminus. Oxidized proteins characteristically give a low-level ongoing 'bleed' of signal spread over many cycles, but complete suppression of degradation does not occur.

(iii) Hydrazones formed as described above possess a strong new band of absorbance centred near 265 nm. This can distinguish them from the native and α-N-glyoxylyl forms of the starting protein, and is seen most clearly in hydrazones formed with peptides that lack aromatic residues.

Applications

Human renin and collagenase substrate peptides (Geoghegan et al., 1993) ; recombinant murine interleukin-1α (an 18-kD cytokine with N-terminal serine) (Geoghegan and Stroh, 1992).

2.5.9. Other chemical coupling agents

In addition to the procedures described above, the following reagents have also been used for preparing peptide-carrier conjugates (see Table 2.1).

Toluene diisocyanate which only affects primary amino groups of the protein (Talamo et al., 1968; Wold, 1972).

3-nitro-2 pyridinesulfenyl group which allows conjugation of peptides to protein via a SH function in the peptide (Albericio et al., 1989).

p-nitrobenzoyl chloride which converts aliphatic amino groups of the peptide to a *p*-nitrobenzoylamide; the latter is then reduced to a *p*-aminobenzoyl derivative and coupled to proteins by diazotization (see Section 2.5.4.1 for a description of the primary and secondary reactions observed with azo coupling). This method was used by Anderer and Schlumberger (1965b) with a series of C-terminal peptides of TMVP and by Deodhar (1960) with angiotensin.

p-aminophenylacetic acid derivatives (Jacob et al., 1985) which link the peptide to carrier protein via an azo bond (see also Rojo et al., 1986).

Cystamine dihydrochloride (Gilliland and Collier, 1980; Johnson et al., 1982) which acts by the formation of disulfide bonds.

N-ethylbenzisoxazolium fluoroborate (EBIZ) which links peptide to carrier protein via an amido bond. This procedure was successfully used by Likhite and Sehon (1967) for angiotensin.

Isobutylchloroformate (IBCF) which has been extensively used for coupling a variety of carboxyl group-containing peptides to proteins. The reaction proceeds in two steps: first, the peptide is

conjugated to IBCF in the presence of a tri-N-alkylamine resulting in the formation of a mixed anhydride. The mixed anhydride
is then added to the protein solution where the peptide reacts with
free amino groups, usually lysine side chains, linking the peptide
to protein via an amido bond (Gendloff et al., 1986; Samokhin and
Filimonov, 1985; Thorell and Larson, 1978).

2.6. Photochemical coupling

2.6.1. Reaction mechanism

Since the introduction of aryl azides as a photoreactive crosslinking
functional group by Fleet et al. (1969), several of these reagents
have become commercially available (Pierce, USA). The main photochemical reagents have been listed by Han et al. (1984) (see also
some examples in Table 2.7). Photoreactive crosslinking reagents
generally involve alkyl or aryl azides ($R–N_3$) which can be pho-
tolyzed to a highly reactive nitrene intermediate at 265–275 nm
range and 350 nm, respectively. The latter then reacts with various
bonds such as C–H or N–H (Peters and Richards, 1977).

Reaction with azido benzoyl hydrazide (ABH) is shown below:

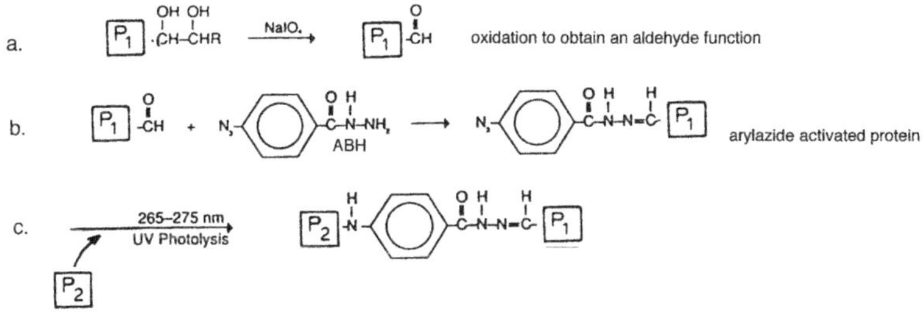

Photoprobes which have the advantage of being inert until photolysis are able to link peptides to any accessible residue of the
carrier. Using aryl azides no direct photochemical damage is observed in the protein when an intense light pulse is applied at 350

TABLE 2.7

Photochemical reagents used for coupling

Photoreactive aryl azides
Azidobenzoyl hydrazide (ABH); M_r
177.2

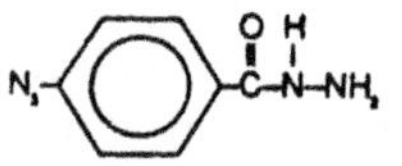

Bis-[β-(4-azidosalicylamino)ethyl]
disulfide
(BASED); M_r 474.5

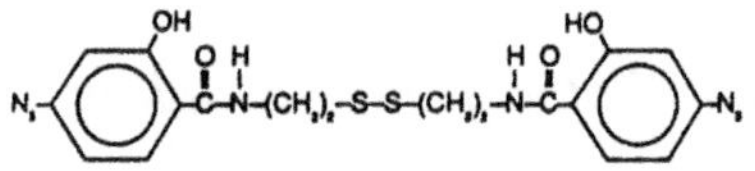

p-azidophenyl glyoxal monohydrate
(APG):
M_r 193.2; 9.3 Å

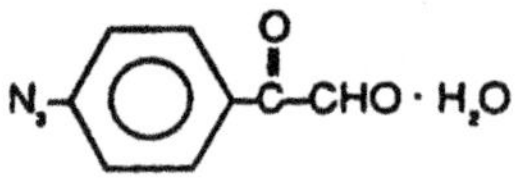

sulfosuccinimidyl   6-(4'-azido-2'-
nitrophenylamino)
hexanoate   (sulfo-SANPAH); M_r
429.4; 18.2 Å

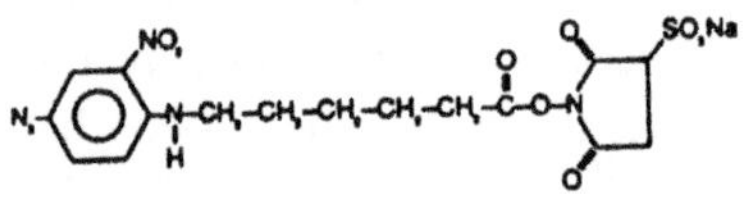

N-(4-azidophenylthio)phtalimide;
M_r 296.3

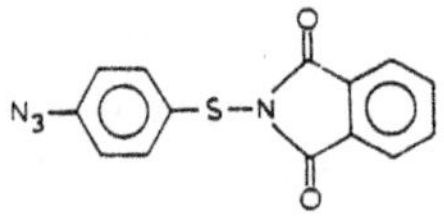

Benzophenone derivative
tert-butyloxycarbonylbenzoyl
benzoyl lysine
(Boc-BB Lys)

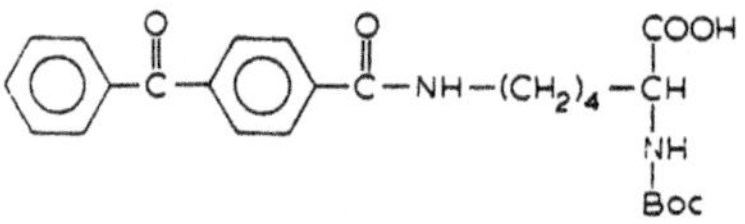

p-nitrophenylalanine derivative
Boc-*p*-NO$_2$-Phe

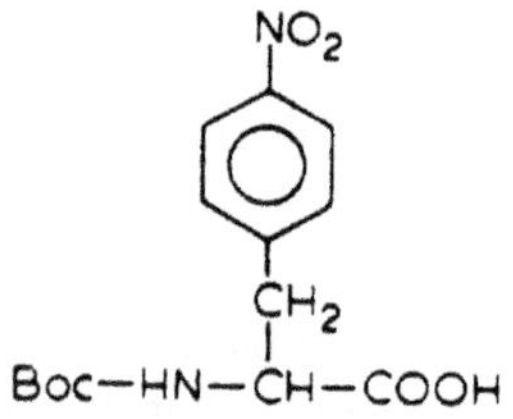

---

nm. In this respect, aryl azides appear to be more appropriate than alkyl azides since modifications can be generated in proteins at 265–275 nm. The half-life of nitrene is of the order of 1 millisecond.

Many applications and experimental details concerning covalent binding by photochemical reagents have been discussed by Han et al. (1984). The method has been found useful for crosslinking macromolecular assemblies such as hormone-receptor complexes, ribosomes, etc. A detailed procedure using azidophenylglyoxal (APG) as photoreactive aryl azide has been described by Boersma et al. (1993). Glyoxals are useful compounds for targeting the guanidyl function of arginine residues. This procedure is thus indicated for coupling arginine-containing peptides to proteins. It has to be noted that some cases of cross-reactivity, at higher pH in particular, have been described with lysine residues.

A drawback in using reagents such as p-azidobenzoate as photoprobes is that active nitrene intermediates are generated which react strongly with the aqueous solvent. In 1973, Galardy et al. (1973) introduced aromatic ketones as a new photochemical probe. Reagents, such as benzophenone, are characterized by a triplet state which apparently does not react with water, does not rearrange or react intramolecularly, and is easily generated at long wavelengths (>320 nm). Parker and Hodges (1985) used such benzophenone photoprobes for linking peptides to a protein carrier. The photoprobes are directly coupled to the protected peptide attached to the solid-phase resin, using the conditions employed for amino acid coupling. The benzophenone species (BB Gly or BB Lys, see Table 2.7) and p-nitrophenylalanine (p-NO$_2$-Phe) are not affected by the hydrofluoric acid used for deprotection and cleavage of the peptide from the resin support. The peptide probes are then photolytically coupled to the carrier at 350 nm as described below. Photolysis can be performed in 8 M urea solution in a pH range of 2.5–8.5. The coupling efficiency obtained by Parker and Hodges (1985) was around 50%, and conjugates containing up to 72 mol of peptide per molecule of BSA have been described (Worobec et al., 1983). This procedure avoids potential modifications of functional groups

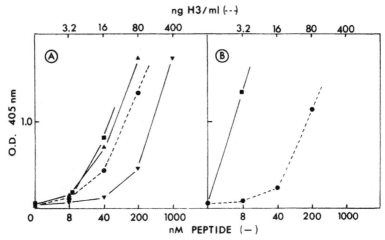

Fig. 2.1. Binding in ELISA of antibodies to H3 (A), and to peptide 130–135 of H3 (B) with various concentrations of H3 and various conjugates of IRG-ERA peptide carrier protein. Sera were diluted 1 : 2000 and allowed to react with histone H3 (●), conjugate IRGERA-BSA (19 : 1) prepared with glutaraldehyde (▲), conjugated IRGERA-BSA (■) and IRGERA-ovalbumin (▼) (with molar ratio peptide : protein of 4 : 1 and 2 : 1, respectively) prepared by photochemical coupling. Antiserum to peptide 130–135 H3 (B) was raised by injecting pep-tide-ovalbumin conjugate obtained with glutaraldehyde. Background OD values detected with normal rabbit serum were less than 0.1. Substrate hydrolysis time was 45 min.

in the peptide. Furthermore, since the photoprobe is inert until pho-tolysis, the synthetic peptide probe can be purified by HPLC before crosslinking to the carrier molecule.

The conditions used in our laboratory for coupling BB Gly-IRGERA (C-terminal hexapeptide of histone H3) to BSA and ovalbumin are described below. The reactivity of this conjugate was tested in ELISA using antipeptide antibodies and anti-H3 antisera (Fig. 2.1) while the IRGERA-ovalbumin conjugate was used to raise specific antisera in rabbits (Briand et al., 1992b).

2.6.2. Procedure

(a) BB Gly IRGERA was synthesized according to Parker and Hodges (1985) and purified by filtration on a G15 Sephadex column.

(b) Dissolve 10.75 mg ovalbumin (0.25 μmol) in 450 μl distilled water and add 50 μl 1 M KH_2PO_4 buffer, pH 6.8.

(c) Dissolve 2.41 mg BB Gly peptide (2.5 μmol) in 500 μl 0.1 M KH_2PO_4 buffer, pH 6.8. In the case of very hydrophilic BB peptides, it is possible to use as much as 10 μmol of the peptide without causing precipitation.

(d) Mix the two solutions in a 1-ml quartz cuvette equilibrated at 10°C and containing a small magnetic stirrer.

(e) Photolysis is carried out at 350 nm for 90 min (at 10°C) under stirring using a Xenon lamp (Photolysis system, Müller Optic, Germany) with a Karatos monochromator condensor. Light intensity is checked by a Kipp and Zohen thermopile.

(f) Dialyze the mixture for 24 h at 4°C against 3 changes of 1 l PBS. Using these conditions, 2 mol of BB IRGERA were coupled to 1 mol of ovalbumin. The coupling efficiency was 20%.

Notes

(i) Conjugates were stable for at least 2 months at 4°C.

(ii) The method is particularly adapted to hydrophilic peptides which are often difficult to couple, without chemical damage, by means of classical reagents.

(iii) The main limitation of the method is that the hydrophobic character of benzophenone decreases the solubility of neutral and hydrophobic peptides with the result that it may be difficult to handle some peptide probes.

Applications The method was used successfully with a large number of macromolecular ligand-receptor systems (see for example Ji and Ji, 1982) as well as with apamin, a 2000 M_r peptide purified from bee venom (Seagar et al., 1986). Photochemical linking of primary aromatic amines to carrier proteins has also been described (Pandey et al., 1986). See also Briand et al. (1992b) and Benkirane et al. (1993).

2.7. Coupling of peptides to liposomes

2.7.1. Reaction mechanism

In recent years, liposomes have gained recognition as potential carriers for various antigens, e.g. haptens, proteins and peptides, in eliciting antibody formation. Liposomes are vesicles prepared from phospholipids; they may differ in size (0.1–10 nm), composition (e.g. one or several phospholipids, with or without cholesterol), charge and structure (uni- or multilamellar). The incorporation of these variables which control liposomal adjuvanticity in the immune response will be addressed later (Chapter 3). The present section is concerned only with the technical aspects of the preparation of liposomes and liposome-peptide conjugates.

Numerous procedures of liposome preparation, including freeze-dried forms, are described in the literature (for reviews, see for example Alving, 1991; Alving and Richards, 1983; Gregoriadis, 1990; Gregoriadis et al., 1989; New, 1995; Szoka and Papahadjopoulos, 1980; Vermuri and Rhodes, 1995). Different methods have been described for attaching the antigen to the liposome. The antigens can be entrapped in the aqueous compartment of the vesicles (i.e. encapsulated antigen) or can be covalently bound to the outer surface of liposomes. Encapsulation is achieved by preparing the vesicles in the presence of antigen, for example by using the 'reverse phase evaporation' technique (Szoka and Papahadjopoulos, 1978). Methods used for the covalent coupling of proteins or peptides to liposomes have recently been reviewed (Heath and Martin, 1986; Schuber, 1995). Several techniques are available which involve azo coupling (Snyder and Vannier, 1984), reagents such as glutaraldehyde (Torchilin et al., 1979), and carbodiimides (Endoh et al., 1981; Neurath et al., 1984a). The conjugation occurs between the amino group of phosphatidylethanolamine (PE), incorporated in the preformed liposomes, and an appropriate functional group of the antigen. Coupling can also be obtained by reacting a protein with an aldehyde, generated by IO_4-oxidation of glycolipid present in the liposome, followed by the Schiff base reduction with a borohydride (Heath et al., 1981). Derivatized proteins or peptides with fatty acids can also be incorporated into the bilayers of the liposomes during their formation (Huang et al., 1980). A general scheme for ligand coupling to preformed liposomes can be summarized as follows:

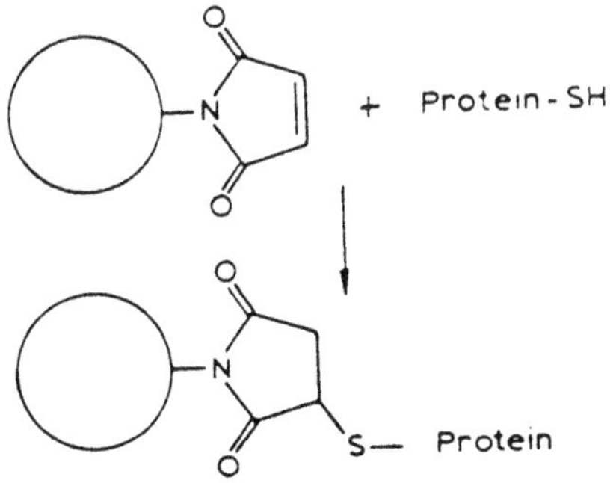

It involves the incorporation of MPB-PE, obtained by re-action of PE and the bifunctional reagent succinimidyl 4-(p-maleimidophenyl) butyrate (SMPB) into liposomes (Martin and Papahadjopoulos, 1982). The maleimide group reacts, under very mild conditions, with a thiol residue present or introduced in the antigen. A similar technique has been developed (Leserman et al., 1980) in which PE was derivatized with another bifunctional reagent, SPDP; in this case a thiol function of the ligand performs a thiol exchange reaction and becomes linked to the liposome through an –S–S– bond (Goldmacher, 1983; Huang et al., 1980). The use of succinimidyl-S-acetylthioacetate was found convenient for the thiolation of proteins in view of their coupling to liposomes (Derksen and Scherphof, 1985).

2.7.2. Procedure (Frisch et al., 1991)

In this section we describe the encapsulation of a synthetic model peptide (CGIRGERA) into large and small unilamellar liposomes and its coupling to preformed vesicles. The coupling involves the reaction between the thiol function of its cysteine residue with the maleimido group of a derivatized phosphatidylethanolamine (MPB-PE).

2.7.2.1. Synthesis of N-[4-(p-maleimidophenyl)butyryl] phosphatidylethanolamine (MPB-PE)

MPB-PE was synthesized according to the method of Martin and Papahadjopoulos (1982). 100 μmol of PE (transesterified egg phosphatidylcholine, Sigma, USA) were dissolved in 5 ml of anhydrous methanol containing 100 μmol of triethylamine and 50 mg of SMPB (Pierce, USA). The mixture was kept under argon at room temperature and the reaction progress was monitored by thin-layer chromatography (TLC) on silica gel 60-F_{254} (Merck, Germany) eluted in a chloroform/methanol/water (65 : 25 : 4, v/v/v) system. The reaction was essentially complete after about 2 h. Methanol was evaporated under vacuum and phospholipids were redissolved in 5 ml of chloroform. A double extraction with saline (1% w/v NaCl in water) was then required to eliminate water-soluble byproducts and unreacted SMPB. MPB-PE was then purified by chromatography on a 1 × 15-cm Bio-Sil hydroxyapatite (Bio-Rad, USA) column activated overnight at 150°C and equilibrated with 100 ml of chloroform. The column was eluted with successively 20 ml of chloroform, 20 ml of chloroform/methanol 40 : 1, 20 ml of chloroform/methanol 30 : 1, 20 ml of chloroform/methanol 25 : 1, 20 ml of chloroform/methanol 15 : 1 and 100 ml of chloroform/methanol 10 : 1. Each fraction was tested on silica gel as described and fractions indicating a single phosphate-positive (molybdenium blue revelation; Sigma, USA) and ninhydrin-negative spot were collected (fractions 15 : 1 and 10 : 1). Solvent was evaporated under reduced pressure and MPB-PE was redissolved in chloroform. At all steps the solutions were flushed and kept under argon. After phosphate determination (Rouser et al., 1970), concentration of MPB-PE was adjusted at 1 or 1.5 μmol/ml of chloroform and stored at $-20°$C in 2-ml sealed (under argon) ampules. The yield of the synthesis was about 95%.

2.7.2.2. Preparation of large and small unilamellar vesicles and peptide coupling

Large unilamellar vesicles (or reverse phase evaporation vesicles, REV) were prepared by the reverse-phase evaporation method of Szoka and Papahadjopoulos (1978). 6.37 μmol of egg phosphatidylcholine (PC), 2.12 μmol of phosphatidylglycerol (PG) (Sigma, USA), 4.25 μmol of cholesterol (Sigma, USA) and 1.5 μmol of MPB-PE were mixed in a 1×10-cm glass tube. Chloroform was evaporated under vacuum and phospholipids were dissolved in 1 ml of diethylether. A 10-mM Hepes buffer, pH 6.5, containing 145 mM NaCl (330 μl) was then added and the mixture was emulsified by sonication for 3 min in a bath-type sonicator (Laboratory Supply Co., Hicksville, NY). Ether was removed under partial vacuum (550 mm/Hg) until a gel-phase was obtained. The gel was broken up by vortexing and ether evaporation was resumed. Finally, the homogeneous suspension of liposomes was placed under vacuum water-pump in order to eliminate residual ether (about 15 min).

Small unilamellar vesicles (SUV) were prepared by the method of Papahadjopoulos and Watkins (1967). Then, 10 μmol lipids (see above) were mixed in a 1×10-cm glass tube. Chloroform was evaporated under vacuum (left under for 2 h in order to eliminate all trace of solvent) and phospholipids were rehydrated (vortexing) with 1 ml of 10 mM Hepes buffer (pH 6.5) containing 145 mM NaCl. The suspension of large unilamellar vesicles obtained was maintained at 25°C and pulse-sonicated with a 3-mm diameter probe sonicator

(Vibra Cells, Sonics & Material Inc., Danbury, CT) at 300 W for 60 min under a continuous flow of nitrogen. After that time, the liposome preparation was centrifuged at 50,000 g for 2 h in order to eliminate the probe fragments. The supernatant contained the SUV preparation which had a 90-nm mean average diameter.

The liposomal suspension (REV or SUV) was then mixed with 660 μl of 10 mM Hepes, pH 6.5, 145 mM NaCl containing 7.5 μmol of the thiol-derivatized peptide in order to obtain a 5:1 thiol/maleimide ratio. The coupling reaction was performed under argon at room temperature overnight. Vesicles were then further treated with 10 μmol of mercaptoethanol in order to derivatize unreacted maleimido residues. Grafted liposomes were separated from free peptide and mercaptoethanol by filtration on a 1 × 15-cm Sephadex G-75 column equilibrated and eluted with a 0.9% NaCl solution. After 4 ml of void volume, liposomes were collected in 2 ml of saline. Vesicles were tested for their phosphate content according to Rouser et al. (1970). Usually, the yield of coupling estimated from available maleimide groups at the vesicles surface (Friede et al., 1993c) is quantitative.

Vesicles are kept under argon at 4°C in the dark until use. They can be frozen and lyophilized as described below (Section 2.7.2.4).

2.7.2.3. Preparation of encapsulated peptide

7.5 μmol of egg PC, 2.5 μmol of PG and 5 μmol of cholesterol were treated as mentioned above. After redissolving the lipid film in diethylether, 330 μl of Hepes 10 mM, pH 6.5, 145 mM NaCl containing 7.15 μmol of the peptide were added and the two phases were emulsified as mentioned above. The liposomes were formed as described above.

Encapsulated peptide was then separated from free material by filtration on a Sephadex G-75 column. The collected vesicles contained about 25% of the initial amount of peptide. They are kept under argon at 4°C in the dark until use.

2.7.2.4. Lyophilized liposomes (Friede et al., 1993c)
Liposome-peptide suspensions are diluted in PBS containing 5% (w/v) sorbitol (Lancaster Synthesis, Eastgate, UK, Ref. 6134) and frozen in dry-ice/acetone. Once frozen, the liposomes can be stored at –20°C. Thawing is performed by letting the samples stand at room temperature. Frozen liposome preparations can be lyophilized. Resuspension is performed by the addition of water (equal to the original volume) followed by intermittent vortexing at room temperature for 10 min. Let stand 15–60 min at 20°C before use. It has to be noted that due to possible leakage, loss of biological activity can be observed after resuspension when peptides have been encapsulated and are not covalently linked to the liposome surface.

2.8. Coupling of peptides to solid supports

2.8.1. General remarks

Solid supports have been used in immunology mainly for preparing immunoadsorbents intended for the purification of antibodies, antigens or cells, although other applications such as microencapsulation of monoclonal antibodies or drugs have also been described (Widder and Green, 1985).

A variety of materials have been used, e.g. nylon fibres, polystyrene beads and tubes, polysaccharide beads, agarose, polyacrylamide, polyvinyl chloride and glass. Numerous activation procedures have been developed and used mainly for the preparation of affinity adsorbents (Aithal et al., 1988; Chersi et al., 1989; Dean et al., 1985; Jakoby and Wilchek, 1974; Kiefer, 1979; Kohn and Wilchek, 1983; Kricka, 1985; Mäkelä and Seppälä, 1986).

Activated beads are commercially available, e.g. EDC-activated agarose (Pierce, USA), CNBr-activated Sepharose and epoxy-activated Sepharose (Pharmacia, Sweden), glutaraldehyde-activated Ultrogel (IBF, France) etc. Spacers have also been introduced in order to preserve the peptide conformation and enhance its accessibility.

In the case of polystyrene tubes, dishes or beads (latex), one method used for introducing functional groups is nitration followed by reduction of the nitro groups to yield active aromatic amines. In the case of nylon (a copolymer of hexamethylendiamine and adipic acid), the terminal amino and carboxyl groups can be modified. The number of these functional groups at the surface can be increased by mild acid hydrolysis (3N HCl) or *O*-alkylation (Kricka, 1985). A method requiring no chemical coupling of the peptide to polystyrene beads has also been described (Karlsen et al., 1990).

Controlled pore glass is the most commonly employed inorganic matrix for immobilizing biological molecules. Activation can be performed by several methods (Polson et al., 1985; Robinson et al., 1971; Weetall and Filbert, 1974).

For examples describing the use of immobilized peptides for immunochemical studies, see Gazin et al. (1986), Hui et al. (1986), Berzins et al. (1986), Muller et al. (1988), Barakat et al. (1992) and Morris et al. (1994).

2.8.2. Procedure using iodoacetyl activated support for immobilization of peptides through sulfhydryl groups (Domen, P. L., 1994, personal communication)

2.8.2.1. Reaction mechanism

Haloacids, such as iodoacetic and bromoacetic, are preferentially reactive with the sulfhydryl group of cysteine under controlled conditions. They can be used to make activated supports which can immobilize sulfhydryl-containing molecules by forming stable thioether bonds between the matrix and the ligand:

$\}$- CH$_2$ - NH - (CH$_2$)$_3$ - NH - (CH$_2$)$_3$ - NH - CO - CH$_2$ - I   +   SH-$\boxed{\text{P}}$ peptide

Iodoacetyl Agarose

$\}$- CH$_2$ - NH - (CH$_2$)$_3$ - NH - (CH$_2$)$_3$ - NH - CO - CH$_2$ - S -$\boxed{\text{P}}$

Although reactions with other groups can occur, these can be controlled by varying the time and pH. Cysteine sulfhydryls react faster than histidine, methionine and lysine groups under the conditions described (Gurd, 1967; Metrione, 1982).

The described procedure uses a support with a spacer arm to reduce steric hindrance. In the case of peptide-carrier systems, the spacer allows direct coupling of peptides to the matrix which is useful for purifying antipeptide antibodies from antisera containing antibodies to both peptide and carrier determinants. Immobilized iodoacetyl is commercially available on a variety of supports, with and without spacers. Alkyl halide-containing gel is light sensitive and should be protected from light until used.

2.8.2.2. Procedure

(a) Sequentially remove the top and bottom cap of a 2 ml SulfoLink® Gel column (Pierce, USA) and drain the storage buffer. The support is iodoacetyl-activated agarose with a 12-atom spacer arm. Alternatively, bulk SulfoLink® gel can be used to produce a column of the desired size by proportionally adjusting the quantity of the reagents described in the protocol. For the bulk material, either mix and wash the gel in a column with approximately twice the capacity of the gel bed volume or use an appropriately sized beaker and paddle to mix the gel and a sintered glass funnel to wash it.

(b) Equilibrate the column by washing the gel with 6 × 2 ml of coupling buffer (50 mM Tris, 5 mM EDTA, pH 8.5). Replace the bottom cap.

(c) Dissolve or dilute 1–10 mg of peptide in 2.5–3.0 ml of coupling buffer. The peptide must have a cysteine terminal end or free sulfhydryl. Retain a portion of the starting material if you want to determine coupling efficiency (see step (i)). Note that sulfhydryl-containing peptides stored in solution may form dimers that will inhibit coupling efficiency. The presence of EDTA in the coupling buffer helps to eliminate dimer formation.

(d) Add the peptide solution to the equilibrated column and replace the top cap. Mix gently at room temperature for 15 min. Let the column stand at room temperature for an additional 30 min without mixing.

(e) Sequentially remove the top and bottom cap and drain the buffer. Wash the column with 3 × 2 ml of coupling buffer. Replace the bottom cap. Save the flow through if you want to determine coupling efficiency (see step (i)).

(f) To block any remaining reactive sites on the matrix, dissolve 15.8 mg of L-cysteine-HCl (Pierce, USA) in 2 ml of coupling buffer and add to the column. Replace the top cap and mix gently at room temperature for 15 min. Let the column stand at room temperature for an additional 30 min without mixing.

(g) Drain the buffer and wash the column with 4 × 4 ml of 1.0 M sodium chloride.

(h) If the column is to be used immediately for affinity purification, equilibrate it with 3 × 4 aliquots of the same buffer that your antibody sample is diluted in (for example, PBS). If the column is to be stored, wash with 3 × 4 ml of degassed 0.05% sodium azide. Replace the bottom cap and add an additional 2 ml of the azide storage solution. Replace the top cap and store the column at 4°C.

(i) If desired, determine coupling efficiency by one of two ways:

    (1) If the peptide contains at least one aromatic tyrosine residue, the coupling efficiency can be determined by comparing the A_{280} (absorbance at 280 nm) of the flow through with that of the starting material.

    (2) The coupling efficiency can be determined by comparing the number of sulfhydryl groups in the flow through with that of the starting material.

        (a) Dissolve 4 mg Ellman's reagent (Pierce, USA) in 1 ml of reaction buffer (0.1 M sodium phosphate, pH 8.0).

        (b) Immediately before use, prepare a standard by dissolving cysteine hydrochloride monophosphate (Pierce, USA) in reaction buffer at the following concentrations: 1.5 mM (26.34 mg/100 ml); 1.25 mM (21.95 mg/100 ml); 1.0 mM (17.56 mg/100 ml); 0.75 mM (13.17 mg/100 ml); 0.5 mM (8.78 mg/100 ml); 0.25 mM (4.39 mg/100 ml).

        (c) For each standard, unknown and a blank, prepare a test tube containing both 50 μl of Ellman's reagent solution and 2.5 ml of reaction buffer.

        (d) Add 250 μl of each standard or unknown to the separate test tubes prepared in step (c). For the blank, add 250 μl of reaction buffer.

        (e) Mix and incubate at room temperature for 15 min.

        (f) Measure the absorbance of the solution in each tube at 412 nm.

        (g) Plot the values obtained for the standards to obtain a standard curve and determine the unknown concentrations from this curve.

Applications

- Peptide of pp60[src] (Gentry et al., 1983);
- Further information is available in the booklets 'SulfoLink® Coupling Gel' and 'SulfoLink® Kit', both published by Pierce, USA.

TABLE 2.8

Determination of the peptide-carrier ratio of conjugates by amino acid analysis (the method is illustrated in the case of the hexapeptide IRGERA of histone H3 coupled to ovalbumin by glutaraldehyde).

Residues	1[a]	2[b]		3[c]		4[d]		5[e]	6[f]	7[g]
		A	B	A	B	A	B			
Asp	31	37				1299				
Thr	15	18				689				
Ser	38	35				1238				
Glu	44		44		1		2325	65	21	21
Pro	14	12				500				
Gly	21		21		1		1650	46	25	25
Ala	31		31		1		1962	55	24	24
Val	31	25				1007				
Ile	17		17		1		1007	28	11	11
Leu	32	27				1144				
Tyr	10	11				376				
Phe	20	19				584				
His	7	7				283				
Lys	20	19				449				
Arg	37		37		2		2964	83	46	23
		$\sum = 218$				$\sum = 7752$				Average value: 23

[a] Theoretical amino acid composition of ovalbumin (mol of residues/mol ovalbumin).

[b] Experimental amino acid composition of ovalbumin used for the coupling. A: residues not present in IRGERA peptide (total = 218). B: residues present in IRGERA peptide.

[c] Theoretical amino acid composition of IRGERA peptide.

[d] Experimental amino acid composition of ovalbumin-IRGERA conjugate. A: residues not present in IRGERA peptide (total = 7752). B: residues present in IRGERA peptide. The values in column 2A are added: the result found is 218. The values in column 4A are added: the result found is 7752. A factor f is obtained from the ratio 4A/2A (in this example $f = 0.028$).

[e] Number of mol of each amino acid residue common to peptide and carrier per mol of conjugate. This value is obtained by multiplying the figures in column 4B by a factor $f = 0.028$ corresponding to the ratio of the summations of columns 2A and 4A (218/7752).

[f] Number of mol of each amino acid residue of the peptide per molecule of conjugate. This is obtained by subtracting the values of 2B from those of column 5.

[g] Number of mol of peptide per mol of carrier calculated for each amino acid residue (values of column 6 divided by those of column 3). As in the case of glutaraldehyde coupling the N-terminal residue (Ile) of the peptide is involved in the binding to the carrier, a lower value is obtained which is not used for calculating the average molar ratio. An average value of 23 is obtained (from Briand et al., 1985).

2.9. Determination of peptide : carrier ratio of conjugates

The most accurate method of determining the number of mol of coupled peptide consists in utilizing a radioactive peptide and determining the total radioactivity of the purified conjugate. The molar ratio peptide : protein can also be easily obtained from the amino acid composition of the conjugate determined after complete hydrolysis (Briand et al., 1985; Shuler et al., 1992). Obviously, the conjugate preparation should be dialyzed before analysis to remove any uncoupled peptide. The method of calculation is illustrated in Table 2.8. Procedures to determine coupling efficiency of peptide to agarose are described above (Section 2.8.2.2).

Methods based on ultraviolet or visible absorption or fluorescence of the peptide have limitations, since, if the peptide reacts with more than one kind of residue in the protein, each derivative may have different spectral characteristics. Also, the molar absorption or emission quantum may differ after conjugation depending on the microenvironment in the protein.

It is not possible to verify that the peptide is covalently linked to the carrier protein by observing the mobility of the conjugate by SDS gel electrophoresis. As shown in Fig. 2.2, bands corresponding to a conjugate may present a migration pattern different from the one shown by the carrier protein alone but not necessarily distinguishable from bands formed by carrier molecules modified by the coupling agent in absence of peptide. A method has been described which controls peptide coupling by mass spectrometry (Tolou et al., 1994). More accurate mass determination is obtained when the number of peptides linked to the protein carrier is low.

A knowledge of the peptide-carrier ratio is important for controlling the stability of conjugates during storage. As shown in Fig. 2.3, peptide conjugates obtained with bisdiazotized benzidine or low concentration of glutaraldehyde are relatively unstable (Briand et al., 1985). When conjugates are to be used over any length of time, it is advisable to verify that the peptide : carrier ratio remains unchanged.

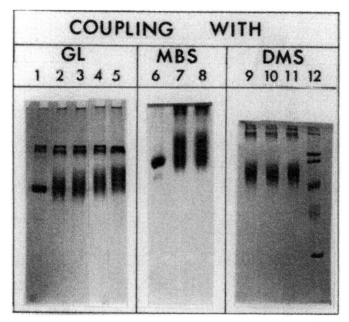

Fig. 2.2. Electrophoretic analysis of peptide-carrier conjugates. BSA-peptide conjugates (10 μg expressed as BSA) were separated by conventional SDS-electrophoresis on 10% polyacrylamide gel (Laemmli, 1970; Tijssen, 1985). 1: control BSA; 2: BSA treated with 1% glutaraldehyde (without peptide); 3: BSA treated with 0.1% glutaraldehyde (without peptide); 4: conjugate peptide 44–61 H2A-BSA (coupling with 1% glutaraldehyde), molar ratio 24 : 1; 5: conjugate peptide 85–100 H2A-BSA (using 0.1% glutaraldehyde), molar ratio 13 : 1; 6: control BSA; 7: BSA treated by MBS; 8: conjugate peptide Arg·14·Ala-BSA (using MBS), molar ratio 20 : 1; 9: conjugate peptide 1–11 H2B-BSA (using DMS), molar ratio 13 : 1; 10: conjugate peptide 40–55 H3-BSA (using DMS), molar ratio 5 : 1; 11: BSA treated with DMS alone (without peptide); 12: low molecular weight markers.

GL: glutaraldehyde; MBS: m-maleimidobenzoyl-N-hydroxysuccinimide ester; DMS: dimethyl suberimidate.

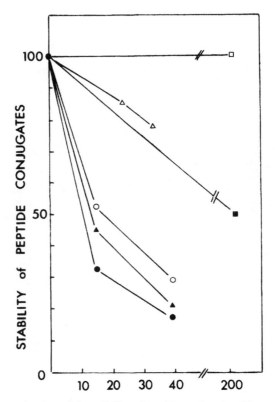

Fig. 2.3. Determination of the stability of peptide conjugates. The peptide/carrier ratio of different conjugates was determined by amino acid analysis at different periods after conjugation. The conjugates were kept in solution at 4°C and dialyzed against PBS before each amino acid analysis. (□—□) peptide 43–50 H2B coupled to BSA with 1% glutaraldehyde (100% = initial molar ratio peptide/carrier of 14); (■—■) peptide 61–74 TMVP coupled to BSA with 0.05% glutaraldehyde (100% = 14 molar ratio); (○—○) peptide (Y) 1–8 H4 coupled to BSA with 0.05% glutaraldehyde (100% = 8 molar ratio); (▲—▲) peptide 1–9 (Y) H2A coupled to BSA with BDB (100% = 13 molar ratio); (●—●) peptide (Y) 1–8 H4 coupled to BSA with BDB (100% = 19 molar ratio); (△—△) peptide (C) 39–47 H2B coupled to BSA with MBS (100% = 14 molar ratio) (from Briand et al., 1985).

2.10. Peptide derivatization

2.10.1. Reversible protection of amino groups with citraconic anhydride

Several coupling methods lead to the random, indiscriminate linking of any amino or carboxyl groups of the peptide to the carrier molecule, with the result that the antigenic and immunogenic properties of the peptide are often extensively modified.

It may be useful, therefore, to protect certain residues of the epitope during the coupling reaction. Treatment with citraconic anhydride is a particularly suitable method for protecting amino groups in a reversible fashion, thereby preserving the antigenic properties of peptides (Atassi and Habeeb, 1972; Briand et al., 1985).

Citraconic anhydride reacts with α- and ε-amino groups to give two equally stable products, as well as with sulfhydryl groups and hydroxyl amino groups. Phenolic hydroxyl groups seem to be unaffected (Atassi and Habeeb, 1972).

Procedure

(a) Dissolve the peptide in Hepes buffer 50 mM, pH 8.5 (0.2 mg/ml).

(b) Add citraconic anhydride (Merck, Germany, 8013 63 or Sigma, USA, C2395) in a molar ratio of peptide amino groups : citraconic anhydride of 1 : 10. Adjust pH continuously to 8.5–9 with 1 M NaOH. Repeat the addition until pH remains constant to 8.5–9. When pH remains stable, add 100 µl citraconic anhydride. If the pH does not change, the reaction has gone to completion. Otherwise readjust with NaOH and repeat the addition of citraconic anhydride.

(c) Incubate the mixture for 1 h at room temperature under slow stirring.

(d) Proceed with actual coupling experiment (see Section 2.5.3 or 2.5.4).

(e) Deprotect masked residues by dialysis against 1 l 5% acetic acid for 3 h at 4°C.

(f) Dialyze for 24 h at 4°C against three changes of 1 l PBS.

2.10.2. Biotinylation of peptides

Biotinylation of peptides has a number of applications. Since avidin and streptavidin have a very high affinity for biotin (association constant, 10^{15} M ^{1}), any peptide tagged with biotin can be visualized with avidin conjugates. For instance biotinylated peptides can be used to evaluate the efficiency of peptide coating in microtitre plates. Sandwich ELISA techniques using avidin immobilized on the plastic surface to present biotinylated peptides have also been developed (Fischer and Howden, 1990). Interaction of peptides with cell surface antigens can be studied (Cole et al., 1987) and coupling of peptides to carrier proteins can be monitored using biotinylated peptides (Jerry, 1993).

Several reactive biotin derivatives can be used to biotinylate peptides (Hermanson, 1996). N-hydroxysuccinimide ester (NHS) derivatives such as NHS-Biotin (Pierce, USA, 20217X) and NHS-LC-Biotin (Pierce, USA, 21335X) react specifically with primary amines under alkaline conditions. Biotin-LC-hydrazide (Pierce, USA, 21340X) can be used to label peptide proteins via carbohydrate groups while iodoacetyl-LC-biotin (Pierce, USA, 21333X) is sulfhydryl-reactive. The ImmunoProbe[TM] biotinylation kit produced by Sigma, USA (BK-101) is based on the use of biotin-amidocaproate-N-hydroxysulfo-succinimide ester (BACsulfo-NHS). Finally, different procedures allow biotin to be incorporated directly during peptide synthesis (Zhang and Tam, 1996).

CHAPTER 3

Immunization with peptides

S. MULLER

3.1. Introduction

As most synthetic peptides are good immunogens when properly presented to the immune system, there is usually no difficulty in raising antibodies against them by classical immunization procedures. In many cases, the titre of antipeptide sera measured with respect to the peptide used for immunization is very high. However, it should be remembered that the most common purpose for raising antibodies against a peptide fragment is to obtain a reagent that will also react strongly and specifically with the complete protein. Those antipeptide antibodies in the antiserum that cross-react with the complete protein have been designated antibodies of predetermined specificity since they react with a single antigenic region of the protein (Lerner, 1982, 1984). Such polyclonal antibodies share with monoclonal antibodies raised against the protein the property of binding to a discrete region of the protein antigen; however, they can differ from the monoclonal antibodies in being relatively less specific for the native conformation of the protein (Boersma et al., 1988) and they usually bind to the protein with a lower affinity constant.

Because of the great potential of peptide-based vaccines (see Chapter 8) much research has been performed during the last years to identify the best strategies to induce antibodies that recognize the native protein and confer protection. New systems of peptide presentation (carriers and vehicles) and new adjuvant formulations have been developed in order to combine efficiency, stability and safety. In this chapter, methods for raising antipeptide sera will be discussed mainly in terms of the ability of the resulting antibodies to cross-react with the whole protein and to neutralize pathogens. Particular attention will be paid to reagents recently developed for potential human vaccination in replacement of unsatisfactory substances such as Freund's adjuvant and various carrier proteins.

Investigators working with experimental animal systems will find practical details concerning the inoculation and bleeding of animals in several reviews (Dresser, 1986; Herbert and Kristensen, 1986; Hurn and Chantler, 1980; Mayer and Walker, 1978; Tijssen, 1985; Vaitukaitis, 1981). Recent review articles devoted to immunization with peptides have also been published (Audhya, 1988; Boersma et al., 1993; Tam, 1994). There have been no systematic studies of the most efficient immunization procedures for obtaining antipeptide antibodies. Since the immune response of individual outbred animals submitted to the same immunization protocol can vary greatly, it would be necessary to collect extensive comparative data to demonstrate the superiority of any particular procedure. Published information on methods used for raising antipeptide antibodies concerns mostly data obtained from a small number of animals. Furthermore, the relative merits of different immunization schedules are rarely compared and unsuccessful attempts to obtain antipeptide antibodies are seldom reported (Briand et al., 1992b; Murdin and Doel, 1987a, b; Palfreyman et al., 1984).

In the case of biologically active peptides administered to humans for therapeutic purposes, the aim is mostly to avoid eliciting an immune response as far as possible. Studies in this area are likely to increase our knowledge on the fate of peptides after they have been injected, and as a spin-off useful clues may be obtained on how to increase their immunogenicity.

3.2. The choice of animal

A number of systematic studies have been made regarding the relative merits of different strains of mice, rats, guinea pigs and rabbits as experimental animals for raising antipeptide sera (Atassi and Young, 1985; Frisch et al., 1991; Murdin and Doel, 1987a, b). Such comparative studies have generally been undertaken with different strains of mice in order to determine the highest responders useful for studying the T-cell response (Francis et al., 1987b; Leclerc et al , 1991; Munesinghe et al., 1991). As a general rule, it is clearly advantageous to use for immunization as many different types and strains of animals as possible as this will minimize the difficulties linked to the presence of a limited immunological repertoire in certain animals. When antisera of low titre are obtained using a particular breed or strain of animal, it is preferable to switch to another type of animal rather than repeating the immunization protocol with another series of individuals of the same breed.

Immunological tolerance, i.e. a specific nonreactivity of lymphoid cells to a given antigen, seems to pose fewer problems when peptide fragments are used for immunization compared to when the complete protein molecule is the immunogen. Tolerance phenomena arise when the injected protein is closely related to a homologous protein present in the animal host. However, when peptides corresponding to conserved regions of homologous proteins are used for immunization, antibodies can be readily obtained as shown, for instance, in the case of the N-terminal tetrapeptide of cytochrome c (Jemmerson et al., 1985), the C-terminal hexapeptide of histone H3 (Muller et al., 1982) or the region 22–45 of ubiquitin (Muller et al., 1988). It is possible that these peptides are immunogenic because they were injected with adjuvant and in the form of conjugates, in which the conserved peptide region was presented in the unnatural environment of the foreign carrier which also provided T-cell help. Immunization with peptides corresponding to conserved regions of autologous regions or closely related antigens may in fact be a useful method for overcoming tolerance to self-antigens. Another issue to bypass the tolerance problem is to immunize a species phylogenetically unrelated to the animal from which the immunogen is derived. For highly conserved mammalian proteins, chickens can be used for antibody production.

As far as dosage of immunogen is concerned, it should be stressed that there is no relation between the size of an animal and the quantity of antigenic material required for efficient immunization: a rabbit of 5 kg requires approximately the same dose of immunogen as a mature goat of 50 kg or a mouse of 25 g (Ritchie, 1986; Van Regenmortel, 1988).

3.3. The immunogen

3.3.1. Free versus conjugated peptides

It is commonly assumed that antigens with a molecular weight smaller than $2–5 \times 10^3$ behave like haptens and are not immunogenic. This belief accounts for the widespread practice of immunizing animals with peptides conjugated to a carrier molecule. There are indeed many reports in the literature indicating that immunization with conjugated peptides leads to antisera of higher titre than immunization with the corresponding free peptides (Alving et al., 1986; Bahraoui et al., 1987; Choppin et al., 1986; Delmas et al., 1985; Lloyd Jones et al., 1991; Schulze-Gahmen et al., 1986).

Studies performed in our own laboratory have shown that immunization with free peptides of a length of 14–25 residues (using the protocol described in Section 3.6.4) could lead to moderate antibody response after 2–3 injections (Fig. 3.1); however, in order to obtain antisera of adequate titre, 4–5 injections were usually necessary. Some authors have reported that satisfactory antibody levels could be obtained by immunizing rabbits and mice with free peptides of a length of 6–8 residues (Antoni et al., 1985; Atassi and Young, 1985; Young and Atassi, 1985; Young et al., 1983). In our laboratory, attempts to raise antibodies by immunization with free hexapeptides corresponding to fragments of histone molecules failed.

Since the main purpose of raising antipeptide antibodies is usually to obtain a reagent capable of reacting with the parent

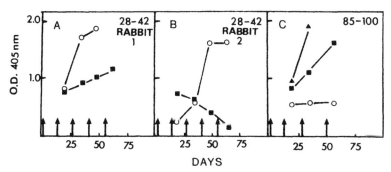

Fig. 3.1. Production of antipeptide antibodies by immunization of rabbits with free peptides of H2A (from Muller et al., 1986). Antibody levels measured by ELISA using plates coated with 400 ng H2A/ml (■); 2 μM homologous peptide-BSA conjugates (▲); 2 μM homologous free peptide (○). Arrows indicate the immunization schedule (100 μg unconjugated peptide/injection).

protein, the success of an immunization protocol depends on the cross-reactive potential of the antiserum and not solely on the titre measured with respect to the homologous peptide immunogen. When a conjugated peptide is used for immunization, the proximity of the carrier molecule may induce a conformation in the peptide which is close to that present in the parent protein. In such a case, the resulting antipeptide antibodies would be expected to show enhanced cross-reactivity with the complete protein molecule. Conversely, as discussed below (Section 3.3.4), interaction of the peptide with the heterogeneous carrier surface, may also yield a number of conformations of the peptide, and this can proportionally decrease the amount of peptide with the appropriate configuration, or perhaps induce the wrong conformation (Friede et al., 1994).

As the length of a peptide fragment increases, the likelihood that its conformation will resemble that found in the corresponding part of the complete protein can also increase. This may explain why longer peptides sometimes react better with antiprotein antibodies than do shorter peptides, and why they can also induce antibodies that cross-react more strongly with the parent protein (Al Moudallal et al., 1985; Dorow et al., 1985; Tanaka et al., 1985; Van Eldick et al., 1983; Van Regenmortel et al., 1986; Welling and Fries, 1985). However, it has also been reported that shorter peptides can fold more easily into the proper orientation required for binding to the antibody (Hodges et al., 1988). This may explain why, for example, antibodies raised against chromatin nucleosome react better with short histone peptides than with intact constitutive histone molecules (Muller et al., 1989).

Several authors have described new strategies to produce conformationally stable peptides that mimic the critical structural features of the protein antigenic site (Kaumaya et al., 1994, 1992; Vuilleumier and Mutter, 1992). For example, Kaumaya et al. (1992) designed and synthesized a peptide in such a way that it adopted a well-defined α-helical secondary and tertiary structure. This engineered conformational peptide was considerably more effective in inducing cross-reacting antibodies, as compared with the corresponding linear peptide.

Cyclization of peptides is another method used for making peptides resemble the conformation of the corresponding segment of the parent protein. Immunization with cyclized peptides has been found to lead to antisera possessing a high degree of cross-reactivity with the intact protein (Arnon et al., 1971; Atassi et al., 1995; Audibert et al., 1981; Cuniasse et al., 1995; Dorow et al., 1985; Dreesman et al., 1982; Kanda et al., 1986; Léonetti et al., 1995; Muller et al., 1990b; Valero et al., 1995). Thus, it seems impossible to predict for any particular peptide whether no conjugation or conjugation to a carrier or cyclization is likely to lead to a structure that better mimics the conformation found in the native protein. For many years, it was commonly assumed that free peptides could adopt a very large number of different conformations in aqueous solution (see Chapter 1). However, experimental observations have shown that this is not always the case and that peptides may in fact adopt a few preferred conformation (Dyson et al., 1985, 1990). The extent to which any peptide is able to mimic a conformation present in the intact protein depends, in the last analysis, on its individual sequence. Since it is not possible to predict in a reliable manner the conformation which a peptide is likely to adopt, the best immunization approach must be determined by trial and error using a variety of immunization procedures with free, conjugated or cyclized peptides in succession until the desired antibodies are obtained.

In view of animal variability, it is also essential to immunize several animals at a time. It is commonly observed that animals which receive the same immunization regimen produce antisera with completely different characteristics. Furthermore, the kinetics of appearance and disappearance of various antibody types during the course of immunization can also vary considerably in different animals. This is illustrated in Fig. 3.1 (A and B) which shows the variation in antigenic response observed with two rabbits immunized with peptide 28–42 of histone H2A (Muller et al., 1986). Although the titre of the antisera measured in ELISA using peptide 28–42 of H2A as antigen increased in successive bleedings, this was not the case for the cross-reactive titre measured in rabbit 2 when histone H2A was used as the antigen.

Another example showing that homologous titres and cross-reactive titres can evolve differently during the course of immunization is given in Fig. 3.1(C). The rabbit was immunized with an unconjugated peptide corresponding to residues 85–100 of histone H2A. The homologous titre in ELISA measured with the unconjugated peptide as antigen did not increase after the second injection, whereas the titre measured with the peptide-BSA conjugate or with H2A increased sharply. Similarly, in a recent study based on the use of rabbit antibodies raised against 39 overlapping peptides of the 52-kD Ro/SSA protein, one of the antisera showed a strong and specific reaction with the parent Ro52 protein in ELISA, Western immunoblotting and immunoprecipitation while no reaction was detectable in ELISA with the peptide immunogen (Ricchiuti et al., 1997). A similar lack of correlation between the antipeptide and cross-reactive antiprotein response has been observed in other systems (Neurath et al., 1984b) and it does not seem to depend on whether the peptide is injected as a conjugate or in free form. These findings illustrate the need to bleed immunized animals repeatedly and to test each bleeding with all relevant antigens. If the complete protein is not available for selecting the best bleedings, as is often the case when the antipeptide serum is made in an attempt to identify a putative gene product, experiments should be done with as many different bleedings as possible.

3.3.2. Immunization with conjugated peptides

Immunization of rabbits with peptides coupled to a carrier protein remains the approach of choice for investigators interested in producing antipeptide antibodies for research purposes, for example, for ultrastructural studies or gene product characterization.

Several protein carriers are commonly used to obtain peptide conjugates suitable for immunization (see Chapter 2, Table 2.3). The use of highly immunogenic substances such as KLH can be detrimental in certain cases, probably because of antigenic competition phenomena (Sarnesto et al., 1983; Taussig, 1971). In the case of peptides that are only poorly immunogenic, it may be preferable to use a less immunogenic protein such as BSA or ovalbumin as carrier.

In Chapter 2, the importance of choosing the correct coupling agent for conjugation has been emphasized. In particular, it seems that conjugation chemistry, if not applied in an appropriate manner, may completely abolish or greatly alter peptide immunogenicity (Briand et al., 1985; Chong et al., 1991; Sheth et al., 1995). As far as the optimal number of mol of peptide per mol of carrier is concerned, it seems that conjugates comprising 5–30 peptide molecules per 100 kD of carrier molecule give the best results. Many studies have been performed with small haptens such as DNP, azobenzenarsonate, and fluorescein to determine the optimal degree of carrier substitution (De Weck, 1974; Desaymard and Howard, 1975; Ivanyi and Cerny, 1969; Klaus and Cross, 1974; Turk and Parker, 1977a). As few as two molecules of hapten per carrier have been shown to lead to a specific antibody response. At high coupling densities, immunogenicity may be reduced, a phenomenon known as immunological paralysis.

The immunogenicity of peptides can be enhanced by coupling them directly to adjuvant such as tuftsin, muramyl dipeptide (MDP) or derivatives and analogues of MDP, fatty acid chains, preformed iscoms or proteosomes (see Section 3.4). Peptides can also be associated to vehicles such as liposomes (Section 3.3.4). In general the latter approach is successful to induce antipeptide antibodies when the peptide contains both a B- and T-cell epitope or when an appropriate adjuvant is incorporated into the same liposomal vesicles.

Antipeptide antibodies have also been raised in mice by intraperitoneal implantation of paper disks derivatized with a synthetic peptide (Viamontes et al., 1986). A peptide corresponding to Cys-thymopoietin 28–39 was coupled by diazo linkages to aminophenyl thioether-derivatized paper disks. After four implantations, the mice developed antibodies reactive with native thymopoietin. In contrast, mice conventionally immunized with peptide alone or with peptide conjugated to thyroglobulin by means of SPDP all failed to produce antibodies. Another successful method was described by Smith et al. (1986) who implanted subcutaneously in mice pieces of nitrocellulose containing adsorbed antigens. Only a single implantation was necessary and spleen cells of the inoculated mouse could be used for producing monoclonal antibodies.

Peptide conjugates can also be studied using an approach in which the synthetic peptide is still bound to the resin used during solid-phase synthesis. As additional residues are added to the growing peptide chain, it is possible to study by a suitable immunoassay the influence of parameters such as composition, length and conformation of the chain on the antigenic activity of the peptide. Spacers have been introduced to render the peptide more accessible to antibodies. This approach has been used to localize continuous epitopes in leghaemogloblin (Hurrell et al., 1978), myoglobin (Rodda et al., 1986; Shi et al., 1984; Smith et al., 1977), apoliprotein AII (Bhatnagar et al., 1983), parathyroid hormone (Delmas et al., 1985), cytochrome c (Paterson, 1985), ribosomal protein S13 (Syu and Kahan, 1989), and foot-and-mouth disease virus (FDMV) protein (Geysen et al., 1984, 1985a). Bahraoui et al. (1987) used a 10-mer peptide linked to its synthesis support (macroporous poly-acrylamide resin) to induce antibodies which recognized the native protein. Kanda et al. (1986) immunized rabbits with an HBs peptide still attached to a polydimethylamide resin and cyclized by reconstitution of a disulfide bridge. The resulting antibodies recognized the HBsAg whereas antibodies raised against the same peptide attached to the resin but not cyclized, did not. Kennedy et al. (1987) used the same approach with peptide 503–532 of the human immunodeficiency virus (HIV) envelope glycoprotein (gp) to raise rabbit and mouse antibodies reacting with the native form of the HIV gp120. The resin used by Kanda and colleagues has a larger pore size than other resins classically used in peptide synthesis thus providing an easier access for reagents. The peptidyl resins are swollen by aqueous buffers which allows interactions with antibodies and other immune receptors (Kanda et al., 1991). Other supports have also been used to test antibodies or to induce antipeptide antibodies, namely, control pore glass (CPG) resin (Chong et al., 1992), and hydrophilic polystyrene-polyoxyethylene graft polymer beads (Bayer and Rapp, 1992; Butz et al., 1994; Zeppezauer et al., 1993).

Good results were also obtained by mixing peptides with methylated BSA which does not cross-react with nonmethylated BSA (Calbiochem, La Jolla, CA; Reference 4554 51; e.g. 250 μg peptide mixed with 3 mg MeBSA; Ricchiuti et al., 1997), or by mixing biotinylated peptides with avidin or streptavidin (e.g. 250 μg peptide mixed with 4 mg avidin; Muller et al., 1998) in the presence of Freund's adjuvant.

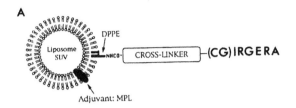

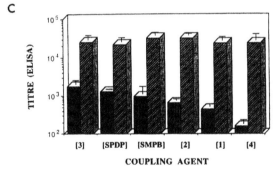

Fig. 3.2. Immunogenicity of several thiol-reactive heterobifunctional crosslink-ing agents: (A) schematic representation of the liposomal construct; (B) structure of the heterobifunctional molecules tested; and (C) immunogenicity of liposo-mal constructs: (solid blocks) antibody level against the heterobifunctional link itself; (shaded blocks) anti-IRGERA peptide antibody level. SUV: small uni-lamellar vesicle; DPPE: dipalmitoylphosphatidylethanolamine; MPL: monophos-phoryl lipid A; SMPB: succinimidyl 4-(p-maleimidophenyl) butyrate; SPDP: N-succinimidyl 3(2-pyridyldithio)propionate.

3.3.3. Possible experimental pitfalls due to the generation of antibodies to the coupling agent used for peptide conjugation

Although it has been known for many years (Goodfriend et al., 1964) that antibodies directed to the coupling agent used for peptide conjugation can be generated using animal immunization with peptides conjugated to a carrier protein, this problem is not always well appreciated. As shown in Chapter 2, a substantial part of the coupling agent usually remains on the carrier-peptide conjugate and, in general, this linker is highly immunogenic. In a comparative study of four bifunctional reagents, Peeters et al. (1989) found that antisera to the peptide conjugates could show antibody titres as high as 10^4–10^5 against reagents such as MBS or SMCC. In contrast, the spacer originating with SPDP induced very little specific antibody. In the same series of experiments, MHS which is more stable than SPDP, showed a moderate immunogenicity as compared with MBS and SMCC. Glutaraldehyde, EDC, MCS, MBS, bisdiazobenzidine were all found to induce a strong antibody response (Bernatowicz and Matsueda, 1986; Boersma et al., 1988; Briand et al., 1985; Deen et al., 1990; Lloyd Jones et al., 1989). It is therefore advisable to prepare two conjugates of the same peptide with different carrier proteins and different coupling methods which will be respectively used for immunization and screening of antibodies. Recently, we have investigated the immunogenicity of six thiol-reactive heterobifunctional crosslinking reagents that allow the conjugation of cysteine carrying peptides (Boeckler et al., 1996). This study was performed with a short peptide of sequence IRGERA to which a CG N-terminal spacer-arm was added for coupling purposes, and the conjugation involved linkers introduced at the surface of liposomes containing monophosphoryl lipid A (MPL) as adjuvant. Irrespective of the length of the linkers (comprised between 3 and 16 Å) and their nature (stable thioether or bioreducible disulfide bonds), all six liposomal constructs elicited a strong antipeptide antibody response (Fig. 3.2). However, a high antibody response against the linker was also found in some cases. Among the six constructs tested (three new polyoxyethylene linkers of different lengths containing thiol-reactive moieties and three classical reagents, SMPB, SPDP and *N*-succinimidyl bromoacetate; Fig. 3.2), the least immunogenic linkers were the bromoacetate derivatives that bind the peptide via a simple thioether bond, whereas, those containing a maleimide group induced a strong immune response (Fig. 3.2).

Several authors have suggested methods to remove these undesired antibodies, for example, by purifying the peptide antibodies by affinity chromatography on appropriate immunoadsorbent (Chersi et al., 1989) or by incubating the peptide antiserum with the coupling agent (Lloyd Jones et al., 1989).

3.3.4. Use of liposomes as peptide vehicles

The potential value of liposomes for eliciting antibodies to peptides is now increasingly recognized and in view of the current interest in the development of safe potent synthetic peptide vaccines, the use of liposomes as vehicles in vaccinal preparation is likely to considerably increase in future. Liposomes indeed offer a number of advantages as they can be made from synthetic components which are by themselves nonimmunogenic, biodegradable, nontoxic, and induce no local or systemic reaction in the immunized animals. The liposomal constructs with peptides coupled at their surface can be lyophilized and stored without loss of biological activity (Friede et al., 1993c).

Several detailed reviews and books have appeared on liposome technology and their applications as vehicles of peptide antigens (Alving et al., 1995; Buiting et al., 1992; Gregoriadis, 1990, 1995; Philippot and Schuber, 1995; Stewart-Tull, 1996; van Rooijen, 1990). The chemical composition and physical properties of liposomes greatly influence their behaviour in the body, distribution into tissues and rate of removal from the blood. Smaller and neutral liposomes are cleared more slowly than are the negatively charged and larger ones. The half-life of liposomal preparations can thus be increased from minutes to hours if small unilamellar vesicles (SUVs) are used in place of multilamellar vesicles (MLVs). In the case of the short peptide IRGERA, the duration of immune stimulation was found to be much longer when SUVs (dia. < 100 nm) rather than larger vesicles such as REVs (see Section 2.7) were used as carriers (Frisch et al., 1991). The discovery of long-circulating (Stealth®) liposomes, prepared by inclusion of 3–7 mol% of methoxypoly(ethylene glycol)-distearoylphosphatidylethanolamine (mPEG-DSPE) in the vesicle-forming lipid mixture has allowed to overcome limitations of 'classical' or 'conventional' liposomes caused by their extensive hepatosplenic uptake and rapid clearance from circulation (Lasic and Martin, 1995; Papahadjopoulos and Gabizon, 1995; Uster et al., 1996; Zalipsky et al., 1995). In general, methods devised to increase stability and rigidity of liposomes have been shown to render the linked peptides more immunogenic (Friede et al., 1993b; Frisch et al., 1991; Yasuda et al., 1977; Zalipsky et al., 1995). Different types of liposomes as well as the methods used for anchoring peptides to them have been described in Section 2.7. Considerable success has been achieved by coupling peptides of biological interest to liposomes, such as peptides of diphteria and cholera toxins, polio virus, FDMV VP1, HIV gp120, HBsAg and haemagglutinin (HA) and neuraminidase of influenza virus (Alving et al., 1986; Francis et al., 1985; Friede et al., 1994; Gregoriadis et al., 1993; Muller et al., 1990b, 1995; Neurath et al., 1984a; Phillips, 1992; Phillips et al., 1996; Xiao et al., 1989). For example, a variety of crosslinking agents and carriers were compared by Neurath et al. (1984a) to assess their efficacy in increasing the immunogenicity of a synthetic peptide corresponding to residues 135–155 of HBsAg. Two rabbits were immunized with each of the 26 different conjugates tested and the antisera were assessed with respect to antipeptide and anti-HBsAg response. Animals immunized with the peptide in free form did not respond. Polymers of the peptide prepared by linking to diaminoalkanes as well as conjugates prepared by binding the peptide to liposomes or to polylysine were found to be immunogenic. A poor correlation was observed between antipeptide and anti-HBsAg response elicited by these conjugates. Glutaraldehyde-fixed liposomes were the best vehicles for inducing an anti-HBsAg response (Neurath et al., 1984a) and gave better results than constructs corresponding to peptides linked to MDP.

A systematic investigation performed in our laboratory (Friede et al., 1993b; Frisch et al., 1991) with the model hexapeptide IRGERA (COOH-terminus of histone H3) has shown that the peptide, whether surface-bound (via an additional cysteine residue) or entrapped in liposomes, did not induce any detectable immune response. When MPL was included in the liposomes, a strong IgG response to the peptide was induced but only when the peptide was bound at the surface of liposomes and not when it was entrapped within the liposomes. It was also found that MPL had to be present in the same population of liposomes suggesting that surface-bound antigen targeted liposomal MPL to B lymphocytes specific for the antigen. We observed that when animals were immunized with the peptide exposed on fluid liposomes containing MPL, induced antipeptide antibodies cross-reacted with the cognate protein, histone H3. In contrast, antibodies raised against the peptide presented on solid liposomes did not recognize histone H3 (Friede, 1995). It was thus concluded that for this particular peptide, the use of solid liposomes was detrimental for the specificity of the antibodies. This result may be due to the fact that the peptide adopts different conformations at the surface of fluid and solid liposomes leading to the induction of different antibody subsets. Clearly, this needs to be studied on a case-by-case basis.

The role played by the conformation of a peptide presented at the surface of liposomes on the induction of cross-reactive antibodies was also demonstrated in the case of two cyclic peptides representing a nine-residue sequence from site A of influenza HA cyclized in such a way that a large (closed by a $-NH-CO-CH_2-CH_2-CONH-$ bridge) and a small (closed by a simple $-NH-CO-$ link) loop were obtained. These two loops only differ by a few Å as determined by molecular modelling, the large one appears more mobile and open than the smaller one (Kieffer et al., 1993) and the small one closely resembles the loop present in the virus HA. When used as peptide-ovalbumin conjugates, it was found that both cyclic peptides (but not the linear peptide) were able to confer protective immunity (up to 70%) as measured by survival after nasal challenge with influenza virus. In contrast, a sharp distinction was found between the small and large loop when immunization of animals was performed with peptides presented at the surface of SUV. In this case, only the small loop was found to confer protection (Friede et al., 1994) and this finding was in good agreement with a previous observation that only the small loop in solution was recognized by antivirus antibodies and inhibited the binding of these antibodies to the virus (Muller et al., 1990b). These results suggest that the flexibility of the large loop allows the peptide, once it is conjugated to the carrier protein, to adopt a structure similar to the one it has in the virus and hence confers protection. This is not the case when the peptide is linked at the liposomal surface which is much more homogeneous compared with the surface of a carrier protein. Thus, and in contrast with what occurs at the surface of liposomes, it appears that when a peptide is bound to a protein, depending on the environment, it can proba-bly adopt a larger diversity of conformations. This may or may not represent an advantage.

According to the definition of Allison and Byars (1986) and Edelman (1992), typical 'vehicles' unlike 'carriers', cannot by themselves provide T-cell help for attached antigens. Thus either synthetic peptides known to contain both B- and T-cell epitopes, or peptides corresponding only to B-cell epitopes but tested in the presence of adjuvant (for example, MPL and/or aluminium salts), can be successfully used as immunogen in association with lipo-somes. However, one of the advantage of liposomes is that they can accommodate different peptide combinations (obtained after copolymerization, colinear synthesis or covalent coupling; see Sec-tion 3.3.6) involving B- and T-cell peptide sequences. Adjuvant and cytokines (for example, interleukin-2) can also be co-entrapped or mixed with the antigen and delivered according to a controlled schedule to the appropriate antigen-presenting cells (APCs). Successful experiments with peptides have been reported by several groups (Alving et al., 1995; Garcon and Six, 1991; Gregoriadis et al., 1993), and recent advances made in the theory and utilization of liposomes are reasonably promising in the quest for effective immunization against complex diseases such as cancer, parasitic diseases and other infections. A human liposomal vaccine against hepatitis A based on the use of inactivated virus has been commercialized (Just et al., 1992). In the case of synthetic peptide vaccines, we are now potentially able to prepare a stable, efficient and safe liposomal formulation involving peptides containing one or several defined B- and T-cell epitopes, a chemically defined and nonimmunogenic bridge (see Section 3.3.3), and a chemically-controlled adjuvant (see Section 3.4). Additional research is needed, however, to further improve the effectiveness of liposomes. In particular, studies are needed to determine the structure of the peptide when it interacts with the liposomal lipid bilayer (Macquaire et al., 1992) and to increase its stability without affecting its immunogenic properties.

3.3.5. Synthetic-branched peptides

As discussed above (Sections 3.3.2 and 3.3.3), the use of protein carriers to present peptides presents a number of drawbacks. Covalent conjugation of peptides to carriers can lead to inappropriate presentation of the epitope or to the appearance of adducts on the protein which are highly immunogenic. Furthermore, protein carriers are themselves immunogenic, and this can have undesired consequences if the same carrier is used for several different peptides (Herzenberg and Tokuhisha, 1980). To overcome such problems several alternative approaches have been proposed in order to present multiple copies of the peptide in a multimeric system in the absence of carrier proteins. Synthetic-branched polypeptides were first introduced as effective carriers for B-cell determinants by the pioneering work of Sela and co-workers (Arnon et al., 1971; Sela, 1969). A structurally simplified family of synthetic branched polypeptides based on a poly[Lys-(DL-Ala$_3$)] backbone were used by Hudecz and Szekerke (1980, 1985). Subsequently, this system was used to prepare branched polypeptides covalently coupled to the monovalent hapten oxazolone (Rajnavölgyi et al., 1989). When mice were immunized with this oxazolone conjugate, hapten-specific IgG antibodies were obtained while no carrier-specific response could be detected. When the conjugate was injected without adjuvant, almost the same level of oxazolone antibodies could be detected as after injection in complete Freund's adjuvant. The authors suggested that the efficacy of these compounds may be caused by a delayed degradation due to the presence of D-amino acid residues in the construct. Applications of this approach with peptides of herpes simplex virus type I (HSV-1) glycoprotein D and protein core of epithelial mucins have been described (Hilbert et al., 1994; Hudecz and Price, 1992).

Another approach using branched oligo-lysines as template for the attachment of antigenic peptides has been developed by J. P. Tam who called it the multiple antigen peptide (MAP) system (Posnett et al., 1988; Tam, 1988). The system consists of a core matrix of lysine residues with amino terminals for anchoring multiple copies of the same or different peptides (Tam et al., 1990; Tam and Lu, 1989). The synthesis of MAP is performed using Boc chemistry or a combination of Boc and Fmoc chemistry. The whole MAP forms a macromolecular complex of about 10 kD in which the lysine core is not exposed. The use of a MAP system was found to be advantageous for coating plates in solid-phase assays (Briand et al., 1992a; Marguerite et al., 1992; Marsden et al., 1992; Tam and Zavala, 1989). Probably because branched (oligomeric) peptides bind more readily to the microtitre plates than do monomeric peptides, and allow multivalent binding between antibody and peptide motif, tests using MAPs are in general much more sensitive than those performed with monomeric peptides. In our experience however, and for the same reasons, we have found that these tests have to be particularly well calibrated to prevent nonspecific reactions with unrelated antibodies (Briand et al., 1992b). The MAP

approach was also successfully used to raise antibodies to short peptides (for example, peptides of FMDV VP1, circumsporozoite (CS)
protein of *Plasmodium falciparum* and *berghei*, surface antigen of
Toxoplasma gondii, Shistosoma mansoni, hepatitis B virus, HIV-
1, influenza HA) in mice, guinea pigs and rabbits (Ahlborg et al.,
1996; Chai et al., 1992; Darcy et al., 1992; Ferru et al., 1997; Francis
et al., 1991; McLean et al., 1991; Nardelli et al., 1992; Naruse et al.,
1994; Schaaper et al., 1990; Tam et al., 1990; Tam and Lu, 1989;
Troalen et al., 1990), and examples of efficient protection against
the corresponding diseases have been described. In certain cases,
the production of antipeptide antibodies was only achieved when
both peptides corresponding to B- and T-cell epitopes were present
in a particular arrangement in the MAP. It should be noted, however,
that several authors reported that antibodies induced against MAP
show a slight or no cross-reaction with the whole protein or fail to
induce protection of infected animals (Briand et al., 1992b; Calvo-
Calle et al., 1993; Darcy et al., 1992; Friede et al., 1994; Rose et
al., 1995). This is particularly true for C-terminal peptides but it
can also hold for peptides located in internal regions of the protein
primary sequence. This result may be due to the inaccessibility of
residues close to the lysine matrix. Indeed when the fine specificity
of antibodies to the sequence 141–160 of FDMV VP1 induced by
using the MAP strategy was analyzed by the pepscan method, it was
found that the antibodies recognized mainly the N-terminal residues
of the peptide (Schaaper et al., 1990), thus confirming previous results (Posnett et al., 1988). Furthermore, it is possible that due to the
density of peptides in the MAP construct, peptides assume an un-
usual conformation that in some cases does not mimic the structure
of either the monomeric peptide or the parent protein. This approach
has, however, been found effective in a number of cases and several
companies use this technology for producing peptide antibodies. A
protocol for immunization of mice and rabbits is given in Section
3.6.9.

Another strategy has been developed by Mutter and co-workers
(Mutter and Tuchscherer, 1988; Tuchscherer and Mutter, 1995;

Vuilleumier and Mutter, 1992). The construction referred here as 'template-assembled synthetic proteins or peptides' (TASP) uses a topological template that serves as 'built-in' device to covalently anchor peptides. Topological templates can be cyclic, e.g. Ac-Cys-Lys-Ala-Lys-Pro-Gly-Lys-Ala-Lys-Cys-NH$_2$ (Rivier et al., 1990; Rose et al., 1995) or linear, e.g. Lys-Lys-Lys-Gly-Pro-Lys-Glu-Lys-Gly-Cys (Callebaut et al., 1996), and peptides are attached to ε-NH$_2$ of lysines in such a way that their spatial conformation is stabilized. The strategy here is not only to design a carrier for peptides but rather to direct the attached peptide blocks to a predetermined three-dimensional packing arrangement which should produce conformationally stable peptides that better mimic the native structure. The TASP approach was used by Kaumaya et al. (1994, 1992) to induce antipeptide antibodies against a topographic antigenic determinant of the testis-specific isozyme of lactate dehydrogenase C4 (LDH-C4); the produced antibodies were found to cross-react with the native parent protein. Specific anti-TASP antibodies that recognize the cognate protein have been raised against the helical segment 87–99 of lysozyme (Mutter and Tuchscherer, 1988), the helical segments 58–74 of the α1 heavy chain domain of HLA-A2 (Tuchscherer et al., 1992), the C-terminal 23 residues of influenza virus HA (Rose et al., 1995) and a short pseudopeptide which mimics the HIV V3 loop (Muller et al., 1999).

3.3.6. Peptidic construction involving B- and T-cell epitopes

The protein carriers used to induce antipeptide antibodies serve not only as peptide vehicle but most importantly provide T-cell epitopes, often absent in short peptides. When, for various reasons (see above), protein carriers cannot be used, several strategies can be followed to provide T-help and thus to enhance the immunogenicity of peptide. For example, animals can be immunized with peptide constructions containing a B- and T-cell epitope associated covalently or incorporated in a multibranched structure such as in a

MAP system or in a TASP. The T-cell epitope moiety will interact with class II MHC molecules on the surface of APCs and B cells and, subsequently, bind to a T-cell receptor (TCR) in the form of a trimolecular complex. The T-helper cells will then provide signals in the form of a number of chemical messengers (e.g. lymphokines) to specific B cells, which result in differentiation, proliferation and antibody production. In the peptidic constructs built in various laboratories, either T-cell help was provided by a foreign T epitope or both B and T epitopes were from the same protein.

Francis et al. (1987b) showed, for example, that B10 D2 (H-2^d) mice which are nonresponders to the free 141–160 VP1 peptide of FDMV can be converted into responders by immunization with the FDMV peptide associated linearly with a defined foreign T-cell epitope from ovalbumin (sequence 323–339) or sperm-whale myoglobin (sequence 132–148 or 105–121). However, the virus-neutralizing activity of the antibodies raised was dependent on the T-cell determinant used. Although sera from mice which received the peptide 141–160 of FDMV VP1 with the added sequence 105–121 from sperm-whale myoglobin contained a high level of anti-141–160 FDMV antibodies, the antisera did not neutralize the virus. A high degree of neutralizing activity was found when the two other constructs were used in H-2^d mice. Other reports describing the immunogenicity of free linear peptides corresponding to T-helper and B-cell epitopes have been published, for example, in the case of peptides of malaria CS (Good et al., 1987), bovine rotavirus major protein (Borras-Cuesta et al., 1988), HBsAg (Leclerc et al., 1987; Milich et al., 1988), *Chlamydia trachomotis* major outer membrane protein (Su and Caldwell, 1992), MUC1 mucin (Denton et al., 1994), measles virus (Hathaway et al., 1995; Obeid et al., 1995) and influenza HA (Fitzmaurice et al., 1996; Zegers et al., 1993). Levi et al. (1995) described protection experiments performed with three influenza peptides containing B, Th and CTL epitopes individually anchored to proteosomes.

Francis et al. (1987b) used free peptide constructs containing amino acid sequences of B- and T-cell epitopes linked colinearly in a B-T arrangement. Su and Caldwell (1992) obtained neutralizing antibodies by using a T-B construct. Several groups have evaluated the activity of such chimeric peptides with regard to the B-T or T-B orientation. It has been reported that when the determinant recognized by T cells was in C-terminal position with respect to the B epitope (i.e. in a B-T construct), the T-cell determinant was responsible for the induction of a higher antibody titre (Cox et al., 1988). Golvano et al. (1990), in another peptide system, confirmed that the position of the T-cell epitope within the construction has a great importance. However, in their study, they found that the T-B construct was the most efficient to induce antipeptide antibodies. The same conclusion was drawn by Partidos et al. (1992a) in the case of constructs containing a T-cell epitope of the fusion protein of measles virus (residues 288–302) and a B-cell epitope of HA of the same virus (residues 188–199). Cox et al. (1988) observed that the proliferative response of T cells to different constructions was equivalent and thus suggested that the differences in the antipeptide antibody responses might result from differences at the level of B-T cell interactions or by the profiles of interleukins secreted by T cells. As an alternative explanation, Francis and co-workers proposed that depending on the construction used, structural differences occurred in the peptide sequences leading to changes in the B-T cell interaction. Golvano et al. (1990) proposed that changes at the level of peptide processing may explain the results. Denton et al. (1994) using circular dichroism spectrometry showed that the B-T and T-B peptides present different secondary structures which may lead to differences in presentation and/or processing of the peptide. In their study, Denton and colleagues showed that the T-B construct had the capacity to induce high antipeptide antibody titres in BALB/c mice whereas no antibody response was obtained against the B-T construct or the B epitope alone. The authors further showed that the sequential order of T- and B-cell epitopes was important for immunogenicity but that it did not affect antibody recognition of the B-cell epitope.

Another type of construct associating B- and T-cell epitopes was tested by Onoé and co-workers (Naruse et al., 1994; Ogasawara et al., 1992). They added the central seven residues 127–133 derived from HA of Aichi/68 influenza strain into the I-A^b binding component consisting of 43–46 and 54–58 residues of a pigeon cytochrome c analogue peptide. The hybrid peptide presented as a MAP induced a high antibody titre against the B-cell epitope, and when included in liposomes and given intranasally to I-A^b mice, it reduced significantly viral growth in lungs challenged with Aichi/68 virus. Multiple B-T constructs have also been successfully derived for antibody production and protection experiments by Chatterjee et al. (1995). Steward and collaborators reported the properties of different B-T chimeras to induce a systemic immune response (Hathaway et al., 1995). In particular they showed that both B-TT and TT-B chimeras induced high antibody titres to the B-cell epitope (the epitope orientation was thus not critical in this case). On the other hand they observed no systemic immune response after immunization with a chimeric peptide containing one copy of the T-cell epitope.

It should be mentioned that there are a few reports describing the production of antipeptide antibodies after simple co-immunization of peptides presenting B-cell epitopes with peptides presenting T-cell epitopes without covalent linkage between the B- and T-cell epitopes (Gregoriadis et al., 1993; Partidos et al., 1992b; Sarobe et al., 1991; Shaw et al., 1993). These results, however, could not be confirmed by Zegers et al. (1993).

Improvements in immunogenicity of peptides is generally achieved by increasing their effective size and the number of repetitive motifs (see Section 3.3.5). Multimeric presentation of peptides in MAP and TASP or as branched constructs has been also shown to be very useful to provide both B- and T-cell epitopes in the same construct (Fitzmaurice et al., 1996; Jackson et al., 1997; Kaumaya et al., 1994; Nardin et al., 1995; Tam, 1994). A number of studies have been conducted using these constructions to induce antipeptide antibodies, neutralizing antibodies or protection of infected animals.

They include peptides of the CS protein of malaria parasite, human T-lymphotropic virus type I and influenza HA (Calvo-Calle et al., 1993; Chai et al., 1992; Fitzmaurice et al., 1996; Lairmore et al., 1995; McLean et al., 1992; Men et al., 1996; Munesinghe et al., 1991; Naruse et al., 1994; Tam et al., 1990; Tam and Lu, 1989; Valmori et al., 1992, 1994). In the *Plasmodium berghei* CS protein system, Tam et al. (1990) showed that a MAP containing four copies of the peptide antigens in a B-T arrangement (Figure 3.3) was much more efficient to induce antibodies that cross-reacted with sporo-zoites as compared with other MAPs. With the MAP B-T(4), 80% protection of infected mice was obtained compared to 50–60% with MAPs T-B(8) and B-T(8). No protection was observed in mice im-munized with the linear B-T peptide or with MAPs containing four or eight copies of each T or B epitopes (T(4), T(8), B(4), B(8)). Munesinghe et al. (1991), studying the repeat region (NANP)3 corresponding to an immunodominant B-cell epitope of the CS pro-tein, showed that optimal antibody response was obtained in mice of different MHC haplotypes immunized with a MAP T-B(4) in which the T-cell epitope chosen for incorporation into the MAP was the 16-mer peptide DPNANPNVDPNANPNV. The reasons for the differences in the immunogenicity of the different MAPs are not known but probably result from the position of the T-cell epitope as regard to the B-cell epitope in the MAP and in the native protein (Calvo-Calle et al., 1993).

As mentioned above, foreign T-cell epitopes can be efficiently used in association with a B-cell epitope. Several groups have thus used a carrier providing 'universal' T-cell epitopes such as tetanus toxoid (TT). However, even when they produce anti-TT antibod-ies, individuals previously vaccinated with TT can fail to mount an effective immune response to a synthetic peptide coupled to TT because of the phenomenon of epitope suppression (Herzenberg and Tokuhisha, 1980; Schutze et al., 1989; Schutze et al., 1985). The possibility to use TT peptides which would stimulate only the Th cells and might be as efficient as the whole TT molecule for pro-viding carrier help without inducing epitope suppression has been

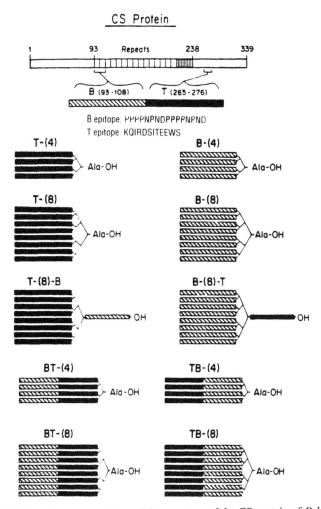

Fig. 3.3. Schematic representation of the structure of the CS protein of *P. berghei*, of the monomeric form of a peptide containing B- and T-cell epitopes associated colinearly and of MAPs studied for their ability to induce antipeptide antibodies and protection (from Tam et al., 1990). Note that in B-T(4) MAP, the site of linear peptide attachment to the lysine core is at the COOH-end of the T-cell epitope.

investigated. A number of such peptides have been used in association with B-cell epitopes to induce protective antibody responses. They include the sequences 830–843 and 947–967 of TT, 288–302 of measles virus, 378–398 of the CS protein of *P. falciparum* (named CST3) and 65–85 of the 65-kD protein of *M. tuberculosis* (Cox et al., 1988; Kaumaya et al., 1994; Kumar et al., 1992; Men et al., 1996; Panina-Bordignon et al., 1989; Rothbard and Taylor, 1988; Sinigaglia et al., 1988; Valmori et al., 1992; Widmann et al., 1992).

3.4. The adjuvant

The adjuvants most commonly used to enhance the humoral response are the water-in-oil emulsions complete or incomplete Freund's adjuvants (CFA and IFA; for details on the composition and the preparation of these adjuvants, see Clausen, 1981; Dresser, 1986; Goding, 1983; Tijssen, 1985). Aluminium salts (aluminium phosphate $AlPO_4$, aluminium hydroxide $Al(OH)_3$, aluminium potassium sulfate $(Al\ K(SO_4)_2)$ have been widely used for human and veterinary vaccination since 1930. They are currently the only adjuvants approved for use in humans by the US Food and Drug Administration. Aluminium adjuvants (alum) are generally safe, but an appreciable granulomatous response has been observed at injection sites in guinea pigs (Turk and Parker, 1977b). Good results were obtained with free or conjugated monomeric peptides and MAPs using alum (Chatterjee et al., 1995; Francis et al., 1991; Geerligs et al., 1989; Green et al., 1982; Houen et al., 1997). It has been reported, however, that although there is usually a good humoral response to aluminium adjuvant (but see Chatterjee et al., 1995), there is little or no augmentation of cell-mediated immune response and protective effect (Bomford, 1980). Aluminium adjuvants are indeed typical stimulators of Th2-type immune response which is accompanied by IL-4 and IL-10 cytokines and leads to production of IgG1 and IgE in mice (see Cox and Coulter, 1997;

Gupta and Siber, 1995 for reviews). Aluminium salts like IFA act mainly as a deposit substance to protect the antigen from degradation. Addition of substances of mostly bacterial origin (e.g. MDP) to aluminium salts leads to much more effective adjuvants

The immunogenicity of small molecules can also be enhanced by associating them to immunostimulation complexes such as ISCOMs[TM] which are open cage-like structures about 40 nm in diameter resulting from the interaction of cholesterol, Quil A (saponin) and glycoproteins such as influenza envelope glycoprotein. First described by Morein and colleagues (Lövgren et al., 1987; Morein, 1988), the system was found to be efficient with haptens such as biotin although it needs to be improved in the case of peptides (Lövgren et al., 1987; Mowat and Donachie, 1991). Recently, a method for incorporating antigenic peptides more easily into ISCOMs was described (Fernando et al., 1995). The authors used glutaraldehyde-polymerized 20-mer peptides containing B- and T-helper cell epitopes from the E7 protein of the cervical cancer associated human papillomavirus type 16. Unpolymerized peptide elicited no measurable antibody. ISCOMs containing polymerized peptide gave higher antibody titres than CFA and a Th1-type response could be measured. The glycoside Quil A was also used in other adjuvant preparations. For example, Lipford et al. (1994) showed that short synthetic peptides of ovalbumin, vesicular stomatitis virus (VSV) nucleoprotein, listeriolysin and cytomegalovirus pp89 when encapsulated in Quil A-containing liposomes triggered a peptide-specific primary $CD8^+$ CTL response *in vivo*. Quil A was also used together with aluminium hydroxide gel in a cocktail containing two KLH-conjugated peptides which was found to protect dogs against challenge with virulent canine parvovirus (Langeveld et al., 1994a).

Another system that combines carrier and adjuvant effects for the presentation of peptides is proteosomes. These are preparations of highly hydrophobic outer membrane proteins of meningococci that naturally form multimolecular vesicles and are safe for human use (Lowell, 1990; Zollinger et al., 1986). The system has been found to be effective for producing antipeptide antibodies (Lowell, 1990; Lowell et al., 1988) and in one report for conferring a partial protective immunity against viral challenge (Levi et al., 1995). Virosomes differ from proteosomes as they contain virus-derived transmembrane proteins e.g. influenza HA (Glück et al., 1994).

A number of much more chemically defined adjuvants have been developed. In particular MDP derivatives, lipopeptides and lipid A analogues have been extensively studied (for reviews, see Adam and Souvannavong, 1992; Gupta and Siber, 1995). Their respective efficacies as compared with Freund's adjuvant, regarding the quantity, affinity, isotype and specificity of antibodies raised have been explored in comparative studies (Bennet et al., 1992; Deeb et al., 1992; Geerligs et al., 1989; Hioe et al., 1996; Kenney et al.., 1989; Lloyd Jones et al., 1990; Przewlocki et al., 1986; Robuccio et al., 1995; Sheth et al., 1995).

Lipid A, the structurally highly conserved lipid moiety of bacterial endotoxins has received considerable attention, and its structure and specific functions have been elucidated. Multiple reviews covering studies on the properties of lipid A have been published (see Johnson, 1994, and references therein). Ribi and co-workers (1984, 1986) have developed a formulation consisting of an oil-in-water emulsion containing the antigen and bacterial products i.e. trehalose dimycolate (TDM) and MPL. Both components of the Ribi adjuvant system (RAS) possess adjuvant activity. MPL or MPL together with TDM have been used in several studies, in particular in combination with liposomes, to induce antipeptide antibodies and CTL responses (Friede et al., 1993b; Frisch et al., 1991; Geerligs et al., 1989; Muller et al., 1995, 1990b; Ribi et al., 1986; White et al., 1995). The adjuvant action of MPL has been extensively studied (reviewed by Johnson, 1994). It was shown that MPL has a direct action on B lymphocytes (Hiernaux et al., 1989) and induces secretion of interferon-γ from T cells and IL-1 from macrophages. Stimulation of macrophages increases their phagocytic activity, thus facilitating antigen uptake, processing and presentation.

MDP compound (*N*-acetyl-muramyl-L-alanyl-D-isoglutamine) is the minimal structure that can substitute for the mycobacteria in CFA (reviewed by Adam and Lederer, 1988). Several MDP derivatives have been chemically synthesized and biologically tested. For the induction of antipeptide antibodies, MDP and MDP analogues have been found to be effective adjuvants in various systems (Arnon et al., 1980, 1983; Audibert, 1987; Iinuma et al., 1995; Jacob et al., 1986/87; Lew et al., 1988; Siddiqui et al., 1978; Singh et al., 1998; Stevens et al., 1986), although some undesirable effects have been reported (Allison and Byars, 1991). When mixed with a conjugate made up of peptide P2 of MS2 coliphage and poly(DL-alanyl)-poly(L-lysine) synthetic carrier, MDP was shown to cause a slight increase in antibody production but when it was covalently linked, the resulting MDP-P2-carrier conjugate administered in PBS elicited in rabbits almost as good an anti-MS2 response as did P2-carrier conjugate in CFA (Arnon et al., 1980). By introducing a butyl ester group into MDP (*N*-acetyl-muramyl-L-alanyl-D-glutamine-*n*-butyl ester), a compound termed murabutide devoid of toxicity but retaining full adjuvant properties was obtained. Murabutide has been used with success in several studies with peptides (Clough et al., 1985; Przewlocki et al., 1986; Telzak et al., 1986), and following successful phases I and II clinical trials appears to be promising for human vaccination (Johnson, 1994). Allison and Byars (1986, 1991) have developed an efficient and nontoxic adjuvant formulation consisting of *N*-acetyl-muramyl-L-threonyl-D-isoglutamine in a squalane pluronic polymer emulsion (SAF-1, Syntex Corporation). As with other MDP formulations, SAF-1 was shown to increase antibody formation and to elicit cell-mediated immunity. The Chiron MF59 adjuvant which contains MTP-PE (muramyl tripeptide-phosphatidylethanol), a lipophilic MDP derivative, induces high levels of serum IL-4 and IL-5 cytokines suggesting a Th2-type response (Singh et al., 1998). In herpes vaccine trials (phases I and II), this 'oil-in-water' adjuvant was demonstrated to be safe and induced a good neutralizing antibody response. However no significant protection was demonstrated in phase III clinical trials (reported in Leclerc and Ronco, 1998).

In a comparison of different adjuvants including Algammulin (a mixture of γ-inulin and alum), several forms of montanide (a series of commercial adjuvants supplied by Seppic, France), alum alone, Squalene Arlacel containing MDP (Ciba-Geigy), SAF-1 and CFA, Lloyd Jones et al. (1990) showed that Algammulin (which has been in phase I clinical trial) was the most effective adjuvant in raising antibodies reacting with both the immunising peptide (a peptide of sequence CKNNNSTNSGI containing an epitope of a malarial surface antigen, MSA2, conjugated to diphteria toxoid protein), and the native antigen. In both mice and rabbits, SAF-1 proved to be relatively ineffective in its immunopotentiation. Squalene Arlacel containing MDP was better but less effective than Algammulin, Montanide, Freund's adjuvant and alum. In another study performed with the synthetic peptide 9–21 of HSV-1 conjugated to BSA or ovalbumin, Geerligs et al. (1989) found that CFA/IFA, alum and RAS (in this order of efficacy) helped to elicit a significant antibody response. Significant protection against a challenge with a lethal dose of HSV-1 was generated when mice were immunized in the presence of CFA/IFA and RAS. Although a delayed type hypersensitivity was observed when immunizations were performed in the presence of alum, no significant protective immunity against the challenge was generated. In a comparison of Freund's adjuvant, alum and Adjuvax^{TM} (a nonantigenic carbohydrate adjuvant supplied by Alpha-Beta Technology Inc., Worcester, MA), as adjuvants for a peptide-TT conjugate, highest titres for the synthetic peptide component (peptide 128–144 of *P. aeruginosa* pilus adhesin) of the conjugate were obtained with Adjuvax^{TM}, while highest titres for the carrier protein components was obtained with Freund's adjuvant (Sheth et al., 1995). In this study, alum was found to be less effective for inducing antipeptide antibodies. Perdew (1994) also reported the production of high titres of antipeptide antibodies using Adjuvax^{TM}.

Besides muramyl dipeptide analogues which represent the minimal structure of the CFA, the tripalmitoyl-S-glyceryl cysteine (P_3C)

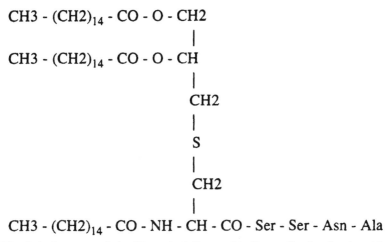

CH3 - (CH2)₁₄ - CO - O - CH2
                              |
CH3 - (CH2)₁₄ - CO - O - CH
                              |
                            CH2
                              |
                             S
                              |
                            CH2
                              |
CH3 - (CH2)₁₄ - CO - NH - CH - CO - Ser - Ser - Asn - Ala

Fig. 3.4. Structure of the N-terminal lipopeptide Pam₃ Cys-Ser-Ser-Asn-Ala (P₃C-SSNA) from the lipoprotein of *E. coli*.

derived from a lipoprotein of *E. coli* has been found as a potential adjuvant for vaccines (Bessler, 1992; Jung and Bessler, 1995).

P₃C-SSNA is identical to the lipoprotein N-terminus with respect to its peptide composition, but contains solely palmitic acid residues. This synthetic peptide (Fig. 3.4) and a multitude of synthetically prepared analogues constitute potent immunoadjuvants either in combination with antigens or after covalent linkage to peptides (Deres et al., 1989; Loleit et al., 1990; Sauzet et al., 1995; Wiesmüller et al., 1989) without requiring further adjuvant or additive. Examples include peptides of FMDV VP1 (residues 135–154), influenza nucleoprotein (residues 147–158) and HIV-1 gp160 (residues 111–121, 303–329, 297–328 and 316–341). Lipopeptides are neither toxic, nor pyrogenic. They are chemically and biologically stable at room temperature. They act as B lymphocyte and macrophage activators, they also induce tumour cytotoxicity in human and murine monocytes/macrophages. Lipopeptides comprising the VP1 135–154 peptide (encompassing both a B- and a T-cell epitope) were found to protect seven out of seven guinea pigs against challenge with the homologous FMDV type (Wiesmüller et al., 1989). High titres of FDMV virus-neutralizing antibodies were also obtained in cattle and swine. A lipopeptide construct containing a B-cell epitope (the poorly immunogenic fragment 1–16 of melittin) and a 16-mer T-cell peptide of sperm-whale myoglobin was found particularly effective for inducing antibodies reacting with melittin compared to other peptide conjugates including P_3CS associated with peptide 1–16 of melittin only (Jung and Bessler, 1995). Conjugates of lipopeptides with viral peptides have also been found to be effective in inducing peptide-specific CTLs *in vivo* (Deres et al., 1989; Schild et al., 1991; Wiesmüller et al., 1992). HSV peptides covalently coupled to two palmitic acid molecules and inserted into liposome structures were able to protect animals against an HSV challenge (Watari et al., 1987). A dipalmitoyl derivative of the 135–159 fragment of FMDV VP1 was found to confer virus protection in mice, guinea pigs and sheep. This construct possessed greater immunogenic and protective activity than the nonacetylated peptide. The synthetic vaccine provided 1 year protection of sheep against FMDV after a single administration and is allowed for veterinary use in Russia (Volpina et al., 1996). P_3C adjuvant and various analogues of the initial molecule were successfully used by Tam and co-workers to avoid the need of mixing MAPs in Freund's adjuvant or alum (Defoort et al., 1992; Huang et al., 1994). Another advantage found in using lipidated MAPs is that they are easily entrapped in liposomes. Nearly 80% of these lipidated MAPs were incorporated into liposomes as compared to 2–5% of MAPs without the lipid anchor. In a study with a 18-residue peptide (residues 312–329) from the third variable region V3 in the gp120 of HIV-1, the lipoMAP system containing two palmitoyl lysines (rather than three as in P_3C) was best incorporated in liposomes for eliciting a significant immune response and lasting CTLs (Huang et al., 1994). The mechanism of lipopeptide-induced adjuvanticity has been reviewed recently (Jung and Bessler, 1995). Because of their low molecular mass, lipopeptide-peptide conjugates can be recognized by the antigen-specific B-lymphocytes. They are taken up by these cells or by other APCs, thereby delivering T-cell epitopes to the natural processing and presentation pathways. Successful and long-lasting production of antipeptide antibodies has been described using a completely synthetic formulation corresponding to P_3C Ala Gly and P_3C Ser Ser (obtained by chemical synthesis) incorporated in SUV carrying the covalently conjugated hexapeptide IRGERA (Fernandes et al., 1997).

Other lipidic constructs have been used with peptides such as α-aminohexadecanoic acid (Hda) possessing a simple 14-carbon, linear saturated aliphatic side chain which was introduced at the carboxyl-terminal end of V3 peptides containing a known MHC class I-restricted epitope. These lipopeptides were very efficient for inducing in vivo Th-cell, CTL- or antibody-mediated responses in $H-2^d$ BALB/c mice (Martinon et al., 1992). Addition of a simple lipidic amino acid as a $N\varepsilon$-palmitoyl-L-lysylamide to a peptide was also found to be particularly efficient to induce virus or parasite-specific CTL (BenMohamed et al., 1997; Deprez et al., 1996; Gras-Masse et al., 1996). Good protection of mice against cutaneous leishmaniasis was obtained after subcutaneous or intraperitoneal immunization in saline with a 16-mer peptide of gp63 (residues 457–482) predicted to represent a T-cell epitope, to which a lauryl-cysteine moiety was covalently added to its N-terminus during synthesis (Frankenburg et al., 1996). As with constructs involving P_3C and P_3C analogues, these systems bypassed the requirement for classical adjuvant in T- and B-cell stimulation.

Small molecules have been used to enhance peptide immunogenicity. A promising immunostimulant is tuftsin which corresponds to the tetrapeptide Thr-Lys-Pro-Arg present in the CH_2 constant domain of Ig (Fridkin and Najjar, 1989). Tuftsin was shown to exert a strong immunopotentiating activity and seems to be nonimmunogenic by itself (Naim et al., 1989). Many synthetic analogues of tuftsin have been prepared and were shown to significantly enhance the immunogenicity of peptides (Ivanov et al., 1994; Trudelle et al., 1987).

The carbohydrate polymer mannan coupled to peptides representing residues 139–147 of HBsAg or residues 129–140 of the pre-S2 region of the protein was also found to be very useful for the efficient production of antipeptide antibodies in the absence of any adjuvant (Okawa et al., 1992). Using human MUC1 as a model antigen in mice, Apostolopoulos et al. (1995) observed distinct CTL and antibody responses when oxidized or reduced mannan was used.

Biodegradable microparticles prepared from polylactides [poly(lactic acid), poly(glycolic acid) and poly(lactic-coglycolic) acid, PLGA] can act as efficient delivery systems for entrapped peptides. Microspheres composed of these polymers which are approved for human use, may be particularly attractive to produce continuous release protein or peptide formulations (Cleland, 1998; Gupta et al., 1998). Although these microspheres still present major difficulties in their development with regard to the purity of the antigen and its stability during the microencapsulation process, they seem to represent a valuable delivery system for synthetic peptide immunogens (Men et al., 1996; Newman et al., 1998; Partidos et al., 1996, 1997). These authors reported that formulations containing PLGA in which peptide constructions were incorporated elicited comparable or greater immune response than those induced by repeated immunizations with the conventional systems. Using PLGA microspheres, in the absence of other adjuvants, Men et al. (1996) observed a strong and sustained proliferative and antibody response in the malaria system. It seems that in mice, PLGA microspheres preferentially induce a Th1-type immune response with high levels of IgG2a, an increased production of interferon γ and low levels of IL-4 and IL-10 (Newman et al., 1998; Singh et al., 1998).

Finally, further adjuvants such as various nonbiodegradable nonionic polymers consisting of polyoxypropylene and polyoxyethylene blocks (Bennet et al., 1992; Hunter et al., 1981, 1995) or cytokines i.e. IL-1 (T- and B-cell maturation), IL-2 (Th2 upregulation) and IFN-γ (Th1 upregulation, enhanced MHC expression) (see for example, Kawamura et al., 1985; Playfair and DeSouza,

1987) are also promising. However, more extensive studies are required to know whether they can be efficiently used with short peptides. Furthermore, cytokines are expensive, species-specific, and they present limitations due to their low stability, toxicity and potential ability to induce autoimmune responses. Adjuvants differ in the relative efficacy with which they stimulate Th1 and Th2 cells. Cox and Coulter (1997) recently reviewed the modes of action of most adjuvants and adjuvant combinations and laid emphasis on their respective abilities to modify the cytokine network (Th1 vs Th2 responses), to preserve the conformational integrity of an antigen and to present it to appropriate immune effector cells (presentation and targeting).

3.5. The route of injection

Information concerning methods of immunizing laboratory animals is almost entirely anecdotal. Yet, it is often claimed that the efficiency of stimulation of the immune system is related to the site of immunization. The differences in efficiency are mainly due to the speed with which the antigen will be lost from the site of injection and the likelihood that it will pass through the lymph nodes or other centres of immunological activity (Hurn and Chantler, 1980). This circulation is radically affected by the adjuvant used. As a result, important differences have been observed at the level of antipeptide antibody titre when different routes and the same adjuvant are used and, if the same route is used, when different adjuvants are administered (Sheth et al., 1995).

In general (see Section 3.6), intramuscular (im), intradermal (id), intraperitoneal (ip) and subcutaneous (sc) injections are used. The method of intradermal inoculations of rabbits introduced by Vaitukaitis et al. (1971) has been successfully used with peptides (Denery-Papini et al., 1994; Ricchiuti et al., 1997). The immunogen is introduced at 40 or more sites spread widely over the back surface. In general Freund's adjuvant enriched with heat-killed tubercle bacillus is used and a single series of inoculations is required. We have observed that antibody levels rise to relatively high titres during several weeks and decrease relatively slowly. Because a single injection is given, the phenomenon of carrier-induced suppression (observed when repetitive immunizations of peptide-carrier conjugates are used) is largely avoided. A detailed protocol using multiple intradermal method is described by Vaitukaitis (1971) and Hurn and Chantler (1980). Inoculation of rabbits by injection of a conjugated peptide (a 15-mer peptide of human growth hormone) directly into the popliteal lymph nodes has also been described (Sigel et al., 1983). This approach is appealing in certain cases because the direct delivery of antigen to the lymphatic circulation decreases the risk of metabolic alterations or loss of the antigen during adsorption and transport. Intravenous injection is often used when animals have to be boosted a few days prior to splenectomy for cell fusion purposes. Intravenous immunization cannot be used with particulate antigens or adjuvants.

As discussed above, considerable information concerning the immunogenicity of peptides can be gathered from the study of peptide delivery systems used as drugs. The pharmacokinetics and pharmacodynamics of peptide drugs are indeed very important considerations in devising optimal drug delivery methods (Eppstein and Longenecker, 1988; Lee, 1986). Two particularly interesting routes for immunization are oral and nasal delivery (Leclerc and Ronco, 1998; Manganaro et al., 1994). These approaches present many potential advantages for delivering vaccines, however, they are still difficult to apply due to our ignorance of the basic mechanisms of host resistance in mucosal tissues. Promising results were obtained with ISCOMs which were found to confer immunogenicity to proteins delivered by the oral route (Mowat and Donachie, 1991). ISCOMs also induce protective immunity against influenza in mice when given intranasally (Lövgren et al., 1990). Data with ISCOMs administered by the oral or nasal route are not available in the case of immunization with peptides. Nasal inoculation of an influenza peptide construct incorporated in multilamellar liposomes was shown to protect mice against infection by several strains of influenza virus (Naruse et al., 1994). More recently, Hathaway et al. (1995) showed that the intranasal administration of a TT-B chimeric construct could induce a systemic immune response. The coadministration of small amounts of cholera toxin B subunit as an adjuvant resulted in a significant enhancement of the response. Oral immunization with lipidated MAPs have been found to elicit mucosal immunity (Tam and Spetzler, 1995). Intragastric adminis tration of a lipoMAP containing P_3C and peptide 308–331 of HIV-1 loop V3 in a tetravalent MAP construction stimulated a secretory mucosal IgA response and IgG antibody production in the serum of immunized animals. Systemic T-lymphocyte stimulation as well as a specific CTL response was found. Takahashi et al. (1991) obtained a very high antibody response in BALB/c mice immunized intranasally with a peptide of 19 residues (sequence 301–319 of the surface protein Ag of *S. mutans*) coupled to cholera toxin B subunit. This finding may have application in the development of a vaccine useful for the prevention of dental caries. Levi et al. (1995) observed a partial protection of mice intranasally immunized with a peptide construction containing a B, Th and CTL epitopes of influenza virus anchored to proteosomes.

3.6 Specific immunization protocols

In view of the wide variety of successful immunization procedures reported in the literature, only a few examples will be presented here, mainly to illustrate the range of conditions that can be used. Procedures followed to produce antipeptide monoclonal antibodies (mAb) after *in vivo* and *in vitro* immunization can be found in Sections 3.6.7 and 3.6.8. Specific protocols using liposomes, MAP and TASP are described in Sections 3.6.9–3.6.10. The use of animals for antibody production is regulated by the Home Office and legislation set out in various relevant acts, particularly the Animals (Scientific

Procedures) Act of 1986 (HMSO Publications Centre, P.O. Box 276, London, 5W8 5DT).

3.6.1. Method of Walter et al. (1980); Patschinsky et al. (1984)

Animals: rabbits, male, 5–6 months old.

Peptides: 8–10 residues long, conjugated to BSA with glutaraldehyde or BDB (see Sections 2.5.1 and 2.5.4).

1st injection: id route at 20 different sites; 1 mg conjugate emulsified in 2 ml CFA.

Subsequent injections: weeks 4 and 8, im and sc injections.

Bleedings: from week 10 onwards.

This procedure is similar to that described by Müller et al. (1982) and Shapira et al. (1984) for immunizing rabbits with synthetic peptides of influenza virus HA; these peptides were conjugated to TT by EDC according to procedure in Section 2.5.3.

3.6.2. Method of Green et al. (1982)

Animals: rabbits.

Peptides: 8–10 residues long, conjugated to KLH by MBS (see Section 2.5.5).

1st injection: 200 μg conjugated peptide emulsified in CFA (1 : 1), sc route.

Subsequent injections: day 14, same injection but with IFA; day 21, ip inoculation of 200 μg conjugated peptide with alum (4 mg); several booster injections given in the same conditions every 5 weeks.

Bleedings: from week 4.

This procedure was also used by Niman (1984) with peptides corresponding to segments of protein sequences predicted from the nucleotide sequences of viral oncogenes and by Tainer et al. (1984) with myohaemerythrin peptides.

3.6.3. Method of Tanaka et al. (1985)

Animals: New Zealand white rabbits.

Peptides: 7–20 residues long, conjugated to KLH with glutaralde-hyde.

1st injection: 300 μg conjugate emulsified in CFA; sc inoculation.

Subsequent injections: sc inoculation of 175 μg conjugate in IFA (week 4); at intervals of 2 weeks to 4 months, sc inoculations of 175 μg/injection.

Bleedings: 10 days after each injection.

3.6.4. Method of Muller et al. (1986) and Dumortier et al. (1998)

Animals: Rabbits, female, 10–12 weeks old, 2–4 rabbits/peptide.

Peptides: 14–20 residues long peptides were used unconjugated; peptides shorter than 14 residues were mostly conjugated to ovalbumin, using a variety of procedures depending on their sequence.

1st injection: 200 μg peptide emulsified in CFA (1 : 1, v/v); multiple sc inoculations at 5–10 injection sites for unconjugated peptides; im inoculation for conjugated peptides.

Subsequent injections: 200 μg peptide (weeks 2, 4, 6 etc.) emulsified in CFA for unconjugated peptides (sc injections), in IFA for conjugated peptides (im injections).

Bleedings: 8 days after each injection starting from week 5.

3.6.5. Method of Nussberger et al. (1985)

Animals: Guinea pigs, female, Hartley, 6 weeks, 250–350 g, 10 animals/peptide.

Peptides: octapeptide, conjugated by means of carbodiimide.

Injection: a single id injection at several points, emulsion in CFA, 500 μg/animal.

Bleedings: 8 days after the injection and then every 2 weeks.

Other procedures for immunizing guinea pigs are described by Audibert et al. (1981), Fujio et al. (1985) and Briand et al. (1997).

3.6.6. Method of Choppin et al. (1986)

The following method has been described for obtaining antipeptide antibodies from ascites of mice.

Animals: BALB/K (H-2^k) female mice, 12–16 weeks old, 5 mice/peptide.

Peptides: 18–24 residues long, conjugated or free.

Schedule:

   day 0: ip injection of a mixture 1 : 9 (v/v) 9‰ NaCl-CFA (200 μl final)

   day 14: ip injection of 10 μg peptide in 200 μl emulsified in CFA (1 : 9, v/v)

   days 23, 32, 43, 53, 83: idem

Generally, ascites form around days 28–32, sometimes only after 6–7 injections. Ascites fluids are collected by ip puncture and the cells are removed by centrifugation (500 g for 5–10 min). A yield of 40–60 ml/mouse is common. A boost can be given intraperitoneally when the production of ascites decreases.

   Generally, ascitic fluids do not clot. Sodium azide at a final concentration of 10 mM can be added to discourage microbial growth. Small aliquots are best stored at –70°C.

   This method, first described by Tung et al. (1976), has a number of advantages over the usual procedures for immunizing mice. Large volumes of ascites can be collected compared to the small quantities of serum obtained by bleeding. An example of ascites antibody activity directed against two peptides of the HLA-B7 heavy

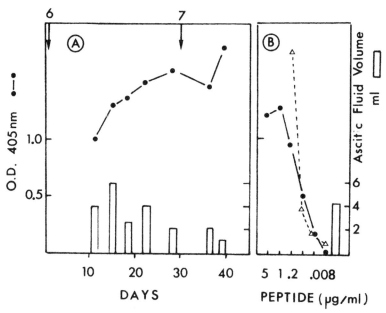

Fig. 3.5. Antipeptide antibody level in ascitic fluid of a BALB/K mouse immunized with peptide 138–157 of HLA-B7 heavy chain (see Section 3.6.6). In (A) the arrows 6 and 7 refer to the 6th and 7th ip injections of peptide conjugated to ovalbumin (10 μg peptide/mouse). A total volume of 22.1 ml of ascitic fluid was obtained from this mouse. For ELISA, ascitic fluids were diluted 1 : 20 and allowed to react with peptide-coated plates (200 ng/ml). In (B), antibody levels to the peptide 99–118 of HLA-B7 heavy chain in ascitic fluid (obtained 11 days after the 6th ip injection) and in a rabbit antiserum are compared. The ascitic fluid was diluted 1 : 20 (●----●), the rabbit antipeptide antiserum was diluted 1 : 100 (△----△).

chain is shown in Fig. 3.5 (Choppin, 1988). This technique has been reviewed by Tung (1983) and various applications have been described by Thèze and Sommé (1979).

3.6.7. Method of Young et al. (1983)

Animals: BALB/c By J (H-2^d) mice; 5 animals/peptide.
Peptides: 6–8 residues long; unconjugated.
1st injection: 100 μg peptide emulsified in CFA; id injections (foot-
    pad).
Subsequent injections: weeks 2 and 4, 100 μg peptide in CFA by ip
    inoculation.
Bleedings: from the tail vein, weeks 2, 4 and 8.

This technique was used to obtain mAb able to recognize native
sperm-whale myoglobin (Atassi and Young, 1985; Schmitz et al.,
1983a, b).

Antipeptide mAbs have also been obtained by immunizing mice
with conjugated peptides. Fok et al. (1982) immunized mice with
the nonapeptide corresponding to the serum thymic factor conjugated to IgG by glutaraldehyde. Shapira et al. (1984) have obtained
antibodies directed against influenza virus HA peptides by immunizing (SJL/J × BALB/c) F1 mice by ip route with peptides coupled
to TT by EDC (50 μg peptide/animal). Other protocols developed
for the production of antipeptide mAbs have been described by Niman et al. (1983), Bellet et al. (1984), Darsley and Rees (1985),
Scheefers-Borchel et al. (1985), Caraux et al. (1985), Antoni et al.
(1985) and Price et al. (1986). Antipeptide mAbs against a peptide of sequence IRGERA and analogues of this peptide have been
generated from mice immunized with the analogues coupled to
neutral small unilamellar liposomes containing MPL as adjuvant
(Benkirane et al., 1995).

Generally, authors have immunized BALB/c mice or mice derived from this strain, mainly for ensuring compatibility during the
fusion with available murine myeloma cells and the propagation
of antibodies *in vivo* by ascitic fluid production. For some immunogens, other mouse strains showing differences in their MHC
haplotypes were used, e.g. SWR strain (Darsley and Rees, 1985),

129 GIX$^+$ strain (Niman et al., 1983), B10 and C57 B1 strains (Atassi and Young, 1985).

3.6.8. Method of De Boer et al. (1987)

De Boer and co-workers have prepared mAbs to thyroglobulin by *in vitro* immunization with a free 19-residue synthetic peptide:

Immunization in vitro: spleen cells (1×10^7 cells/ml) from nonimmunized BALB/c mice were cultured in serum-free medium supplemented with 50% (v/v) thymocyte-conditioned medium (TCM), 50 μl 2-mercaptoethanol and sterile filtered peptide (0.1–1 μg/ml). After 3 days of culture, the cells were sedimented (7 min, 800 g) and used for fusion with marine myeloma cells (SP2/0 cells). The classical procedures for cell fusion and cloning were then used.

Preparation of TCM: thymus glands were removed from 10- to 14-day-old BALB/c mice and passed through a sterile 50-mesh stainless steel screen. Thymus cells (5×10^6 cells/ml) were cultured in serum-free medium containing 50 μM 2-mercaptoethanol. The cells were cultured for 48 h at 37°C in 7.5% CO_2. The TCM was then collected by centrifugation (7 mm, 800 g) to remove the cells and was stored at –70°C.

Yield (2 experiments with 0.1 μg peptide/ml in the immunization mixture): a total of 314 wells containing hybrids was obtained, 16 wells contained hybridomas secreting mAbs reactive with the homologous peptide and 11 of them were also reactive with the intact protein.

3.6.9. Method of Lu et al. (1991) with MAP

Animals: New Zealand white rabbits, 3.5 kg, female (2 rabbits/MAP)

Peptide: octameric MAP

1st injection: 1 mg in 0.5 ml PBS and 0.5 ml CFA; sc injection (0.5 ml/rabbit).

Subsequent injections: sc injections with IFA on days 21, 42 and 63.

Bleedings: before each inoculation.

Briand et al. (1992b) immunized rabbits (2 rabbits/MAP) with 150–200 μg octameric MAP by sc inoculation, in the presence of CFA for all injections.

For immunization of mice, animals received 50 μg/animal/injection by ip injection (Posnett et al., 1988) or sc inoculation (McLean et al., 1992).

3.6.10. Method of Tuchscherer et al. (1992) with TASP

Animals: BALB/c or C57 B1 mice, 7–10 weeks old, female.

Peptide: MHC-TASP (TASP containing four copies of the peptide 58–74 of the α1 heavy chain domain of HLA A2 molecules).

1st injection: 50 μg/mouse in 100 μl, sc inoculation at the base of the tail, emulsion in CFA (v/v).

Subsequent injection: twice 50 μg/mouse in IFA, sc inoculation 3–4 weeks after priming.

Bleedings: animals bled weekly.

In our laboratory (Muller et al., 1999), we have immunized female New Zealand rabbits (2 rabbits/TASP) with a TASP containing five copies of the tripeptide KPR with a CG arm and linked to small unilamellar liposomes containing MPLA as adjuvant. Animals received sc inoculations (about 100 μg peptide/injection) at intervals of two weeks. Antipeptide antibody response appeared after 3–4 injections and high titres of antibodies reacting with the tripeptide were obtained after 5–6 injections. Antibodies cross-reacted with the parent protein in Western blotting.

3.7. Concluding remarks

In most situations it is desirable that a given antipeptide antibody be specific for a particular antigen and not react with other structurally related antigens. In reality this ideal picture is sometimes difficult to obtain and it is necessary to always investigate potential cross-reactions as far as possible. It is recommended to systematically check the reaction in a competitive binding situation (see Chapter 4), in particular when antipeptide antibodies are used in immuno-cytochemical and immunoblotting assays such as those used for the identification of complex protein structures.

Peptide immunoassays

M. H. V. VAN REGENMORTEL

4.1. Introduction

It is beyond the scope of this volume to describe all the immuno-assays that can be used with synthetic peptides. Numerous text-books are available which describe the immunological testing of small and medium-sized molecules (Butler, 1991; Diaman-dis and Christopoulos, 1996; Herzenberg et al., 1997; Johnstone and Turner, 1997; Price and Newman, 1997; Van Oss and Van Regenmortel, 1994).

When synthetic peptides corresponding to protein fragments are studied for the purpose of localizing the epitopes of a protein, the most common approach consists of measuring the capacity of the peptides to inhibit the reaction of the protein with its homologous antibodies. Various immunoassays in an inhibition for-mat can be used for this purpose, for instance precipitation tests (Atassi, 1977a), radioimmunoassay (Milton et al., 1980), comple-ment fixation tests (Benjamini, 1977; Milton and Van Regenmortel, 1979), enzyme-linked immunosorbent assay (ELISA) (Altschuh and Van Regenmortel, 1982), fluorescence and chemiluminescence immunoassays (Diamandis and Christopoulos, 1996) and biosensor assays (Richalet-Sécordel et al., 1994a). It should be noted that in all these inhibition assays, the peptide is used free in solution.

It is important to realize that the type of immunoassay format used can determine whether a peptide shows antigenic activity or not. In the classical studies of Atassi (1977a) on the antigenic structure of myoglobin, five continuous epitopes of 6–7 residues were identified by inhibition of the precipitation reaction between

179

myoglobin and its specific antibodies (see Chapter 1). These results could not be confirmed in a subsequent study in which all the possible overlapping hexa-, hepta- and octapeptides of myoglobin were synthesized on a polymer of polyacrylic acid and tested for antigenicity while still bound to the solid-phase. In this later study, only one major epitope was identified in residues 48–55 (Rodda et al., 1986), i.e. in a region which had been found earlier to contain no antigenic activity. Furthermore, the epitopes identified by Atassi were not picked up by the method of Rodda et al. (1986) which uses peptides attached to the solid phase. It seems that such conflicting results arise because peptides adopt different conformations in different assays. In addition covalent or noncovalent attachment of peptides to a carrier or a solid-phase may cause certain epitopes to be masked. Studies in which synthetic peptides were tested by different immunoassays in the same laboratory using the same antisera have shown that the antigenic activity of peptides often differs when they are tested as free peptides in solution, conjugated to a carrier or adsorbed to a solid-phase (Muller et al., 1986; Quesniaux et al., 1986).

The enzyme-linked immunosorbent assay (ELISA) is the assay most commonly used for measuring the antigenic activity of synthetic peptides (Butler, 1991; Crowther, 1995; Kemeny, 1991; Kemeny and Challacombe, 1988; Lauritzen et al., 1994). This chapter describes some of the ELISA formats that have been used with peptides and will review some of the difficulties likely to be encountered in such tests. In spite of the numerous advantages of solid-phase assays, it should be remembered that; (1) any peptide immobilized on a solid-phase will have part of its surface unavailable for binding to antibody; (2) adsorption of a peptide on a polymer surface will affect its conformation; and (3) the kinetics and equilibrium characteristics prevalent in liquid-phase interactions are altered when one of the reactants is immobilized (Stevens et al., 1986).

In recent years, biosensor instruments based on surface plasmon resonance have become increasingly used for analyzing the antigenic activity of peptides and this technique will also be described in detail. Biosensors measure interactions in real time and they allow the calculation of kinetic rate constants and equilibrium affinity constants of peptide-antibody interactions with relative ease (Saunal et al., 1997). Since knowledge of antibody affinity is important for the proper design of immunoassays, methods used for measuring the affinity of an antigen-antibody interaction will also be briefly reviewed.

4.2. Types of solid-phase immunoassays

The simplest type of solid-phase immunoassay that can be used with peptides is one in which the synthetic peptide is allowed to react with antibodies while still attached to the resin support used for its synthesis (Modrow and Wolf, 1990; Smith et al., 1977). By immunological testing at each step of the synthesis, it is possible to assess the contribution of each successive amino acid to the antigenic reactivity of the growing peptide.

4.2.1. The pepscan technique

Geysen et al. (1984) have introduced a method known as pepscan which allows the rapid concurrent synthesis of hundreds of peptides on polyethylene rods. In this technique the synthesized peptides are tested for antigenic activity without removing them from the support. The rods are assembled into a polyethylene holder with the format and spacing of a microtitre plate, which allows the peptides to be tested easily by ELISA. Another approach consists in coupling peptides synthesized by standard solid-phase methods directly to radiation-grafted polyethylene using reagents such as m-maleimido benzoyl-N-hydroxysuccinimide ester or glutaraldehyde (Geysen et al., 1985a, b). The pepscan method uses polyethylene pins arranged in a 8×12 matrix (Rodda et al., 1986). The peptides can be tested for antigenic activity while still bound to the surface of the individual pins, or they can be cleaved before testing. The additional cleavage step makes it possible to analyze the purity and identity of the peptides. Both Boc and Fmoc protection strategies have been used for multiple peptide synthesis on pins (Geysen et al., 1987; Valerio et al., 1991). The technique has been improved by a new design of the pin (Maeji et al., 1994, 1995) which allows a better control of the reactive area and by the development of polymers, such as hydroxypropyl methacrylate that have better solvation characteristics in both water and organic solvents (Rodda and Tribbick, 1996). Some users of the pepscan technique acetylate the N-terminus of peptides on pins, in order to remove the charge that is absent in the parent protein sequence (Geysen et al., 1987). However, blocking the free endings reduces peptide solubility and does not necessarily improve the capacity of the peptide to cross-react with antiprotein antibodies.

Detailed procedures for measuring the binding of antibodies to pin-bound peptides using ELISA have been described (Rodda et al., 1996; Rodda and Tribbick, 1996). In general, the ELISA absorbance of replicate pin peptides varies by $\pm 20\%$ within an assay. The background of the assay can be calculated by ranking the absorbance values of an entire set of overlapping peptides and averaging the lowest 50% of the values (Geysen et al., 1987; Trifilieff et al., 1991). Alternatively, the mean of the lowest quarter of the absorbance values, plus three times the standard deviation of the mean value can be taken as a cutoff point for specific binding (Rodda and Tribbick, 1996). Another test of specificity consists in using the whole antigen for competing with the binding of specific antibodies to the peptides.

It is possible to use pin-bound peptides as an affinity support for the fractionation of serum antibodies, using buffers of either high or low pH for eluting the antibodies from the pins (Tribbick et al., 1991).

It must be emphasized that the pepscan format favours bivalent binding of antibody and facilitates the detection of low levels of cross-reactivity. In a pepscan study of antibodies raised to two peptides of tobacco mosaic virus protein (TMVP), it was found that a sequence identity of only three residues in a peptide was sufficient to give rise to an antigenic cross-reaction (Trifilieff et al., 1991). As shown in Fig. 4.1, an antiserum to unconjugated peptide 115–134 of TMVP reacted with hexapeptides 20–25, 109–114, 113–118, 114–119, 115–120 and 116–121. The reactivity with peptides 113–118 and 116–121 was expected since they contain at least four residues of the sequence 115–134 against which the antibodies were raised. The reactivity of peptides 20–25 and 109–114 was more surprising and was caused by the presence in these peptides of two tripeptide sequences (Glu_{22} Leu_{23} Ile_{24} and Asp_{109} Ala_{110} Thr_{111}) that are also found in peptide 115–134, i.e. Glu_{131} Leu_{132} Ile_{133} and Asp_{116} Ala_{117} Thr_{118}. Apparently, in the antiserum to peptide 115–134 some antibodies recognized the sequence Glu Leu Ile whereas others recognized the sequence Asp Ala Thr. This is confirmed by the somewhat weaker reaction (Fig. 4.1) observed with peptide 129–134 (Ile Val Glu Leu Ile Arg) which also contains the tripeptide Glu Leu Ile. To confirm these findings the peptides 9–32, 90–117, 115–124 and 125–134 were synthesized by classical solid-phase peptide synthesis and tested in two ELISA formats for their capacity to react with antibodies raised against the 115–134 peptide (Trifilieff et al., 1991). As shown in Table 4.1, the peptides 19–32, 115–124 and 125–134 which contain the sequences Asp Ala Thr or Glu Leu Ile reacted in ELISA either when adsorbed to the plate or as liquid-phase inhibitors. On the other hand, peptide 90–117 which contained also the sequence Asp Ala Thr showed no reactivity in either assay format, indicating that peptide reactivity depends on the assay format.

Another unexpected finding observed in this study was that an antiserum raised to peptide 149–158 of TMVP conjugated to ovalbumin reacted with a large number of hexapeptides of TMVP situated outside the region 149–158 of the viral protein. When the sequences of TMVP and ovalbumin were compared, it was found that there were two common tetrapeptide and 14 common tripeptide

TABLE 4.1

Reactivity in two ELISA formats of different peptides of TMVP with antiserum to peptide 115–134 data from Trifilieff et al. (1991)

Synthetic peptide	Reactive tripeptide sequence present in peptide	Peptide tested when adsorbed to plate	Free peptide tested as inhibitor	Hexapeptides found reactive in pepscan (Fig. 4.1)
115–124	$D_{116}A_{117}T_{118}$		+	113–118, 114–119, 115–120, 116–121
125–134	$E_{131}L_{132}I_{133}$	+		129–134
19–32	$E_{22}L_{23}I_{24}$		+	20–25
90–117	$D_{109}A_{110}T_{111}$		+	109–114

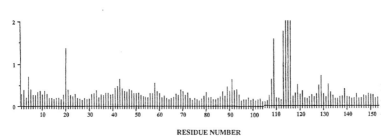

RESIDUE NUMBER

Fig. 4.1. Scan of TMVP hexapeptides synthesized by the pepscan technique, tested by ELISA with antiserum to peptide 115–134. Each peptide is numbered according to the position in the TMVP sequence of its N-terminal residue (reprinted from Trifilieff et al., 1991 with permission).

sequences in these two proteins. One of the common tetrapeptides (Gln_{22} Leu_{23} Ile_{24} Asn_{25}) and five of the common tripeptides (sequences 28–30, 39–41, 60–62, 84–86 and 131–133) were located within the TMVP hexapeptides that reacted with antibodies to the ovalbumin-conjugated peptide 149–158. These findings suggested that the unexpected reactivities were due to a cross-reaction between antibodies to ovalbumin and the TMVP hexapeptides synthesized on the pins. It seems, therefore, that the presence of atoms from as few as three residues provides sufficient binding energy to give rise to immune recognition. This conclusion is in accord with the findings of Chappey et al. (1994) that antigens need not be larger than about 400 M_r in order to bind strongly to antibodies (i.e. with an affinity constant of about 10^9 M^{-1}).

It must be emphasized that the results of Trifilieff et al. (1991) do not imply that every tripeptide region in a protein immunogen necessarily gives rise to antibodies. There is also no reason to expect that the presence of a common tripeptide sequence between two proteins is sufficient to give rise to an observable antigenic cross-reactivity between two native proteins (Dietzgen and Zaitlin, 1986; Zimmermann and Van Regenmortel, 1989). If two proteins possess only a short sequence in common, it is highly unlikely that this small region will be both immunogenic and antigenically reactive in the two native proteins. However, if the molecule used for immu-

TABLE 4.2

Solid-phase immunoassays used with peptides

Procedure		Successive steps of assay		
1	Peptide	$\underline{Ab}^R$	anti-R^G-E	
2	Peptide-conjugate	$\underline{Ab}^R$	anti-R^G-E	
3	$\underline{Ab}^R$	Protein	$\underline{Ab}^R$-E	
4	$\underline{Ab}^C$	Protein	$\underline{Ab}^R$	anti-R^G-E

Ab = antibody; R = rabbit; C = chicken; G = goat; E = enzyme label; anti-R ^{G} = goat antirabbit globulin reagent. Underlined antibodies refer to antibodies raised against the peptide.

nization is denatured (Lando and Reichlin, 1982; Scibienski, 1973) and the pepscan technique is used for detecting antigenic cross-reactivity with another protein, the probability of discovering such cross-reactions is greatly enhanced.

4.2.2. ELISA

Instead of being covalently attached to the solid support, the free peptide is more commonly made to adsorb to a plastic solid-phase, for instance to the wells of a microtitre plate. In general, peptides that are at least 15 residues long will become adsorbed to plastic after incubating the peptide solution in the microtitre wells overnight. However, this is not an absolute rule, as longer peptides sometimes do not become adsorbed (Muller et al., 1987) while shorter ones do (Houghten, 1985). This procedure (Procedure 1, Table 4.2) is the simplest method for measuring the activity of antipeptide sera. Serial dilutions of the antiserum are incubated in the peptide-coated wells and the bound antibodies are revealed by an enzyme-labelled anti-immunoglobulin reagent or by radiolabelled protein A.

A variety of approaches have been advocated to improve the attachment of peptides to the solid-phase such as incubation with glutadehyde, poly-L-lysine or cyanogen bromide (Brennand et al., 1986; Corthier and Franz, 1981; Lehtonen and Viljanen, 1980; Suter, 1982). When such chemicals are used with short peptides, it should first be established that the immobilizing reagent does not modify the antigenicity of the peptide and that pretreating the plates does not lead to indesirable high background readings.

Several approaches that have been used to improve the coating efficiency of peptides on ELISA plates are listed in Table 4.3. The enhanced reactivity obtained when a peptide is presented as a multiple antigen peptide (MAP) on a polypeptide core is shown in Fig. 4.2. A considerable increase in assay sensitivity can be obtained with octameric branched peptides (Briand et al., 1992b; Tam and Zavala, 1989). When 4–5 glycine spacers are introduced between the branched lysine core of the MAP and the peptide epitope, the sensitivity of antibody detection can be further increased (Fig. 4.3) and the amount of branched peptide needed to produce a given signal is reduced (Marsden et al., 1992).

Loomans et al. (1997, 1998a, b) have shown that the coating efficiency of a peptide can be considerably improved by adding a small N-terminal extension such as an acetyl-thio-acetyl group or a polylysyl moiety to the peptide during synthesis. This reduces the amount of peptide needed in ELISA by several orders of magnitude.

Another useful method for improving the cross-linking of peptides to microtitre plates consists in coating the plates first with polylysine followed by the addition of 1% glutaraldehyde solution and subsequent washing to remove the excess of glutaraldehyde (Ball et al., 1994). Polylysine readily adsorbs onto plastic surfaces and is easily cross-linked to synthetic peptides by interactions between free amines and the reactive aldehyde groups of glutaraldehyde (Fig. 4.4). One advantage of this approach is that no special peptide synthesis steps are needed and that peptides that have been prepared for other purposes can be used, provided they possess a free amine. In some cases, a directional coupling of peptides to polylysine, via an additional terminal Cys residue and an heter-

TABLE 4.3

Improved coating efficiency of peptides on ELISA plates

Methods	Enhancement factor	Reference
MAPS (branched peptides on PL core)	$10^3 \times$	Tam and Zavala (1989)
MAPs with glycine spacers	10^3–$10^5 \times$	Marsden et al. (1992)
N-terminal linking of acetyl-thioacetyl group and of (Lys), to peptide	10^3–$10^5 \times$	Loomans et al. (1998b); Loomans et al., (1997, 1998a)
Poly-L-lysine (PLL) treated plates	$10 \times$	Ball et al. (1994)
PLL treated plates with directional Cys-coupling	4–$10 \times$	Gegg and Etzler (1993)
Carbodiimide treatment (EDC and NHS)	$4 \times$	Søndergard-Andersen et al. (1990)
Carboxylated plates	10–$100 \times$	Nivelean et al. (1995)
Glutaraldehyde-treated plates		Hobbs (1989)
Alcian blue-treated plates		Lagacé et al. (1994)
Activation of polystyrene by UV		Boudet et al. (1991)
γ-irradiation of polystyrene and EDC treatment		Dagenais et al. (1994)
Resin-bound peptides		Modrow et al. (1989)
Peptide coupling to carriers		Briand et al. (1985)
Peptide coupling to biotinylated carrier	$10 \times$	Böcher et al., (1997); Richalet-Sécordel and Van Regenmortel (1991)
Biotinylated peptides on streptavted plates	$10 \times$	Ivanov et al. (1992) Ngai et al. (1993)
Activated dextran coated plates		Gregorius et al. (1995)

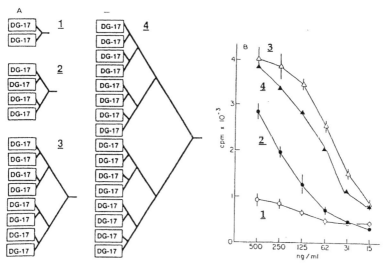

Fig. 4.2. Increased antigenic activity of a 17-residue peptide synthesized as multiple antigen peptides (MAP) on a core matrix of Lys residues. The peptides were tested in radioimmunoassay with a monoclonal antibody against the CS protein of *Plasmodium berghei*. (1) dimeric MAP; (2) tetrameric MAP; (3) octameric MAP; (4) hexadecameric MAP (reprinted from Tam and Zavala, 1989 with permission).

obifunctional cross-linker can be advantageous (Gegg and Etzler, 1993).

When the peptide is shorter than 15 residues, it is preferable to use it as a peptide conjugate in the immunoassay (Procedure 3, Table 4.4). Methods used for coupling peptides to carrier proteins are described in Chapter 2. It is, of course, essential in this instance to couple the peptide to another carrier than the one used to prepare the peptide conjugate intended for immunization. It is not always realized that the peptide antiserum, in addition to containing antibodies directed to the peptide moiety and to the carrier protein, is likely also to contain a considerable proportion of antibodies directed to the coupling agent used for conjugation (Briand et al., 1985; Edwards et al., 1989; Gegg and Etzler, 1993; Goodfriend et al., 1964; Peeters et al., 1989). It is thus necessary to use in the

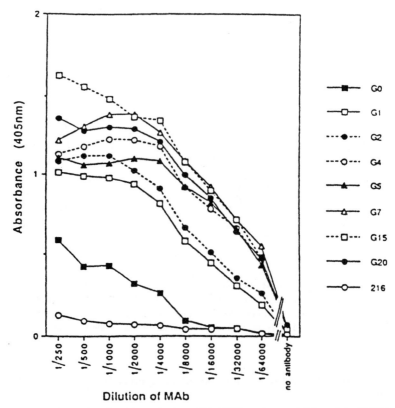

Fig. 4.3. Effect of 1–20 spacer glycines (G1–G20) on the sensitivity of the ELISA reaction between a monoclonal antibody and a MAP heptapeptide from herpes simplex virus binding protein. The addition of 5 glycine spacers between the peptide epitope and MAP core was found to be optimal. Peptide 216 is a control peptide (from Marsden et al., 1992 reprinted with permission).

immunoassay a peptide conjugate prepared with both a different carrier protein and a different coupling agent. If this precaution is not taken, antibodies directed for instance against glutaraldehyde- or carbodiimide-modified residues may contribute to the overall reaction. This will lead to a spurious overestimation of the level of peptide antibodies present in the antiserum (see Fig. 4.5).

TABLE 4.4

Competitive solid-phase immunoassays used with peptides

Procedure	Successive steps of assay			
1	Peptide	Ab^R	anti-R^G-E	
2	Ab^C	Protein	Ab^R + peptide	anti-R^G-E
3	Peptide-conjugate	Ab^R + peptide	anti-R^G-E	
4	Ab^R	Peptide-L + peptide		
5	anti-M^G	Ab^M	peptide-L + peptide	
6	Biotin-conjugate	Avidin	Ab^M-biotin	Peptide-L + peptide

For meaning of abbreviations, see Table 4.2. L = label, e.g. radiolabel, enzyme or biotin, M = mouse.

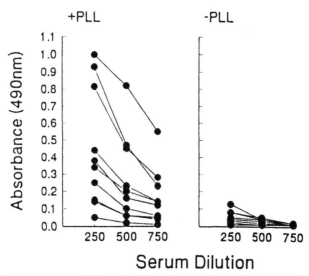

Fig. 4.4. Improved crosslinking of a 30-residue viral peptide to microtitre plates treated with poly-L-lysine (PLL). The peptide was either passively adsorbed (-PLL) or crosslinked to PLL (+PLL) and tested in ELISA with 10 antisera to the virus (from Ball et al., 1994 reprinted with permission).

In order to measure the subpopulation of antibodies in a peptide antiserum that is able to cross-react with the cognate complete protein, the microtitre plates are coated with protein instead of peptide. The plastic wells can be coated, for instance, by incubation with a 0.1–1.0 μg/ml protein preparation diluted in carbonate buffer, pH 9.6, or phosphate buffer, pH 7.0. Optimal incubation conditions (reagent concentration, pH, time of incubation, choice of blocking solution, etc.) must be determined empirically.

It should be emphasized that, contrary to some claims (Green et al., 1982) an ELISA format using plates coated with protein does not necessarily measure antibodies able to cross-react with the native protein antigen. It is now well established that proteins become at least partly denatured when they are adsorbed to a solid-phase (Al Moudallal et al., 1984; Altschuh et al., 1985; Butler et

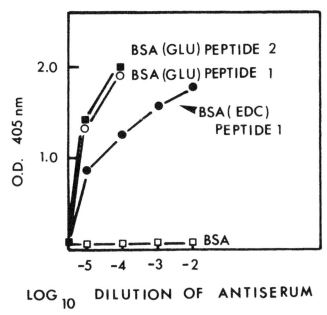

Fig. 4.5. Binding in ELISA of antiserum raised against peptide 1 (conjugated to KLH with glutaraldehyde) with homologous and heterologous peptides. The antigens were used at a concentration of 2.5 μmol. Peptide 1 corresponds to sequence 80–89 of histone H4 (TVTAMDVVYA) conjugated to BSA with glutaraldehyde (○) or with e.c.d.i. (carbodiimide) (●). Peptide 2 corresponds to sequence 130–135 of histone H3 (IRGERA) conjugated to BSA with glutaraldehyde (■). Note that the reaction of antibodies specific for peptide 1 can only be demonstrated with a peptide 1 conjugate prepared with a different coupling agent from the one used to prepare the immunogen (adapted from Briand et al., 1985).

al., 1986; Dierks et al., 1986; Kennel, 1982; Mierendorf and Dimond, 1983; Soderquist and Walton, 1980; Spangler, 1991). The widespread use of monoclonal antibodies, which are often specific for a particular conformation of the antigen, has contributed to the growing realization that proteins adsorbed to surfaces often undergo conformational changes (Al Moudallal et al., 1985; Darst et al., 1988; Friguet et al., 1984; Vaidya et al., 1985).

If it is important to measure only those antibodies in the peptide antiserum that recognize the native protein molecule, it is necessary to use either a double antibody sandwich immunoassay in which the protein is bound to a first layer of antiprotein antibodies (Procedures 3 and 4, Table 4.2) or a competition type of assay (Procedure 2, Table 4.4). It should be noted that the initial attachment of the antigen to a first layer of immobilized antibody may also lead to a local change in protein conformation by an allosteric effect (Dubs et al., 1992), although this is likely to be less prevalent than the drastic changes induced by direct adsorption of the protein to the solid-phase.

When peptide antisera are screened for the purpose of determining the titre of antibodies cross-reacting with the whole protein or for evaluating whether the antisera contain neutralizing antibodies (for instance in experiments designed to develop a synthetic peptide vaccine), it is best to use an assay in which the native conformation of the antigen is preserved. Antibodies that recognize a denatured form of the viral antigen but not the native conformation are unlikely to possess neutralizing or protective potential.

The methods discussed so far (Table 4.2) are particularly suited for analyzing the properties of antisera raised against peptides. However, when the antigenic reactivity of synthetic peptides is tested for the purpose of mapping epitopes in a protein, an ELISA competition format is more appropriate. The simplest form of assay consists of absorbing an antiserum raised against the protein with peptides and testing the antiserum for the presence of residual antibodies able to bind to the protein immobilized on the solid-phase (Procedure 1, Table 4.4). The degree of antigenic reactivity of the peptide is inversely proportional to the level of protein antibody that can still be detected by the labelled anti-immunoglobulin reagent. However, the concentration of the different reagents has to be adjusted with care to ensure maximum sensitivity since the extent of inhibitory activity exhibited by different peptides may depend on the concentration of protein used for coating the wells (Altschuh and Van Regenmortel, 1982).

To ensure that the peptides compete with antibodies specific for the native protein, the protein must be immobilized on the solid-phase via a first layer of protein antibodies (Procedure 2, Table 4.4). In this type of double antibody sandwich assay, the antibody used for capturing the antigen should be obtained from a different animal species than the test antibody. Avian antibodies which are serologically unrelated to mammalian immunoglobulins (Leslie and Clem, 1969) are a particularly good choice for use as capturing antibodies since they will not be detected by an enzyme conjugate directed against mammalian globulins (Al Moudallal et al., 1984; Van Regenmortel and Burckard, 1980). Another approach consists of using Fab_2 fragments devoid of the Fc portion of immunoglobulin molecules for capturing the antigen. In this case, the same intact antibody molecule can be used later in the assay since its binding can be revealed by an anti-Fc enzyme conjugate (Barbara and Clark, 1982).

Solid-phase immunoassays can also be used to compare the antigenic reactivity of a series of peptide analogues, for instance in experiments designed to assess the contribution of individual amino acids to the antigenic reactivity of peptides. This can be done by the methods developed by Geysen et al. (1984) and Houghten (1985), for analyzing replacement sets of peptide analogues in which each residue of the peptide is, in turn, replaced by the other 19 amino acids (Getzoff et al., 1987; Rodda et al., 1986). Since peptides attached to the support used for their synthesis or adsorbed non-covalently to the solid-phase may have little activity, it is preferable to assess the comparative antigenicity of a series of peptide analogues by a competitive immunoassay (Quesniaux et al., 1986). A simple assay consists of assessing the capacity of peptide analogues to inhibit the binding of antibodies to a peptide conjugate immobilized on the solid-phase (Procedure 3, Table 4.4). Another approach consists of letting a series of peptide analogues compete with a labelled peptide (Procedure 4., Table 4.4). In this case, it is important to establish that the binding properties of the antibody are not affected when it is adsorbed to the solid-phase. Since this effect can be particularly troublesome with monoclonal antibodies (Butler et al., 1986), it may be preferable to trap such antibodies on the plastic by a first layer of anti-mouse immunoglobulins (Procedures 5 and 6, respectively, Table 4.4) or by a biotin–avidin bridge (Suter and Butler, 1986).

4.3. Solid-phase immunoassay procedures

Many different solid-phase immunoassay formats have been developed and have been described in detail (Butler, 1991; Butler, 1996; Crowther, 1995; Gosling, 1996; Tijssen, 1985). Only a few procedures that were found to work satisfactorily with peptides will be described here. Depending on the properties of the molecules under study, each investigator should determine the optimal conditions in terms of incubation time, reagent concentration, buffer composition, type of blocking solution, etc. (Brown et al., 1997).

4.3.1. Indirect ELISA using immobilized peptide (Procedures 1 and 2, Table 4.2)

This test can be used to quantitate the amount of antibodies present in antisera raised against a peptide or the corresponding protein which are capable of reacting with an immobilized peptide. It consists of the following steps.

(a) Microtitre plates (e.g. polyvinyl; Falcon, USA, Reference 3912) are coated by incubation overnight at 40°C for 2–6 h at 20 or 37°C with 100–300 μl of 0.2–2.5 μM peptide solution diluted in carbonate buffer, pH 9.6 (15 mM Na_2CO_3; 35 mM $NaHCO_3$; 0.2 g/l NaN_3). If the peptide does not become adsorbed when this buffer is used, other buffers in the pH range 4–8 should be tried (Geerligs et al., 1988). When peptide conjugated to a carrier protein is used for coating the wells, the concentration of conjugate expressed as peptide should also be in the range 0.2–2.5 μM (Tuaillon et al., 1992).

(b) Repeated washings (at least three) with phosphate-buffered saline, pH 7.4 containing 0.05% Tween-20 (PBS-T).

(c) Blocking of remaining sites on the plastic by incubation with 10 mg/ml bovine serum albumin in PBS-T, for 1 h at 37°C.

(d) Repeated washings with PBS-T.

(e) Incubation with the antiserum to be tested, diluted in PBS-T, for 2 h at 37°C. The range of two-fold dilutions appropriate for a peptide antiserum is usually from 1/100 to 1/12 800, although dilution end points of 10^{5}–10^{6} may sometimes be observed.

(f) Repeated washings with PBS-T.

(g) Incubation with a suitable anti-immunoglobulin enzyme conjugate, diluted in PBS-T in the range 1/500–1/30000, for 30 min to 3 h at 37°C. If the peptide antiserum was raised in a rabbit, the enzyme conjugate could be goat antirabbit globulin (H + L chains) conjugated to alkaline phosphate (Stemmer et al., 1997). When human sera or murine Mabs are tested, goat antihuman IgG, goat antihuman IgM (Jackson, West Grove, PA) or rabbit antimouse IgG (H + L) conjugated to horseradish peroxidase (Nordic, Tilbury, The Netherlands) can be used (Tuaillon et al., 1992).

(h) Repeated washings with PBS-T.

(i) Incubation with an appropriate enzyme substrate for 1–3 h at 37°C. If the enzyme conjugate was prepared with alkaline phosphatase, the substrate p-nitrophenyl phosphate at 1 mg/ml in 0.1 M diethanolamine buffer, pH 9.8, is used. This substrate is available as tablets (Sigma, St Louis, Reference 104105) or in powder form (Boehringer, FRG, Reference 107905). If the enzyme conjugate was prepared with horseradish peroxidase (The Jackson Laboratories, West Grove, PA), the reaction can be visualized by addition of 3,3′,5,5′-tetramethyl-benzidine (Janssen Chimica, Beerse, Belgium) in the presence of H_2O_2 for 15 min at 37°C. The reaction is stopped by addition of HCl (final dilution 0.25 M) and the absorbance measured at 450 nM. Several other enzyme-substrate systems are commercially available (Tijssen, 1985).

(j) Reading of the optical density (at 405 nm in the case of alkaline phosphatase) in a suitable ELISA reader such as the Titertek Multiskan MC (Flow Laboratories) or the Autoreader Micro ELISA (Dynatech).

To determine the cutoff line of the assay, it is customary to test several normal sera with the peptides. Test sera are considered positive with respect to peptide reactivity when absorbance values are higher than the average value obtained for normal sera plus 2 or 3 standard deviations. In general, the average intra- and interplate coefficient of variation in ELISA should be ≤5% (Tuaillon et al., 1992).

Typical titration curves of peptide antisera raised against the C-terminal hexapeptide of histone H3 with the corresponding peptide and with the whole histone are illustrated in Fig. 4.6.

Instead of using the indirect immunoassay approach, it is also feasible to use antipeptide labelled antibodies. This method was used for instance to detect the cyclic undecapeptide, cyclosporin, in an inhibition enzyme immunoassay and was found to be more sensitive than liquid-phase RIA or other types of solid-phase immunoassay (Quesniaux et al., 1987a). In this competitive assay using enzymelabelled monoclonal antibodies, 0.2 ng of cyclosporin caused 50% inhibition of binding (Fig. 4.7). Under the conditions used, the within-assay coefficient of variation was in the range 1.5–10.5%.

4.3.2. Double antibody sandwich assay

In this type of assay the antigen will become attached to two different layers of antibodies and it must therefore present more than one accessible epitope. This means that either a protein or at least a fairly long peptide must be used as antigen.

As enzyme conjugate, it is possible to utilize an antipeptide serum labelled with an enzyme (Procedure 3, Table 4.4). However, this means that it is necessary to label each antiserum to be tested.

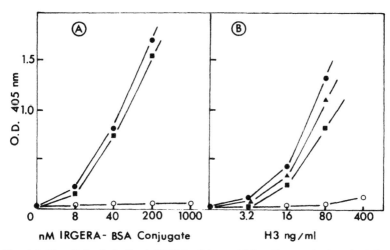

Fig. 4.6. Reactivity in indirect ELISA of two rabbit antisera raised against the C-terminal hexapeptide of histone H3 (residues 130–135 of sequence IRGERA). Antisera diluted 1 : 1000 were tested against an IRGERA-BSA conjugate (coupling ratio 21 : 1) prepared with glutaraldehyde (in A), and against the complete H3 histone molecule (in B). A concentration of 16 ng/ml of H3 corresponds to about 1 nM. (●) Antiserum to IRGERA-ovalbumin conjugate was prepared by photochemical coupling (coupling ratio 2 : 1); (▲) antiserum to IRGERA-ovalbumin conjugate prepared with glutaraldehyde (coupling ratio 13 : 1); (■) antiserum to H3; (○) antiserum to an unrelated peptide conjugated to ovalbumin by photochemical coupling. The ELISA procedure with alkaline phosphatase conjugates described in Section 4.2.1 was used. Substrate hydrolysis time was 45 min.

It is therefore more practical to use an indirect procedure with antisera obtained from two animal species such as chickens and rabbits (Procedure 2, Table 4.4). Conjugated antibodies against rabbit immunoglobulin will not react with chicken antibodies (Al Moudallal et al., 1984). An example of such an assay is presented in Fig. 4.8. The assay consists of the following steps.

(a) Wells are coated by incubation (2 h at 37°C) with 1–10 μg/ml chicken immunoglobulins diluted in PBS-T. These immunoglobulins can be obtained from laying hens immunized

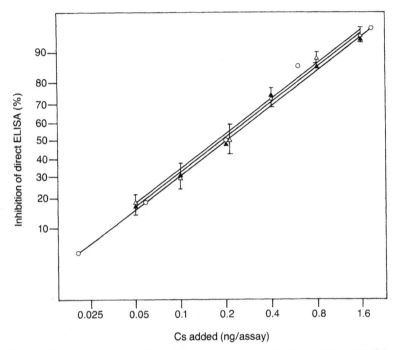

Fig. 4.7. Detection of the cyclic peptide cyclosporin by inhibition of direct ELISA. Microtitre plates coated with 0.25 μg/ml of BSA-cyclosporin conjugate were incubated with enzyme-labelled monoclonal antibody (1 μg/ml of antibody) for 2 h at 4°C in the presence of increasing quantities of cyclosporin inhibitor. Inhibition standard curves correspond to three experiments performed on different days (Δ, ○, ▲). Bars indicate two standard deviations (from Quesniaux et al., 1987a).

with the protein and are easily extracted from the eggs yolks (Polson et al., 1980; Van Regenmortel, 1993).

(b) Repeated washings with PBS-T (see Section 4.2.1).

(c) Blocking with 1% BSA in PBS-T, followed by washing.

(d) Incubation with the protein diluted in the range 20–500 ng/ml in PBS-T, for 2 h at 37°C.

(e) Repeated washings with PBS-T.

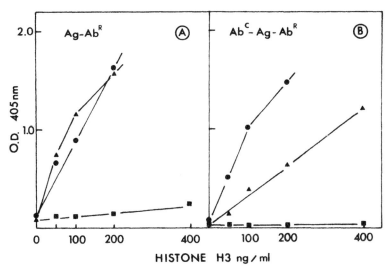

Fig. 4.8. Comparative reactivity in indirect ELISA (A), and in double antibody sandwich ELISA (B) of two antisera raised against the hexapeptide IRGERA of histone H3. The same antisera as in Fig. 4.6 were used, i.e. raised against a conjugate prepared with glutaraldehyde (●) and against a conjugate prepared by photochemical coupling (▲). Normal rabbit serum was used as control (■). (A) H3-coated plates were incubated with antipeptide rabbit antisera (diluted 1 : 1000) for 2 h at 37°C. After blocking and washing an antirabbit globulin alkaline phosphatase conjugate was incubated for 1 h. Substrate incubation time was 1 h (see Section 4.2.1). Plates were coated with 10 μg/ml chicken anti-H3 globulins for 2 h at 37°C. Subsequent incubations were with H3 (2 h) and with antipeptide rabbit antisera (2 h). Enzyme conjugate and substrate were as in (A).

(f) Incubation with the antipeptide rabbit serum diluted in the range 1/100–1/10000 in PBS-T containing 1% BSA, for 2 h at 37°C.

(g) Repeated washing with PBS-T.

(h) Incubation with goat antirabbit globulin enzyme conjugate, and further steps as outlined in Section 4.2.1.

This assay can also be used in an inhibition format, in which case the antipeptide serum is incubated for 1–2 h with the peptide or a series of peptide analogues (Procedure 2, Table 4.3). To prevent the peptides from binding to the antibody-coated plates, this incubation must be carried out outside of the microtitre wells (Tuaillon et al., 1992). In common with all competitive assays, this method is particularly suited for comparing the antigenic reactivity of a large number of different peptides.

4.3.3. Solid-phase radioimmunoassay (RIA)

The various assays listed in Tables 4.1 and 4.3 can also be used in the RIA format by replacing the enzyme conjugate by a radio-labelled antibody or alternatively by detecting the antigen-antibody complex by means of ^{125}I-labelled protein A. Following the incubation step with radiolabelled reagent (for instance, ^{125}I-protein A from Amersham, UK, 60–100 μCi/μg, using 4×10^4 cpm/ml incubated for 1 h at 37°C) and repeated washings to remove excess radiolabelled reagent, the wells are cut from the plate and read in a gamma counter (Muller et al., 1982b).

Practical instructions concerning the performance of different types of radioimmunoassays are available in several textbooks (Chard, 1996; Parratt et al., 1982). When a competitive assay is used (Procedure 4, Table 4.3), peptides containing a tyrosyl residue can be radiolabelled with ^{125}I-sodium iodide using the chloramine-T method (Greenwood et al., 1963). Peptides containing cysteine and methionine residues can be labelled with Iodogen (Pierce Chemicals, Rockford, Illinois) using the method of Fraker and Speck (1978)

4.4. Dot immunobinding assay

Immunoblotting procedures in which proteins are transferred from a gel after electrophoretic separation on nitrocellulose membranes and are detected by an immunological assay were introduced by Towbin et al. (1979). Subsequently, it was shown that peptides could be immobilized on nitrocellulose by crosslinking them to the membrane using glutaraldehyde or formaldehyde. Small peptides are most conveniently presented by means of a spacer molecule such as 1,6-diaminohexane and can be immobilized on nitrocellulose activated by divinyl sulfone (Lauritzen et al., 1990, 1993). The method has been described in detail by Lauritzen et al. (1994).

4.5. Spotscan assay

This method developed by Frank (1992, 1995) consists in synthesizing a series of up to 96 different peptides assembled on a 8×12 cm cellulose membrane. The end groups at the N- and C-termini of each peptide are blocked since the free N-terminus is acetylated and the C-terminus participates in the covalent anchor to the cellulose sheet. The spot method has been found useful for mapping both B cell epitopes (Allauzen et al., 1995; Commandeur et al., 1994; Halimi et al., 1996; Volmer-Engert et al., 1994) and T-cell epitopes (Adler et al., 1994) using overlapping octa- or decapeptides. However, longer peptides can also be tested (Molina et al., 1996) and commercial synthesis kits are available (Genosys, Cambridge, UK). Following the synthesis of peptides, the membrane is washed with methanol and 0.05 M Tris buffered saline and then incubated overnight with a casein-containing blocking buffer. After rinsing, the test antibody is added for 2 h, followed by a suitable antiglobulin enzyme conjugate. Following substrate addition and colour development, the bound antibodies can be removed by washing with various solutions such as 8 M urea, 1% sodium dodecylsulfate or dimethylformamide. The membrane can then be used for additional tests with other antibodies (Frank and Overwin, 1996). When used for identifying epitopes recognized by sera from autoimmune patients, the spotscan was found to give less nonspecific background readings than the pepscan technique (Halimi et al., 1996).

4.6. Biosensor assays

In recent years, a new biosensor technology based on surface plasmon resonance has become available which greatly simplifies the analysis of quantitative interactions between biomolecules. This new technology commonly known as biomolecular interaction analysis (BIA) makes it possible to visualize the binding process in real time on a computer screen. The increase in refractive index that occurs when one of the interacting partners binds to its ligand immobilized on the surface of a sensor chip is followed as a function of time. None of the reactants needs to be labelled which avoids the commonly observed artefactual changes in binding properties that occur when molecules are labelled. Numerous reviews describing this new technology are available (Fägerstam and Karlsson, 1994; Granzow, 1994; Jönsson and Malmqvist, 1992). This section will concentrate mainly on the use of biosensors for studying peptide-antibody interactions.

4.6.1. Description of the BIAcore instrument

The most commonly used biosensor instrument is the BIAcore™ developed by BIAcore AB (Uppsala, Sweden). Another instrument, called Iasys, based on a resonant mirror system is commercialized by Affinity Sensors (Cambridge, UK). Since the BIAcore has been used in over 90% of the published research literature so far, the discussion will be limited to data obtained with this instrument. A comparative study of commercially available biosensor instruments has been published (Hodgson, 1994).

The BIAcore instrument consists of an optical detector system, exchangeable sensor chips, a processing unit and a personal computer for control and evaluation. The processing unit contains the surface plasmon resonance (SPR) monitor, an integrated microfluidic cartridge and an autosampler for dispensing samples automatically (Jönsson and Malmqvist, 1992). The sensor chip is a glass slide, coated on one side with a gold film which is covered with a dextran layer extending about 100 nm from the surface. The dextran is carboxymethylated which makes it possible to immobi- lize molecules with primary amines after activation of the matrix with carbodiimide-N-hydroxysuccinimide. Various other immobi- lization chemistries can also be used (Johnson et al., 1995). A particularly useful strategy is to add a Cys residue at one end of the peptide to be tested and immobilizing it using thiol activa- tion chemistry (Chatellier et al., 1996; O'Shannessy et al., 1992; Richalet-Sécordel et al., 1994a).

The optical detection system is based on surface plasmon reso- nance, a physical phenomenon which makes it possible to measure changes in refractive index occurring at the surface of the chip. Since the refractive index is related to the concentration of material in the medium, the system is able to detect the binding between a ligand immobilized on the chip and an analyte flowing over the surface. A microflow cell with a volume of 0.06 μl is used and the bulk flow rate lies in the range 1–100 μl/min, which allows a typical interaction to be analyzed in less than 10 min. Four indepen- dent flow cells are present on each sensor chip. Variations in SPR signal corresponding to the concentration of bound molecules are monitored continuously and presented as a plot of resonance units (RU) versus time, known as a sensorgram. A signal of 1000 RU corresponds to a surface concentration change of 1 ng/mm^2. After each analysis, the sensor surface can be regenerated by introducing a small volume of a dissociating agent which removes the analyte from the covalently immobilized ligand. As many of 100 analytical cycles can be performed on the same surface.

Compared to other solid-phase immunoassay systems, biosensor instruments have the following advantages.

(1) The conformation of the immobilized ligand tends to be pre- served because it is covalently bound to a hydrophilic dextran matrix. In contrast, in classical solid-phase assays, the ligand is immobilized by adsorption to plastic which tends to lead to

denaturation of proteins or alteration of peptides (Butler, 1992; Darst et al., 1988).

(2) Every step in a multi-layer assay can be directly visualized and it is immediately apparent if one of the components in the system is defective.

(3) Interactions are measured in real time, which allows kinetic rate constants and equilibrium affinity constants to be calculated (Karlsson et al., 1991; Karlsson and Roos, 1997; Saunal et al., 1997). Knowledge of the affinity of antibodies for a peptide is important for the proper design of immunoassays and for assessing to what extent a peptide mimics the structure and binding activity of a protein epitope (Zeder-Lutz et al., 1993b). BIAcore measurements have been found to be very useful for measuring the degree of antigenic mimicry achieved with retro-inverso peptide analogues of various epitopes (Benkirane et al., 1995; Guichard et al., 1994; Muller et al., 1995).

4.6.2. Analysis of peptide-antibody interactions with BIAcore

The BIAcore instrument can be used to analyze the antigenic activity of peptides immobilized on the sensor chip or used as inhibitors of the reaction between an antigen and specific antibodies (Altschuh et al., 1992; Kantrong et al., 1995; Schellekens et al., 1994). When a peptide is found to harbour an epitope, the contribution of individual residues to the antigenic activity can be assessed by measuring the binding of peptide analogues presenting single substitutions (Zeder-Lutz et al., 1993a) or deletions (Zvi et al., 1995). By measuring the kinetic rate constants characterizing the interactions of the antibody with the wild type and substituted peptides, it is possible to determine which residues contribute to the energy of interaction. The results of such an experiment are illustrated in Fig. 4.9 which shows the association and dissociation rate constants of a recombinant Fab fragment interacting with various immobilized peptides. The peptides correspond to analogues of an epitope of tobacco mosaic virus protein located in the vicinity of residues 134–146 that present single residue substitutions (Altschuh et al., 1992; Chatellier et al., 1996). It can be seen that the substitutions mainly affected the dissociation rate constant of the interaction.

Several groups have used the biosensor technology for optimizing peptide probes used in the diagnosis of the human immunodeficiency virus 1 (HIV-1). Various linear and cyclic peptides corresponding to immunodominant epitopes of the gp120 and gp41 proteins of HIV have been studied using either peptides covalently attached to the chip, peptides conjugated to a carrier protein or free inhibitor peptides (Lucey et al., 1993; Mani et al., 1994; Richalet-Sécordel et al., 1994a, b; Van Cott et al., 1992). In one study, Mabs and rabbit polyclonal antibodies were raised against a cyclic peptide corresponding to a chimeric sequence of a consensus V3 loop of HIV-1 gp120. These antibodies, when tested by ELISA and BIAcore, were found to cross-react extensively with peptides corresponding to the V3 regions of different HIV-1 strains. The antibodies recognized the cyclic form of the homologous peptide better than the linear form (Fig. 4.10). When V3 peptides of different viral strains were compared for their ability to inhibit the binding of antibodies to the chimeric immobilized peptide, it was possible to identify which residues were critical for antibody recognition (Richalet-Sécordel et al., 1994a, b). The chimeric peptide was also found to be a good diagnostic probe for detecting antibodies in the sera of patients infected with various HIV-1 strains (Richalet-Sécordel et al., 1994a, b). The ELISA titres of Mabs with respect to various V3 peptides correlated well with the amount of competitor peptide needed to inhibit 50% of the binding of Mabs to the immobilized chimeric peptide present on the sensor chip. In view of the good correlation between ELISA titres and BIAcore data, it seems that biosensor data are useful for selecting peptides to be used in classical diagnostic solid-phase immunoassays.

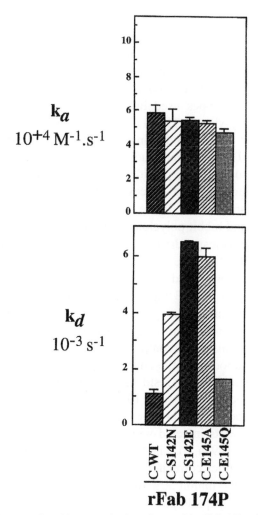

Fig. 4.9. Influence of residue substitutions in peptide 134–151 of tobacco mosaic virus protein on its association (k_a) and dissociation (k_d) rate constants of interaction with recombinant Fab fragment of monoclonal antibody 174P. An N-terminal Cys residue was added to each peptide for immobilization to the sensor chip using thiol activation chemistry. WT: wild type peptide; S142N: substituted peptide with Ser_{142} replaced by Asn. (adapted from Chatellier et al., 1996 with permission).

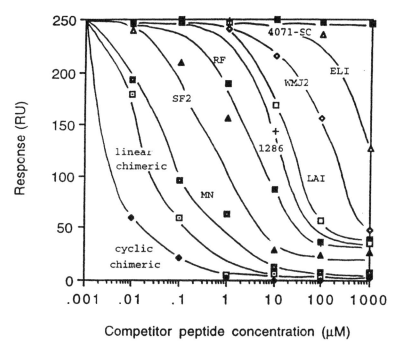

Fig. 4.10. Inhibition of binding in BIAcore of the reaction between chimeric peptide 303–338 and a monoclonal antibody to the V3 loop of human immunodeficiency virus 1, by increasing amounts of V3 peptides of different HIV-1 strains. Note the higher inhibitory capacity of the homologous cyclic peptide compared to the linear peptide (from Richalet-Sécordel et al., 1994a with permission).

4.6.3. Immobilization of peptides on sensor chips

The following reagents are required: N-hydroxysuccinimide (NHS), N-ethyl-N'-[(3-dimethylamino)propyl] carbodiimide hydrochloride (EDC) and 2-(2-pyridinyldithiol)ethaneamine hydrochloride (PDEA).

Peptides can be immobilized on the carboxylated dextran matrix of sensor chips through their primary amino groups using reactive esters (Johnsson et al., 1991). Immobilization runs are performed at a flow of 5 μl/min in 10 mM Hepes, 150 mM NaCl, 3.4 mM EDTA,

0.005% surfactant P20, pH 7.4 (HBS buffer) at 25°C. The carboxylated matrix is first activated with 50 μl of an 1/1-EDC/NHS mixture. Peptides are injected at a concentration of 2 mg/ml in a suitable buffer such as formate buffer pH 3.5. Remaining NHS esters are blocked by injection of 35 μl of 1 M ethanolamine-HCl pH 8.5. Non-covalently immobilized peptides are removed by washing the sensor chip surface with 15 μl of 100 mM NaOH.

Peptides containing a terminal Cys residue can be immobilized using thiol chemistry (O'Shannessy et al., 1992). The sensor chip surface is first activated by injecting 4 μl of EDC/NHS followed by 25 μl of 81 mM PDEA in 0.1 M sodium borate pH 8.5. Excess NHS esters are blocked with 35 μl of 1 M ethanolamine-HCl pH 8.5. Then 35 μl of peptide at 20 μg/ml in 10 mM sodium acetate pH 4 were injected. Excess reactive sulfhydryl groups are deactivated with 25 μl of 0.1 M cysteine in sodium acetate buffer containing 1 M NaCl. The surface is then washed with 15 μl of 0.1 N HCl (Chatellier et al., 1996).

4.7. Measurement of affinity constants

Numerous techniques exist for measuring the affinity constant of peptide-antibody interactions and they have been described in considerable detail (Day, 1990; Phizicky and Fields, 1995; Saunal et al., 1997; Steward and Chargelegue, 1997:; Van Regenmortel and Azimadeh, 1994: Zeder-Lutz et al., 1993c). The present section will only briefly describe the use of BIAcore for measuring kinetic rate constants and equilibrium affinity constants.

The interaction between antigen and antibody at equilibrium may be expressed as:

$$A + B \underset{k_d}{\overset{k_a}{\rightleftharpoons}} AB$$

where A represents free antigen, B free antibody, AB the antigen-antibody complex, k_a (M^{-1} sec^{-1}) the association rate constant and

k_d (sec $^{-1}$) the dissociation rate constant, respectively. According to the law of mass action, the equilibrium constant can be expressed either as an association equilibrium constant.

$$K_A = \frac{k_a}{k_d} = \frac{[AB]}{[A][B]} \quad (\text{units M}^{-1})$$

or a dissociation equilibrium constant

$$K_D = \frac{k_d}{k_a} = \frac{[A][B]}{[AB]} \quad (\text{units M})$$

For determining the equilibrium affinity constant, it is necessary to measure either the concentration of free antigen, free antibody or of the bound molecules after separating the free molecules from the complexes. The separation can be done by centrifugation, filtration or simply by washing when the interaction occurs on a solid phase. In solid phase assays where the peptide is adsorbed on plastic, varying amounts of antibody can be added to the microtitre wells and the amount of bound antibody can be measured after removing free antibody by washing.

It is also possible to measure free antibody at equilibrium with BIAcore. After immobilizing the antigen on the sensor chip, the antibody is introduced in a flow and its binding is visualized in real time and expressed in resonance units (RU). A calibration curve of response level (in RU) versus antibody concentration is established using a series of dilutions of an antibody of known concentration. To measure the affinity, a constant amount of antigen is mixed with increasing amounts of antibody and incubated for one hour. The mixture is than injected on the sensor chip containing the immobilized antigen and any free antibody will bind to this surface and can be quantified. This method does not require the preliminary separation of free from bound antibody and can be used with antigen of any size (Zeder-Lutz et al., 1993c).

While the quantities of complex formed depend on the equilibrium affinity constant, the time necessary to reach equilibrium depends on the kinetic rates, k_a and k_d. The biological relevance of an interaction is often more dependent on the kinetic rates than on the equilibrium affinity. It has been shown, for instance, that the capacity of viral antibodies to neutralize virus infectivity depends on the dissociation rate constant (Van Cott et al., 1994). Single substitution in antigenic peptides corresponding to T-cell epitopes are often able to change the activity of a peptide from stimulatory to antagonistic and such differences were found to be correlated with changes in the kinetic constants of the interaction (Lyons et al., 1996; Matsui et al., 1994).

Procedures used in kinetic analysis with BIAcore have been described in several reviews (Karlsson and Roos, 1997; Karlsson et al., 1994; Myszka, 1997; Saunal et al., 1997). Information on kinetic constants can be extracted from sensorgrams using various evaluation methods such as linearization, analytical and numerical integration (Morton et al., 1995). A nonlinear least squares method is normally used. This method proceeds in an iterative manner to find a theoretical curve that matches closely the experimental sensorgram, on the basis of minimal residual values (O'Shannessy et al., 1993). Global fitting in combination with numerical integration calculation is regarded as the method of choice for analyzing simultaneously sets of data obtained at different analyte concentrations (Karlsson and Fält, 1997; Karlsson and Roos, 1997).

Detailed experimental protocols for measuring the kinetic rate constant of peptide-antibody interaction are available (Chatellier et al., 1996; Saunal et al., 1997). The range of kinetic constants that can be measured with precision with BIAcore is 10^2 to 5×10^6 M^{-1} sec for k_a and 10^{-5} to 10^{-2} sec^{-1} for k_d. Outside of this range, quantitative information on the interaction can still be obtained by equilibrium measurements.

4.8. Monitoring of the immune response to peptides

Solid-phase immunoassays have been widely used to follow the development of the immune response in animals immunized with

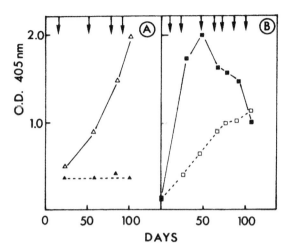

Fig. 4.11. Variability of the antibody response to peptides in rabbits subjected to the same immunization protocol. (A) Antibody levels measured by indirect ELISA in two rabbits (△ and ▲) immunized by a series of subcutaneous injections (indicated by arrows) with 100 μg of a 15-residue-long peptide of histone H2A. Antisera were diluted 1 : 500. Plates were coated with 2 μM unconjugated peptide. (B) Development of antibody response to an 18-residue-long peptide conjugated to ovalbumin in two rabbits (□ and ■) immunized by one subcutaneous and several subsequent intramuscular injections (arrows). Antibody levels were measured by indirect ELISA using plates coated with 2 μM unconjugated peptide and antisera diluted 1 : 1000.

synthetic peptides. Since the outcome of an immunization protocol is unpredictable, it is essential to bleed the animals frequently and to test each serum for the presence of antibodies reacting with different forms of the peptide as well as with the cognate protein. The variability of the immune response to peptides in rabbits receiving the same immunization schedule is illustrated in Fig. 4.11.

For instance, a 15-residue-long peptide (residues 12–26 of histone H2A) when used as a free, unconjugated peptide was found to elicit an immune response in only one of two rabbits (Fig. 4.11). A few reports have appeared indicating that small synthetic peptides of 5–10 residues could be immunogenic when administered in free form (Young and Atassi, 1982). However, the affinity of the antibodies obtained in this way was about 10^3-fold lower than the values obtained with carrier-conjugated peptides (Mariani et al., 1987).

The data presented in Fig. 4.11 show that antiserum titres do not necessarily continue to rise during the course of immunization, indicating the need to collect serum at frequent intervals.

Antibody levels in antisera can also be readily measured with biosensors (Karlsson et al., 1993; Richalet-Sécordel et al., 1997). Van Cott et al. (1992) have quantitated antibody to specific epitopes from HIV-1 positive individuals enrolled in vaccine trials. They showed that the same sensor chip containing an immobilized peptide could be used about 90 times for measuring antibody concentration with only a small loss in reactivity.

CHAPTER 5

Use of antipeptide antibodies in molecular and cellular biology

S. MULLER

5.1. Detection of gene products with antipeptide antibodies

A powerful method for identifying previously undetected proteins consists in revealing their presence by means of antibodies raised against synthetic peptides, the sequence to be synthesized being deduced from the nucleotide sequence of the protein gene. The peptide sequences selected for synthesis usually correspond to regions of the protein that are believed to be particularly antigenic on the basis of prediction algorithms (see Chapter 1). These algorithms are derived from established correlations between antigenically active regions and structural features of the protein such as chain termination, hydrophilicity and segmental mobility. Antisera raised against these peptides are expected to recognize epitopes on the protein synthesized *in vivo*. The feasibility of this approach has been demonstrated in many studies, for example for the detection of viral proteins, tumour antigens, putative cell receptors and proteins linked to cell differentiation.

When the proteins are synthesized in living organisms, other immunological approaches have been used for identifying them. Some investigators, for example, tested fusion proteins of which a part was encoded by an inserted DNA sequence and the remainder was encoded by a vector gene. These fusion proteins were used either to stimulate antibody production (Beesley et al., 1990; Broekhuijsen et al., 1987; Clarke et al., 1987; Coppel et al., 1983; Kleid et al., 1981; Schlomai and Zadok, 1984), or to select by affinity chromatography those antibodies present in a polyspecific antiserum that recognize the protein encoded by the cloned sequence (Crewther et al., 1986; Hall et al., 1984).

The aim of this section is to describe some of the methods involving antipeptide antibodies that have been used for finding gene products in a cellular extract and for detecting translation products of viral RNA in cell free extracts *in vitro*.

Specific experimental details concerning DNA cloning and transcription and translation techniques have been described extensively in numerous texts and reviews (Lefkovits, 1997; O'Reilly et al., 1992; Sambrook et al., 1989). A number of suitable vectors have been developed for cDNA bacterial expression such as pBR322, λgtl1, pEX. The detection of expressed cloned sequences by antibody screening methods is simplified by using expression vectors that produce insoluble hybrid protein products and by working with bacterial hosts that are defective in protein degradation pathways.

As pointed out by Lerner (1984), it is important, in order to correctly identify a particular gene product, to use antibodies raised against peptides corresponding to several different regions of the putative protein. First, a single antipeptide antiserum may not recognize certain forms of the unprocessed gene product. Second, in order to ensure that the detected product pertains to the studied protein, it is important to show that antibodies directed to more than one peptide recognize the protein and that nonrelated antibodies do not bind to it. By using a double antibody sandwich immunoassay with antipeptide antibodies specific for two different epitopes of the protein, the possibility of erroneously identifying a protein owing to nonspecific reactions is virtually eliminated. The specificity of the observed reaction can also be demonstrated by inhibition experiments with the free peptide. As the total amount of protein used in screening assays is often very high, problems caused by coprecipitation and nonspecific absorption of antibody are often encountered and it is therefore essential to use suitable controls to establish binding specificity.

In the following sections, the main applications of antipeptide antibodies for identifying gene products will be briefly summarized and a few selected techniques will be described.

5.1.1. Detection of putative proteins on the basis of nucleic acid sequences

Antipeptide antibodies have been found particularly useful for identifying DNA and RNA tumour virus proteins implicated in cell transformation, and it is in this field that putative proteins were first successfully characterized by means of antipeptide antibodies. Sutcliffe et al. (1980) succeeded in identifying in infected cells a new retroviral gene product, the protein R from Moloney leukaemia virus (Mo-MuLV). They used an antiserum to a pentadecapeptide corresponding to the C-terminal region of the R protein predicted from the nucleotide sequence. Using a similar approach, Papkoff et al. (1981) identified a product from the *mos* gene of Moloney murine sarcoma virus (Mo-MuSV).

Antipeptide antibodies have been used to demonstrate the existence of relationships between different proteins. For instance, Robbins et al. (1983) and Devare et al. (1983), using this approach, observed a relationship between the sis oncogene protein of simian sarcoma virus (SSV) and a normal human protein of known function, the human platelet derived growth factor. These studies were carried out by means of antipeptide antisera raised against the N- and C-terminal regions of the predicted oncogene protein of SSV. Niman (1984) confirmed this result using antibodies to a peptide of 17 residues which corresponded to an internal segment of the SSV transforming protein.

Proteins encoded by viral v-*myc* and cellular c-*myc* oncogenes were also identified by means of antipeptide antibodies. Some *myc* oncogene products have been shown by means of antipeptide antibodies to be evolutionarily highly conserved (Persson et al., 1984). The oncogene c-*myc* has also been identified in normal cells (Hann

et al., 1983). The proteins that were detected by means of antipeptide antibodies were phosphorylated and localized in the cell
nucleus of infected cells. In noninfected cells, the *myc*-related protein did not appear to be phosphorylated (Hann et al., 1983). The
myc gene consists of three exons and two introns, exons 2 and 3
coding for the cellular homologue of the v-*myc* protein. Gazin et al.
(1986) showed that a protein with an apparent size of 58 kD was
a dimer of a 32 kD protein and represented a product derived from
the *myc* exon 1. Both 58 and 32 kD proteins were recognized using
five different antipeptide antisera elicited by peptides, ranging from
21 to 28 residues, which corresponded to nonoverlapping regions of
the putative product of this exon.

Antipeptide antibodies have also been used for identifying gene
products in the case of the large T antigen of simian virus 40 (SV40)
and polyoma virus (Dietrich, 1985; Walter et al., 1980, 1982).
In these experiments, antibodies to the C-terminal hexapeptide of
polyoma virus medium T antigen were used as well as antibodies to
a hexapeptide from the C-terminus of SV40 large T antigen (Walter,
1986).

Many studies have also been carried out on the coding sequences
of hepatitis-B viral genes (Neurath and Kent, 1988; Neurath et al.,
1986a, b). One of the open reading frames on hepatitis-B virus
(HBV) DNA comprises the coding region for the viral envelope
proteins, known as the *env* gene. This gene has the capacity to code
for three related proteins: the S protein (226 amino acids), the M
protein, containing an additional 55 amino acids at the N-terminal
end of S protein (coded by a portion of the *env* gene upstream of
the S gene known as pre-S2), and the L protein, corresponding to
the sequence of M protein with an additional 108 N-terminal amino
acids (encoded by the pre-S1-region). Using antibodies raised to
synthetic peptides corresponding to the pre-S gene, Neurath et al.
(1985a) showed that all three *env* encoded proteins were present in
HBV particles and that pre-S epitopes played an important role in
hepatitis-B virus infection and in the human immune response to
HBV. The presence of pre-S sequences has been shown to enhance

the immune response to S protein (Coursaget et al., 1985; Milich et al., 1985). An immunoenzymatic assay was developed (Neurath et al., 1985b, 1986b) for detecting the presence of pre-S sequences in HBV preparations and this test also made it possible to evaluate hepatitis-B vaccines for the presence of sequences corresponding to the pre-S regions. In this assay, antibodies to the synthetic pre-S peptide (residues 120–145) were used to coat polystyrene beads.

Antibodies to peptides have also been used to track viral or cellular protein precursors during their processing. For example, Semier et al. (1982), and Baron and Baltimore (1982a, b) have demonstrated the existence of a common precursor for the poliovirus replicase and the polio RNA-linked VPg. Other examples of this approach are the analysis of precursor proteins encoded by the *gag* gene of human T-cell leukemia virus (Hattori et al., 1984), and of proteins found in cells infected with Mo-MuLV (Green et al., 1981) and influenza virus (Lerner, 1984; Sutcliffe et al., 1983). Many other applications have been reported, for instance, the identification of proteins postulated to be present in malignant tumours, e.g., the protease transin (Matrisian et al., 1986), the pS2 protein found in human breast cancer cells MCF-7 (Nunez et al., 1987), the p21 proteins, encoded by the *ras* family of cellular genes, which are modified at a single amino acid residue (at position 12 in the sequence) in their oncogenic forms (Clark et al., 1985; Wong et al., 1986), and tumour-specific bcr-abl joining region in chronic myeloid leukemia as well as in acute lymphoblastic leukemias (Van Denderen et al., 1989).

Immunodetection by means of antipeptide antibodies was also used successfully for identifying several unknown mitochondrial proteins whose existence had been predicted on the basis of unidentified open reading frames in mitochondrial DNA (Chomyn et al., 1983; Mariottini et al., 1983). This study also showed that antipeptide antibodies are valuable probes both for assigning frames and for detecting the products of overlapping genes.

Biologists involved in embryogenesis and organogenesis often use antibody probes to study the expression of genes which are activated or suppressed during development. For example, antipeptide antibodies were used to study the expression pattern of connexin gene products at the early developmental stage of the mouse cardiovascular system (Delorme et al., 1997) as well as the expression of different genes during embryogenesis in *Caenorhabditis elegans* (Tabara et al., 1999).

5.1.2. Antipeptide antibody probes for structural and functional studies of gene products

The baculovirus system and other expression vectors have proven particularly useful in the generation of large quantities of protein for structural and functional studies. Different expression vectors were thus used to study antigenicity and immunogenicity of protein and peptides (Hofnung and Charbit, 1993). By inserting the same peptide at different sites of a vector protein or in different vector proteins, several authors have investigated the peptide antigenicity in the context of the folded protein and the influence of distinct molecular environments on the antigenic activity of a particular peptide sequence. Examples of such studies concern the antigenicity and immunogenicity of myohemerythrin (Alexander et al., 1992), peptides of foot-and-mouth disease virus (Beesley et al., 1990; Benito and Van Regenmortel, 1998; Broekhuijsen et al., 1987; Clarke et al., 1987) and of herpes simplex virus (Van der Ploeg et al., 1989).

5.1.3. Immunodetection of in vitro translation products using antipeptide antibodies

In vitro translation products have been characterized by many different methods. Most of them require that the proteins be labelled during their synthesis by incorporation of radioactive amino acids. However, if antibodies specific for the translation products are avail-

able, they represent an alternative powerful method for identifying
and quantifying these products. The specificity of these antibodies
makes it possible to avoid the problems caused by multiple translation that occur when many mRNA species are present. The strategy
used for identifying translation products involves either immunoprecipitation experiments or a separation of translated products on
SDS-gel, followed by transfer to nitrocellulose sheets and immunodetection by specific antibodies (Clemens, 1984; Towbin et al.,
1979). This approach was used, for instance, by Berna et al. (1986)
in their characterization of the nonstructural proteins of alfalfa mosaic virus (AMV) found in infected tobacco plants. Antisera to
synthetic peptides corresponding to the C-termini of the three predicted nonstructural proteins, P1, P2, P3, were used to detect these
proteins in crude membrane fractions of AMV-infected leaves. In
a wheat germ translation system, the three antisera also recognized the respective translation products derived from the viral RNA
species 1, 2 and 3 (see Section 5.1.4.3). Antipeptide antibodies were
also used, for example, to study the linear regions exposed at the
surface of the *in vitro* translated U1 snRNP-C protein (Dumortier et
al., 1998) and 52-kD Ro/SSA protein (Ricchiuti et al., 1997).

*5.1.4. Selected techniques used for the immunological detection of
gene products*

Detailed accounts of the relevant techniques have been published
in numerous publications (e.g. Ausubel et al., 1994–1997; Lenstra
and Van Vliet, 1996; O'Reilly et al., 1992). In this section, the basic methodology used in immunochemical studies of gene products
will be described. Three examples from different fields will be used
to illustrate the range of possible applications.

5.1.4.1. Gene isolation with antibody probes using λgt11
expression vector (G. de Murcia, personal communication)
Young and Davis (1983a, b) have developed a very efficient technique for isolating gene sequences by screening *E. coli* expression
libraries with antibody probes, using the bacteriophage expression
vector λgt11. This vector has become increasingly popular for the
construction of cDNA or genomic libraries, mainly because of its
ability to express high levels of the desired proteins. Cloning into
the unique *Eco*RI site located in the 3′ end of the λgt11's Lac Z
gene can result in the expression of the foreign DNA as a part of a
β-galactosidase fusion protein in a lawn protease deficient *E. coli*
strain. These fusion proteins are generally stable enough to be detected with antibody probes. The procedure for isolating genes by
immunoscreening developed by Snyder et al. (1987) was slightly
modified as follows.

Construction of a recombinant DNA library in λgt11
Genomic libraries are used for organisms such as Drosophila or
yeast that have a small genomic size and few introns in their coding
sequences. In this case the number of genomic recombinants that
must be screened in order to isolate the gene of interest in not too
large. For organisms such as mammals which have a large genome,
it is necessary to use cDNA libraries. The construction of cDNA
and genomic libraries has been described in detail (Ausubel et al.,
1994–1997; O'Reilly et al., 1992; Sambrook et al., 1989).

Preparation of antibody probes
Both polyclonal and monoclonal antibodies have been used successfully for isolating genes by means of λgt11 libraries. When
polyclonal antibodies are used, problems are sometimes encountered owing to the presence of anti-*E. coli* antibodies in the serum.
These contaminating antibodies can be removed by incubating the
antiserum with an *E. coli* lysate bound to Sepharose 4B (Young and
Davis, 1983a), or nitrocellulose filters (Schleicher & Schüll BA 85,
0.45 µm) (Johnson et al., 1985). The sensitivity of the assay can

be enhanced by using affinity-purified antibodies (O'Brien et al., 1986).

Screening λgt11 libraries with antibody probes

The method developed by Young and Davis (1983a, b) and modified by Huynh et al. (1985) consists of the following steps.

E. coli Y1090 cells are infected with phages of the λgt11 library and plated on LB soft agar, at approximately 10^5 plaques per 150 mm plate.

The plates are incubated for 4 h at 42°C.

A dry nitrocellulose filter previously saturated with 10 mM isopropyl-β-D-galactopyranoside (IPTG) and air-dried is placed on the agar and incubated for 9 h at 37°C. The filter position is marked with a needle dipped in waterproof ink.

The filters are removed from plates and are washed for 5 min in TBS (10 mM Tris, pH 8, 150 mM NaCl).

For duplicate screening a second IPTG-treated filter is overlaid on plates and incubated for an additional 3 h at 37°C.

Filters are incubated in the antibody solution at a solution at a suitable dilution in TBS containing 0.05% Tween 20 (TBS-T) and 5% powdered milk (12.5 ml/large filter) for 2 h at room temperature (Johnson et al., 1984).

The filters are washed 3 times in TBS-T for 10 min.

Detection of the antibody probes:

(a) ^{125}I *protein A* Treat filters with ^{125}I-labelled protein A (>30 mCi/mg) (Amersham IM 144) at a concentration of 1 μCi in 10 ml TBS-T per large filter for 1.5 h. Wash filters three times in TBS-T for 10 min. Dry filters and expose at −70°C to Kodak X-Omat AR film and a Cronex Lightning Plus intensifying screen.

(b) *Horseradish peroxidase conjugated second antibody* Incubate filters for 2 h with horseradish peroxidase-conjugated second antibody at a 1 : 1000 dilution in TBS-T, 5% powdered milk at room temperature. Wash the filters three times in TBS-T for 10 min. Incubate the filters 30 min in the following solution: 10 ml of 10 mM Tris, pH 7.4, 200 μl orthodianizidine, 4 μl H$_2$O$_2$ 30%.

Remove an agar plug at the position of each positive signal and incubate it in 10 mM Tris, pH 7.5, 10 mM MgSO$_4$.

Replate the phages at a lower density (use serial dilutions, for example 10^3, 10^4, 10^5) and rescreen until all plaques on the plate produce a positive signal.

Preparation of E. coli lysates

The most common method for examining translation products derived from λgt11 recombinants consists of lysogenizing positive phages in *E. coli* Y1089 (Glover, 1985). After induction of the lytic cycle, IPTG is added, and the proteins of the lysates are examined on SDS-polyacrylamide gel and by Western blot analysis. If difficulties are experienced with this method, the following procedure is recommended: 5×10^3 p.f.u. are plated on a lawn of *E. coli* Y1090; one 90-mm diameter plate is prepared for each lysate. After 4 h incubation at 42°C, 1 ml of 10 mM IPTG is added to the plates and the plates are incubated for an additional 5 h at 37°C. Lysates are recovered with 0.5 ml 25% β-mercaptoethanol/10% SDS/6 M urea/300 mM Tris, pH 6.8. Aliquots (25 μl) are subjected to SDS-polyacrylamide gel and Western blot analysis in order to identify the fusion protein.

Comments

The antibody solution, when kept at –80°C between successive uses, can be reused up to 15 times.

To avoid false positives it is better, especially for the first screening, to screen in duplicate and to pick only the positives that appear on the two filters.

Another technique for detecting the bound primary antibody consists in incubating the filters after probing with ^{125}I-labelled protein A, with the horseradish peroxidase-conjugated second antibody. In this case, only the plaques giving positive signals by the two systems are further analyzed. This usually ensures that false positives caused by nonspecific binding of ^{125}I protein A to the nitrocellulose filters are avoided.

The bound primary antibody can also be detected with alkaline phosphatase-conjugated second antibody (Protoblot immuno-screening system, Promega Biotec, Madison, USA) or with a biotinylated secondary antibody followed with avidin-labelled horseradish peroxidase. Several reagents developed by Amersham Pharmacia Biotech are also recommended (ECL™ Western blotting).

5.1.4.2. Immunochemical detection of proteins related to the human c-myc exon 1 (Gazin et al., 1986; C. Gazin, personal communication)

Five 20–30 residue-long peptides selected from the sequence derived from the human c-*myc* exon 1 were synthesized and antisera were prepared against them by immunizing three rabbits with each of the nonconjugated peptides (Chapter 2).

Hela cells collected and resuspended as described by Green et al. (1983) were homogenized by sonication and centrifuged during 30 min at 40,000 rpm in a Beckman 50 Ti rotor. Cellular extracts corresponding to 2×10^6 cells were loaded on 5 mm wells of SDS-PAGE (12.5%) as described by Laemmli (1970). The samples were subjected to electrophoresis in an electric field of 1400 V (gel dimension $180 \times 170 \times 2$ mm).

Transfer onto nitrocellulose sheet and immunodetection

After migration, the proteins were transferred onto nitrocellulose paper (Schleicher & Schüll, BA 83, 0.45 μm) as described by Burnette (1981) except that the precooled buffer (180 mM glycine – 30 mM Tris-0.2% SDS) contained 20% ethanol. Transfer was carried out for 3 h in an electric field of 30 V.

After the transfer, the membrane was placed in a plastic sealable bag and incubated twice with 50 ml PBS containing 3% BSA and 20% ethanol for 3 h at 37°C with gentle shaking.

The blot was then incubated successively with antipeptide antiserum diluted 1 : 300 in PBS-3% BSA-1% sheep serum overnight at 4°C and with ^{125}I protein A (Amersham IM 144) 0.7 μCi/ml in PBS-3% BSA, EDTA 0.5 mM for 2 h at room temperature. After each step, the blot was washed three times for 30 min with PBS-0.1% Triton.

Finally, the blot was air-dried and exposed at −70°C to Kodak XAR5 film and intensifying screen. For some experiments, immunoblots were freed of bound immunoglobulins by means of 3 M guanidine thiocyanate (twice for 1 h) and used again for incubation with another antiserum.

Affinity chromatography

In order to confirm the specificity of the reaction between a polypeptide and antipeptide antibodies the following procedure described by Gazin et al. (1986) can be used. This method uses two different peptides coupled to a solid-phase and the two corresponding antisera.

Each peptide was coupled to activated CH-Sepharose 4B (Pharmacia), or to polylysine agarose (Sigma) preactivated with 0.5% glutaraldehyde (Sigma, electron microscopy grade) for 45 min at 4°C in PBS. After extensive washing (with 500 bed volumes of demineralized water) for 10 min at 4°C, 2 mg of each peptide were added to 1 ml of wet gel. The polylysine agarose support was found to have lower nonspecific adsorption than the Sepharose support.

200 μl of each antipeptide antiserum were diluted in PBS-T - 3% BSA and incubated with 1.5 ml of the conjugated peptide for 18 h at 4°C with rotation. Residual antibody activity that did not bind to the peptide was characterized by ELISA and immunoblotting. In order to analyze the activity of the antibodies that bound to the peptide the same experiment was repeated with 3 ml of antiserum. A small column of peptide conjugate with adsorbed antibodies was washed with 50 bed volumes of cold PBS and 10 volumes of PBS containing 1 M NaCl. The column was re-equilibrated with PBS and then incubated in a batch-wise manner for 3 h at room temperature with three bed volumes of PBS containing 50 μg/ml of the homologous peptide, in order to release the antibodies. The eluant

was then extensively dialyzed against PBS at 4°C before use in immunodetection.

By repeating the experiment with two peptides corresponding to two different regions of the protein, the specificity of detection of any polypeptide is practically guaranteed.

5.1.4.3. Use of antipeptide antibodies for the immunodetection of plant viral nonstructural proteins (C. Stussi-Garaud, personal communication)

Immunodetection of viral nonstructural proteins is generally difficult to achieve because these proteins are synthesized in minute amounts in infected cells or during a short period of time. In the case of viruses for which the viral genome sequence is known, the expected protein sequences can be deduced from the genome sequence and antibodies can be raised against peptides corresponding to well chosen regions of these proteins (see Chapter 1). Peptides of more than 15 aminoacids can be injected to rabbits either uncoupled or conjugated to carrier proteins (see Chapter 2). In many cases, good antibody levels are obtained after injections with the unconjugated peptides. When antisera are raised against conjugated peptides, they contain antibodies against the carrier protein and residues modified by the coupling agent, and therefore it may be necessary to purify specific antipeptide antibodies by affinity chromatography (see Chapter 3).

Antipeptide antibodies showing a strong reactivity with the homologous peptide in ELISA are not always able to recognize the cognate full length viral protein due to modifications of epitope accessibility in peptide compared to the corresponding sequence in the native or denatured full length protein. The best way to verify is to test the antisera with the viral protein obtained by *in vitro* translation of the viral messenger RNA (when available) in the presence of radioactive precursors. Immunodetection of *in vitro* translated radioactive viral protein can be performed by Western immunoblotting followed by autoradiography of the membrane to prove comigration of radioactive and immunolabelled viral protein bands.

Procedure

In vitro translation: For example, radioactive proteins are synthesized in the presence of [^{35}S] methionine in a wheat germ translation system. The radioactive proteins are partially purified (Godefroy-Colburn et al., 1985), or immunoprecipitated (Demangeat et al., 1990) and loaded on a SDS-PAGE (Laemmli, 1970) containing 6–12% polyacrylamide, depending on the size of the polypeptides.

Western immunoblotting: After electrophoretic migration, the proteins are transferred onto a membrane (nitrocellulose or Immobilon) essentially as described by Towbin et al. (1979). Transfer is for 2 h in electrophoresis buffer used for SDS-PAGE, except that SDS is generally omitted and that 20% ethanol is added when transfer is done on nitrocellulose membrane. In the case of high molecular weight proteins (>100 kD), transfer is in some cases significantly improved by placing an 'empty' 6% polyacrylamide gel (containing SDS and electrophoresis Tris-glycine buffer) on the cathode side of the gel that contains the samples. This method increases the local SDS concentration to favour the migration of the proteins from the gel to the membrane while preventing their release in the transfer buffer. The final efficiency of transfer is between 85 and 100% depending on the size of the proteins.

After transfer, the membrane is rinsed with PBS and saturated by a 5 min incubation at room temperature with 5% powdered fat-free milk in PBS containing 1% Tween 20. Antisera are then added at the required dilution (to be optimized from the ELISA experiments performed to screen the antipeptide antisera) in PBS containing 1% Tween 20. Secondary antibodies coupled to enzymes (e.g. peroxidase or alkaline phosphatase) are finally added at the dilution indicated by the manufacturer (but can often be used at higher dilutions). The immunoreactions are revealed by adding the appropriate substrate (Harlow and Lane, 1989; Stott 1989, 1994; Vidard, 1998).

After selection of antisera capable of recognizing the translation products of viral mRNA, the antisera can be used to probe these proteins in infected cells. This can be achieved in total crude extracts of plants by disrupting cells directly into the denaturing buffer used for SDS-PAGE. In order to increase the viral to cellular protein ratio or to localize the proteins in a given cell compartment, it may be necessary to prepare subcellular fractions by differential centrifugation of extracts obtained upon disruption of cells in a buffer preserving the subcellular elements. The protein content of the fractions are then analyzed by Western immunoblotting as described above. The antisera can also be used to further immunolocalize the viral proteins *in situ* (see below).

In these experiments, it is important to check that the antipeptide antisera do not recognize any protein in a total translation extract prepared in the absence of the viral mRNA or in healthy plant extracts, and that the pre-immune sera do not react with viral proteins. Antipeptide antisera may cross react with cellular proteins because the peptides contain epitopes made of short sequences which are also present in some cellular proteins. In this case, cross-reactions are in fact specific reactions. The primary and secondary antibodies may also bind nonspecifically to cellular proteins giving rise to a high background labelling. Blocking reagents such as gelatin, BSA, milk or various blocking reagents proposed by different manufacturers can be added in the incubation media in order to decrease this nonspecific signal

These methods are widely used in a variety of applications. Examples of studies performed with plant viruses are given below to illustrate the various techniques described above. The first experiments were done on AMV by Berna et al. (1986). This multipartite RNA virus codes for three nonstructural proteins and the coat protein. P1 and P2 are part of the replication complex, and P3 is the movement protein required for cell-to-cell movement together with the coat protein. Using antibodies raised against peptides corresponding to the 15–30 C- terminal amino acids of P1, P2 and P3, the proteins were detected in an *in vitro* translation system, and in subcellular fractions of infected tobacco leaves. The P3 protein was further localized in cell wall fractions of infected plants (Godefroy-Colburn et al., 1986) and *in situ* by immuno-electron microscopy near plasmodesmata connecting adjacent cells (Stussi-Garaud et al., 1987). The tobacco mosaic virus (TMV) and cauliflower mosaic virus (CaMV) movement proteins were detected by similar techniques in an *in vitro* translation system and in subcellular fractions of infected plants (Albrecht et al., 1988; Moser et al., 1988). Other work was done on grapevine fanleaf virus (GFLV), a nepovirus from the *Comoviridae* family. The multipartite positive-strand RNA genome of this virus contains a 24 aminoacid protein (VPg) covalently-linked to the 5′ RNA end. Chemical synthesis of VPg was achieved and the peptide was used to raise antibodies. These antibodies allowed detection of viral VPg-linked proteins produced during the processing of newly synthesized viral polyproteins and of the viral RNAs themselves in total RNA extracts from infected protoplasts or from plants after Northern blotting (Margis et al., 1993). These antipeptide antibodies have been used to visualize by immunofluorescence the viral replication complex of GFLV in tobacco BY2-cell suspensions infected with synthetic RNA transcripts corresponding to viral RNAs (Gaire et al., 1999).

Tomato black-ring virus is another nepovirus for which several antipeptide antibodies were raised against the C-terminal sequence of the polyproteins encoded by genomic RNAs and against internal sequences corresponding to the expected C-terminal regions of the processed proteins. These antibodies allowed studies of polyprotein processing during *in vitro* translation and their detection in subcellular fractions of infected plants (Demangeat et al., 1991, 1992).

5.1.5. General comments

Since the first studies of Walter et al. (1980) and Sutcliffe et al. (1980) demonstrating the usefulness of antipeptide antibodies for identifying DNA products, this approach has been widely used in a variety of studies in molecular and developmental biology, immunology, neurobiology and virology. Both conventional poly-clonal and monoclonal antipeptide antibodies have been used for identifying gene products and for recognizing the cells in which these proteins are expressed. These studies helped to clarify the function and also shed light on the post-translational processing of proteins. Considerable information has also been obtained regarding oncogene and proto-oncogene products, MHC gene products and hormone receptors.

A survey of the literature indicates that one of the most successful strategies for obtaining suitable reagents consists of raising antisera against the C- or N-terminal regions of the protein. Peptides of a length of 6–20 amino acid residues are mostly used and usually are conjugated to a carrier for immunization purposes (Tanaka et al., 1985; Walter, 1986). Somewhat longer peptides are synthesized when internal regions of the putative protein are used (Gazin et al., 1986; Neurath et al., 1985a; Niman, 1984; Paucha et al., 1984; Tanaka et al., 1985).

Antipeptide monoclonal antibodies have been used only rarely (Bellet et al., 1984; Le Guern et al., 1987). It seems that the high specificity of monoclonal antibodies for a particular epitope conformation tends to make them less suitable reagents for a type of application which requires extensive antigenic cross-reactivity. Also, the use of monoclonal antibodies in immunoprecipitation and immunoblotting experiments leads to more frequent nonspecific reactions.

Although there is a tendency not to report negative results, there is evidence that not every peptide selected on the basis of the usual prediction algorithms necessarily induces antibodies able to cross-react with the corresponding protein. It is sound policy, therefore, to raise antibodies against several synthetic peptides corresponding to both terminal and internal regions of a protein. In addition to increasing the likelihood of obtaining suitable reagents, this will make it possible to use double antibody sandwich assays which greatly decreases the possibility of confusion due to nonspecific reactions (Walter, 1986).

5.2. Use of antipeptide antibodies in immunohistochemistry and immunocytochemistry

5.2.1. General considerations

The potential of antipeptide antibody probes to identify and localize intracellular antigens has been used in a variety of immunohistochemical methods. Over the last two decades there has been an increasing number of publications describing new staining protocols, and numerous antibody reagents specific for cellular, microbial and other antigens are commercially available. Detailed technical protocols and recommendations can be found in recent reviews (e.g. see Brandtzaeg, 1998; Brandtzaeg et al., 1997; Cochet, 1998; Gonda, 1994; Kumar, 1994; Liddell and Weeks, 1995; Mayer and Walker, 1987).

Different methods of specimen preparation used in light fluorescence and electron microscopy have been described as well as various direct, indirect, double or triple labelling strategies. Immunofluorescence and immunoenzyme histochemistry is widely used, both in biological research and in diagnostic histopathology and microbiology. Although immunohistochemistry methods are simple, the results depends on several variables. Some of the pitfalls that can be encountered and can be avoided by using positive and negative controls are described in the reviews listed above. Antipeptide antibodies were used for example to localize the histone H3.3 variant in germ line chromatin of *Drosophila* males (Akhmanova

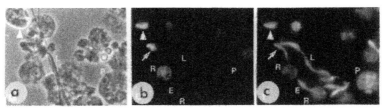

Figure 5.1. Localization of highly acetylated histone H4 in cytological preparation from rat testis using an antiserum raised against peptide AGGKGGKG-
GKGGK acetylated at each of the four lysine positions which cross-react with
the N-terminal sequences of rat H4 (SGRGKGGKGLGKGGAK). The antiserum
to the acetylated peptide recognizes elongating spermatids (arrowhead), only a
part of the earliest step of elongated (condensing) spermatids (arrow) and a few
of three round spermatids. (a) phase contrast; (b) immunofluorescence measured
using rhodamine conjugated second antibody; and (c) fluorescence measured with
DNA-specific dye DAP (from Meistrich et al., 1992).

et al., 1997) and to identify highly acetylated histone H4 during
spermiogenesis (Meistrich et al., 1992; Figure 5.1).

Antipeptide antibodies were also used to study the expression of
various proteins during development, for example, in mammalian
systems, in plants and yeast (e.g. Delorme et al., 1997; Dussossoy
et al., 1996; Furuta et al., 1997; Tao et al., 1998), or to identify the
localization of a protein in distinct cell compartments (e.g. Berna et
al., 1991; Hagg et al., 1997; Oakley et al., 1997). Specific examples
are described below.

5.2.2. Examples of procedures

The following procedures were used to immunolocalize viral proteins *in situ* using antipeptide antibodies. This is generally achieved
on infected leaves harvested at different times post infection: leaves
were cut in 1–2 mm strips which are fixed in standard fixative
reagents for microscopy. These reagents are glutaraldehyde (4%), or
glutaraldehyde (0.1–2%) in the presence of formaldehyde (1–4%),
or formaldehyde alone (4%), in 100 mM phosphate buffer (for 4 h

to 1 night at 4°C), followed in some cases by a 1.5 h post-fixation at 4°C with an aqueous 0.1% osmium tetroxide solution. After dehydration in a graded series of ethanol concentrations (30, 50, 70 and 100%), the leaf strips are embedded either in London LR White resin or in Epon resin. Polymerization is allowed to occur for 60 h at 60°C. The first resin is often more appropriate for immunogold labelling because it is more hydrophilic. In Epon resin, the immunogold labelling is often less intense but tissue preservation and visualization is much better. Milder fixations with formaldehyde, acetic acid and ethanol (FAE) followed by embedding in paraffin can also be used for optical microscopy. The fixed and embedded tissues are then used for immunolocalization of viral antigens at the optical or electron microscopic level.

For immuno-optical microscopy, semi-thin sections (0.5–1 μm) are deposited on multiwell glass slides and left to dry for 1 night at 40°C. Immunoreactions are performed by adding 20 μl drops of each reagent on the sections. The first incubation is done with antipeptide sera at optimized dilutions for 4 h at 4°C in PBS containing 0.05% Tween 20 and blocking reagents. After four washes (10 min each) with this buffer, secondary antibodies coupled either to enzymes (peroxidase or alkaline phosphatase) or to fluorochromes (FITC or rhodamine) are added for 2 h. After two washes with the buffer, and two washes with doubled distilled water, the sections are treated with the enzyme substrate if necessary and observed by transmitted light microscopy. When fluorochrome-coupled conjugates are used, observations are done by epifluorescent microscopy with the appropriate filters. Images are memorized either by standard microphotography or by capture with a video or numerical camera connected to a computer equipped with the appropriate softwares.

For immunoelectron microscopy, ultrathin sections (90 nm) are collected on slotted nickel grids coated with a formvar membrane. Immunoreactions are performed as above except that grids are floated on 20 μl drops of each reagent. The secondary antibody solution is in most cases a colloidal gold-coupled antibody solution (5–20 nm gold grains). The grids are finally contrasted with a 4% aqueous uranyl acetate solution. They are observed under an electron microscope at 75 kV.

As control for specificity, immunolabelling experiments should be performed with an antiserum preadsorbed with the purified peptide in order to inhibit the viral protein labelling. The concentration of the purified peptide to be used must be optimized, depending on the antisera dilution, in order to saturate all the binding sites of the IgGs. It should be noted that for immunomicroscopy, specificity controls must be performed on serial sections showing the same cellular or viral structures.

As stated by Brandtzaeg (1998) 'the human mind seems to be the only limitation for use of these powerful probing methods, which can be applied to tissue and cellular localization of antigens ranging from amino acids and proteins to infectious agents and subsets of leucocytes'. This statement is certainly true if—as pointed out by Brandtzaeg—the results are interpreted with great caution and if the adequate controls, including particular attention to the quality of antipeptide antibody probes, are introduced in the successive steps of the experiment.

CHAPTER 6

The use of peptides for diagnosing viral infections

M. H. V. VAN REGENMORTEL

6.1. Mimicry of viral epitopes with synthetic peptides

In spite of the availability of sensitive nucleic acid-based diagnostic methods, most laboratory diagnostic tests for virus diseases are still based on the detection of pathogen-specific antibodies in the serum of diseased individuals. Following exposure to a viral infection, antibodies of the IgM class specific for a variety of viral antigens appear in the serum within a few days, soon followed by antibodies of the IgG class. These antibodies are useful diagnostic reagents and can be detected in solid-phase immunoassays by their ability to react with intact virus particles, dissociated viral structural subunits or nonstructural virus-coded proteins. Since the use of viral antigenic probes entails handling infectious material at some stage of the procedure (e.g. infected cell cultures, serum samples, stools etc.), there has been an increasing tendency to replace such probes with synthetic peptides to avoid this potential hazard. The use of synthetic peptides for the diagnosis of viral diseases has also been stimulated by the development of improved methods of solid-phase peptide synthesis and by our ability to synthesize linear peptides that mimic the three-dimensional conformational features of viral epitopes. In addition to synthetic peptides, viral proteins produced by recombinant DNA technology are also commonly used as diagnostic probes. Both types of probes have their advantages and disadvantages. Recombinant antigens usually present several different epitopes that may or may not retain the native structure present

237

in the viral protein. To avoid false positive results due to contamination with cross-reacting cellular proteins, a high level of purity of recombinant products is usually necessary which may not be easy to achieve without concomitant alteration of the viral antigen. The preparation of synthetic peptides with an adequate level of purity is usually easier to achieve.

Both continuous epitopes and continuous paratopes are easily obtained by peptide synthesis. Continuous epitopes correspond to short peptide fragments of the viral protein that can bind to antibodies raised against the intact protein, while continuous paratopes correspond to individual CDR sequences that bind antigen with the same specificity as the intact antibody, albeit with lower affinity (Kang et al., 1988; Welling et al., 1991; Williams et al., 1991). In a recent study of the HyHEL-5 antilysozyme antibody, it was found that linear peptides corresponding to each of the six CDRs of the antibody were able to bind lysozyme (Laune et al., 1997). When CDR peptide analogs containing alanine substitutions were tested for their ability to bind lysozyme, most residues important for binding were residues known by X-ray crystallography studies to be located at the epitope-paratope interface. A possible application of the binding capacity of continuous paratopes in viral immunology has been described by Sallberg et al. (1994). These authors constructed a bispecific peptide by linking the CDR-H3 sequence of an antibody directed to the V3 loop of human immunodeficiency virus (HIV-1) to a conserved epitope (residues 39–50) of the VP1 protein of enteroviruses (Fig. 6.1). This chimeric peptide which recognized the HIV-1 V3 loop as well as antibodies specific for the VP1 epitope of enteroviruses was able to specifically redirect the binding reactivity of monoclonal antibodies and human polyclonal antibodies specific for enteroviral VP1 and to make them recognize HIV-1. Such findings illustrate the usefulness of the concepts of continuous paratopes and epitopes for describing the binding activity of synthetic peptides. Although it is not possible to draw a sharp distinction between continuous and discontinuous epitopes (see Chapter 1), the epithet 'continuous' is useful for describing

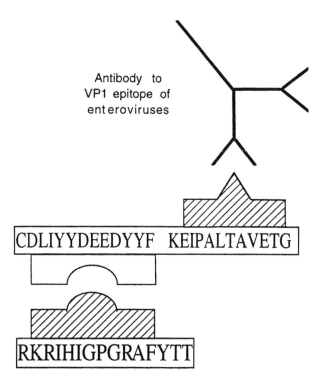

Antibody to
VP1 epitope of
enteroviruses

CDLIYYDEEDYYF KEIPALTAVETG

RKRIHIGPGRAFYTT

V3 domain of HIV-1

Fig. 1. Chimeric peptide comprising both a continuous paratope (CDLIYY-
DEEDYYF) corresponding of an antibody directed to the V3 loop of HIV-1,
and an epitope (KEIPALTAVETG) of the VP1 of enteroviruses (residues 39–50).
The continuous paratope binds to the epitope present on the V3 loop and
the VP1 epitope binds to enterovirus antibodies (from Sallberg et al., 1994).

short peptide fragments of 6–10 residues that are capable of binding
specifically in an immunoassay.

   The binding activity of continuous epitopes and paratopes can
sometimes be enhanced by constraining their conformation by cyclization (Haack et al., 1997; Joisson et al., 1993; Vuilleumier
and Mutter, 1992; Williams et al., 1991). For instance, Levi et al.
(1993a) showed that cyclization of the peptide corresponding to

the CDR-H3 of an antibody directed to the V3 region of HIV-1 increased its binding activity and rendered the peptide capable of inhibiting HIV-1 replication.

Continuous epitopes of viral proteins are commonly identified by analyzing the antibody-binding capacity of sets of overlapping synthetic peptides encompassing the entire sequence of the protein (see Section 1.4.3, Chapter 1). Alternatively, it is possible to test the antibody-binding capacity of sets of randomly synthesized peptides. Chemical synthesis or phage display techniques make relatively easy to obtain randomly generated combinatorial peptide libraries containing complete sets of hexapeptides (6.4×10^7) or octapeptides (2.5×10^{10}) (Table 6.1). Such molecular libraries often contain peptides that bind to the antiviral antibodies but show little or no sequence similarity with any part of the viral proteins (Appel et al., 1996; Hirabayashi et al., 1996; Lenstra et al., 1992; Mattioli et al., 1995; Zwick et al., 1998). Such epitopes are called mimotopes and are thought to mimic discontinuous epitopes of the viral antigen, although it cannot be excluded that they mimic continuous epitopes without showing much sequence similarity with them. In order to qualify as a mimotope, the peptide should not only bind to the viral antibody but should also be able to elicit antibodies that react with the original antigen it is supposed to mimic (see Section 1.3, Chapter 1). Only in this case can it be said that the antigenically active peptide is a true mimotope (Hirabayashi et al., 1996).

Phage-displayed random peptide libraries comprising more than 10^7 sequences have been used to identify mimotopes of different epitopes of human hepatitis B virus envelope protein (Folgori et al., 1994; Meola et al., 1995), hepatitis C virus (Pereboeva et al., 1998) and measles virus (Steward et al., 1995). Immunological screening of the phage library can be done by an antigen- independent procedure by means of human sera from individuals immunized with the viral antigen. Some of the mimotopes of HBsAg obtained in this way had no sequence similarity with the viral antigen although they were able to mimic it antigenically and immunogenically (Delmastro et al., 1997). Other mimotopes showed some sequence similarity

TABLE 6.1

Number of peptides in random peptide libraries

Dipeptides	$20^2 = 400$
Tripeptides	$20^3 = 8,000$
Tetrapeptides	$20^4 = 160,000$
Pentapeptides	$20^5 = 3.2 \ 10^6$
Hexapeptides	$20^6 = 6.4 \ 10^7$
Heptapeptides	$20^7 = 1.28 \ 10^9$
Octapeptides	$20^8 = 2.56 \ 10^{10}$
Nonapeptides	$20^9 = 5.12 \ 10^{11}$
Decapeptides	$20^{10} = 1.10^{13}$

with different parts of the viral antigens and could thus be viewed as mimicking continuous epitopes (Table 6.2) (Chen et al., 1996; Grihalde et al., 1995).

Although the term mimotope was originally defined as an anti-genically active peptide having no sequence similarity with the epitope it mimics (Geysen et al., 1986), current usage gives the term a broader meaning. Since the antigenic activity of a continuous epitope can be mimicked by means of a mimotope peptide showing little sequence similarity with it, the absence of sequence similarity does not necessarily indicate that the mimotope mimics a discon-tinuous epitope of the antigen. Some indication about the possible identity of the mimicked epitope can be obtained by calculating the frequency of finding similar sequences in two random sequences (Chen et al., 1996). However, the evidence is only statistical and requires the presence of conserved stretches of residues in the indi-vidual sequence fragments constituting the putative discontinuous epitope. The value of the mimotope concept is not diminished be-cause of the vagueness of its structural definition since the term is used mainly to describe the immunological reactivity of peptides rather than their structure. It is the ability of mimotopes to mimic the

TABLE 6.2

Sequences of mimotopes that mimic epitopes of hepatitis B (HBsAg) and hepatitis C viruses identified using phage peptide libraries (Delmastro et al., 1997).

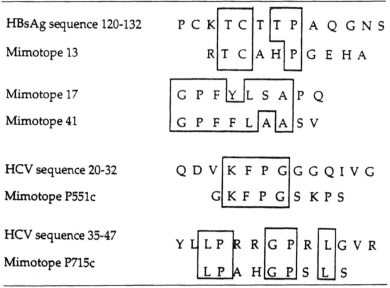

Boxes outline sequence similarity among mimotopes and original antigens. Mimotopes 17 and 41 have no sequence similarity with HBsAg but are able to mimic it antigenically and immunogenically.

antigenic and immunogenic activity of epitopes (Delmastro et al., 1997) which is the ultimate justification for retaining the concept.

Infection of humans with HIV-1 has been found to generate autoantibodies reactive with autologous Fab fragments (Süsal et al., 1996) and with T-cell receptor α- and β-epitopes (Lake et al., 1994; Marchalonis et al., 1995, 1997).

6.2. Synthetic peptides used for viral diagnosis

The use of synthetic peptides corresponding to a single epitope increases the specificity of a diagnostic immunoassay in the same way as monoclonal antibodies do compared to polyclonal antiserum. This is an important advantage of peptide-based immunoassays since it allows infections caused by closely related virus strains or subtypes to be distinguished (Gnann et al., 1987a; Modrow and Wolf, 1990).

Synthetic peptides are most commonly used as probes for detecting viral antibodies produced during infection. (Leinikki et al., 1993; Modrow and Wolf, 1990). However, they also may be used to raise antipeptide antibodies for detecting viral antigens in biological materials such as nasopharyngeal swabs and aspirates, or in blood, saliva, urine, stool specimens and cell cultures (Brahm et al., 1988; Dillner et al., 1989; Hovi and Roivainen, 1993; Vihinen-Ranta et al., 1996). When peptides are used to immunize animals, they can be administered as free peptides if they are at least 15 residues long. Alternatively, they can be administered as peptide-carrier conjugates, as peptide-liposomes conjugates or as branched peptides on a core of lysine residues (see Chapter 2).

A diagnostic assay can be made specific for individual viral strains or serotypes by selecting peptides that correspond to serotype-specific epitopes. Alternatively when the peptides correspond to epitopes that are conserved in different virus species or genera, a single diagnostic probe can be used to detect a wide variety of viruses. For instance, a synthetic peptide corresponding to residues 37–53 of the VP1 protein of poliovirus was found to detect antibodies against many additional enteroviruses (Cello et al., 1993; Roivainen et al., 1991). Antibodies raised against this conserved region of VP1 were also able to detect polio- echo- and coxsackieviruses in cell cultures (Hovi and Roivainen, 1993).

The first peptide-based immunoassays used for demonstrating the presence of viral antibody in sera during the course of infection were developed for Hepatitis B virus (Bhatnager et al., 1982; Lerner et al., 1981). Peptides derived from the pre-S1 and pre-S2 sequences of the hepatitis B virus surface particles, were used to assess the functional importance of antibodies directed against these sequences (Neurath and Kent, 1985; Neurath and Thanavala, 1990).

Subsequently, many additional viral infections of humans and animals have become amenable to diagnosis using synthetic peptides as probes (for reviews, see Leinikki et al., 1993; Modrow and Wolf, 1990).

Synthetic peptides have been used as probes in ELISA for the diagnosis of many viral infections including those caused by dengue (Aaskov et al., 1989), cytomegalovirus, enteroviruses (Cello et al., 1993), Epstein-Barr virus (Becker et al., 1989), hepatitis A, B, C and F viruses (Mattioli et al., 1995; Rosa et al., 1995), herpes simplex virus (Levi et al., 1993b), human immunodeficiency virus (Brown et al., 1997; De Koster et al., 1995; Gnann et al., 1987a, b), human papilloma virus (Sharma et al., 1996), human parvovirus B19, human T-cell leukemia virus, Japanese encephalitis virus (Huang et al., 1996) and respiratory syncytial virus (Langedijk et al., 1996).

Antipeptide antibodies have also been used to detect the presence of viruses in infected plant tissue (Berna et al., 1986; Wellink et al., 1987; Ziegler et al., 1985), and for studying the antigenic properties of plant viruses (Jaegle et al., 1988; Joisson et al., 1993). By raising antibodies to peptides corresponding to conserved regions of the coat protein of potyviruses, diagnostic reagents were produced that could detect the presence of many different potyviruses in infected plants (Joisson et al., 1992).

6.3. Peptide-based immunoassays

The most commonly used diagnostic assay based on synthetic peptides is the enzyme-linked immunosorbent assay (ELISA). Typically, a peptide is adsorbed directly to the plastic of microtitre plates but a variety of other approaches have been used to improve the coating efficiency of peptides on ELISA plates (see Table 4.3, Chapter 4). Antibodies raised against peptides corresponding to the N-terminal, variable region of a potyvirus coat protein, are useful for detecting particular serotypes or strains of a potyvirus

(Crescenzi et al., 1997). Since peptides tend to have different conformations when they are free in solution, conjugated to carriers by various coupling agents or adsorbed to the solid phase, the antigenic activity of synthetic peptides tends to vary considerably in different immunoassay formats. Since the particular peptide conformation that antibodies produced during viral infection will preferentially recognize cannot be predicted prospective diagnostic peptides need to be tested in a variety of assay formats. Peptides can be used as resin-bound peptides (Modrow et al., 1989), peptide carrier conjugates (Richalet-Sécordel and Van Regenmortel, 1991) or MAPs (Marsden et al., 1992).

By combining two to four peptides in a single ELISA, virus-specific antibodies can usually be detected in about 90–95% of the serum samples from infected individuals. In particularly favourable cases, antibodies can be detected in 100% of the sera using only one or two peptides. In the case of Japanese encephalitis virus, two peptides from the core protein detected antibodies in 100% of human sera (Huang et al., 1996). One NS4 peptide of hepatitis C virus detected antibodies in 90% of human sera (Khudyakov et al., 1995) whereas one E2 peptide of human papilloma virus type 16 detected antibodies in 87% of patients with cervical carcinoma (Sharma et al., 1996). Two peptides of hepatitis E virus detected antibodies in 84% of human sera (Coursaget et al., 1994) whereas four peptides of hepatitis δ-antigen detected antibodies in 93% of human sera (Poisson et al., 1993). The best results are usually obtained when one or more peptides are used in combination with an intact recombinant viral protein. Combining several peptides leads to an additive effect since the peptides corresponding to immunodominant epitopes act as efficient antibody detectors while the recombinant antigen detects minor antibody populations.

The optimal size and sequence of a peptide intended for diagnosis can be established using biosensors based on surface plasmon resonance (Richalet-Sécordel et al., 1996). Peptides are immobilized by their N-terminus on the carboxymethylated dextran layer present on the sensor chip, or alternatively via a cysteine residue using thiol chemistry (Richalet-Sécordel et al., 1994, 1994a; Van Cott et al., 1992). The peptides can also be used as inhibitors of the reaction between a viral antigen and specific antibodies. Antibody binding to peptide analogs can be analyzed quantitatively with great precision in the absence of nonspecific background binding and this allows the design of peptides with optimal binding activity. This approach has been used, for instance, for optimizing peptide probes used in HIV diagnosis. Various linear epitopes of the gp120 and gp41 proteins of HIV were compared in various formats, as immobilized peptides, as free inhibitor peptides or as conjugated peptides. Since there was a good correlation between biosensor measurements of peptide activity and the corresponding ELISA titres of the same peptide preparations, the biosensor data were useful for selecting the best peptides to be used in diagnostic solid-phase immunoassay (Richalet-Sécordel et al., 1994, 1994b).

Various strategies have been used to enhance the level of conformational similarity between peptides and the intact viral protein or virion. These include cyclization of the peptide, introduction of amino acid substitutions such as α-aminoisobutyric acid to increase helix formation and conjugation to protein carriers or liposomes to create a microenvironment reminiscent of the one experienced by the peptide when it is part of the native viral antigen (Gegg and Etzler, 1993; Gomez et al., 1998; Marsden et al., 1992).

Antisera to peptides corresponding to viral epitopes are also useful for detecting viral antigen in ultrathin sections of infected tissue using immunofluorescence and other histochemical techniques (Modrow and Wolf, 1990).

CHAPTER 7

Peptides in diagnosis of autoimmune diseases

S. MULLER

7.1. Introduction

The term autoimmune disease refers to a variety of illnesses in which immune processes are directed against self tissues. They may be predominantly humoral (i.e. with the production of antibodies also called autoantibodies) or cellular in origin, or a combination of both. Autoantibodies may be the actual pathogenic agent of disease (e.g. antibodies to glomerular basement membrane in the Goodpasture's syndrome), the secondary consequence of tissue damage, with or without additional detrimental effect, or the harmless result of an etiologic agent. Targets recognized by autoantibodies have been found in cell nuclei, cytoplasm, cell membranes, plasma proteins, hormones, enzymes, and also in receptors for physiological ligands. Autoantigens may be proteins, nucleic acids, phospholipids, lipoproteins, sugars, or steroids. Generally, the original immune stimulus that gave rise to the production of autoantibodies is unknown. Precise identification of the epitopes recognized by autoantibodies is one approach to understand the etiological and pathogenic mechanisms that lead to autoimmunity. Furthermore, identification of autoepitopes, in particular at the level of small protein fragments, has largely contributed to the recent development of tests allowing the detection and quantification of certain autoantibodies. A new generation of tests (such as ELISA) has largely replaced older methods such as precipitation (double diffusion Ouchterlony assays, single radial Mancini immunodiffusion assays) and agglutination tests. Complex antigens, that are often difficult to purify and prepare in large quantities, have been replaced by synthetic peptides and recombinant fragments. It should be noted, however, that as far as is known, none of the companies selling kits for autoimmune disease diagnosis use synthetic peptides as antigens. They use either whole purified or recombinant proteins or long recombinant fragments.

The aim of this chapter is to describe and discuss some basic techniques using synthetic peptides which have been developed to characterize autoimmune diseases. Several detailed reviews have appeared on this topic in recent years (e.g. Elkon, 1992; Pettersson, 1992; van Venrooij and Maini, 1993), and compilations of epitopes of a large number of autoantibodies have been published (e.g. Galperin et al., 1996; Peter and Shoenfeld, 1996; van Venrooij and Maini, 1994). Rather than repeating what has been written, this chapter will summarize the results obtained with a few model antigens and examine the advantages and limitations of each assay.

7.2. Methods of detection and quantification of autoantibodies with synthetic peptides

7.2.1. Epitope mapping with synthetic peptides

Several approaches have been used to map epitopes of autoantigens with synthetic peptides. One of these has been to test autoimmune sera in ELISA with overlapping peptides covering the entire length of the protein. This strategy has been applied to histones (Stemmer et al., 1994), the 52-kD SSA/Ro protein (Ro52; Ricchiuti et al., 1994a), protein D1 of Sm antigen (SmD1; Barakat et al., 1990; Sabbatini et al., 1993b), proteins A and C of U1 small nuclear ribonucleoprotein (snRNP) antigen (U1A, U1C; Barakat et al., 1991; Halimi et al., 1996) and the human thyroprotein (TSH) receptor (Morris et al., 1994). In some studies, mostly for economical reasons, only a few peptides have been tested. Their selection was based on data obtained by screening representative sera with larger natural or recombinant fragments (Frank et al., 1994; Hirakata et al., 1993; Ohguro et al., 1993; Wahren et al., 1992). Thus, Riemekasten et al. (1998) tested patients' sera with overlapping cellulose-bound peptides (see below), and then selected peptides to be tested in ELISA within the major sites recognized by antibodies. Alternatively, the choice of peptides was made after the identification of functional or particular structural domains thought to be located at the surface of the protein. This approach has been used for example for the 60-kD SSA/Ro protein (Ro60) which contains a zinc finger motif in residues 305–323 (Barakat et al., 1992) and poly(ADP-ribose polymer)ase (PARP) which contains two zinc fingers called F1 and F2 involved in DNA strand break repair (Decker et al., 1998; Muller et al., 1994). Computer algorithms allowing to predict the location of epitopes have also been used (see Section 7.4).

Classical solid-phase immunoassays (ELISA, RIA) have been used for testing patients' sera with synthetic peptides. For example, peptides of 15–30 residues are directly adsorbed to a plastic solid-phase, in general the wells of a microtitre plate (see Chapter 4 for detailed procedures). Some authors (e.g. Elkon, 1992) have advocated the use of peptides conjugated to a carrier protein (BSA, ovalbumin) rather than unconjugated peptides in order to avoid the problem of coating efficiency (which depends on the solubility and charge of each peptide) and because this requires less peptide per assay. When unconjugated peptides are used, their effective binding to the plate has to be checked, for example by using antipeptide antibodies or by incubating with enzyme-conjugated streptavidin when biotinylated peptides are used (see Section 2.10.2). Likewise when peptide conjugates are used as antigen, the yield of effective peptide coupling must be controlled (see Section 2.9). As stressed in Chapter 2, the procedure used for coupling the peptide to carrier is of great importance to avoid alteration of its antigenicity. Chemical conjugation has to be carefully chosen according to the peptide sequence. Unrelated peptides should be utilized as control in each assay. Because patients' sera can contain a diversity of autoantibodies, whose range of specificities is not known with certainty, these control peptides need to be selected with care. In our laboratory, we generally use a panel of different peptides including for instance peptides derived from plant viruses (e.g. tobacco mosaic virus) which are unlikely to be bound by patients' antibodies. When conjugated peptides are used, it is also necessary to check for the absence of reaction with the carrier to which an unrelated peptide has been associated by the same conjugation chemistry. It should be noted that bovine milk or serum, which are often used as blocking reagents in ELISA, can contain self antigens such as DNA and histones (Waga et al., 1987). Patients' sera can also contain circulating self antigens. For example, the presence of nucleosomes and proteinase-3 (the target antigen of cytoplasmic antineutrophil cytoplasmic antibodies, cANCA) in the serum of normal and/or autoimmune patients has been demonstrated. These soluble antigens may affect the detection of certain autoantibodies and may be responsible for some discrepancies in the literature. Finally, antialbumin autoantibodies have been detected in the serum of autoimmune and infected patients (Sansonno et al., 1996).

It has been shown that certain classes of autoantibodies are surprisingly common in the normal population. For example, between 5 and 15% of the normal population appear to have low levels of anti-SSA/Ro antibodies (Gaither et al., 1987). The presence of natural antibodies which generally (but not only) belong to the IgM class and are of low affinity (although they may be of high avidity) has lead investigators to develop sensitive tests to discriminate between those antibodies and others linked to pathological states. In our laboratory, patients' sera are usually diluted 1 : 1000 in routine ELISA tests and only IgG antibodies are tested. In order to establish the cutoff value for positivity of the assay, a large number of sera from different (at least 50) healthy individuals should be tested with all new peptides investigated, and the absence of cross-reaction between each peptide and the second antibody (antihuman Ig conjugated to horseradish peroxidase or alkaline phosphatase) has to be checked with each new batch of anti-Ig enzyme conjugate.

Epitope mapping of a number of self-proteins with patients' sera has been performed by using a complete set of overlapping octamer peptides synthesized on the tip of polyacrylate grafted polyethylene rods arranged in an 8×12 microtitre plate array according to the method introduced by Geysen et al. (1987). The complete sequence of Ro60 protein (Scofield and Harley, 1991), SSB/La protein (Tzioufas et al., 1997), SmD1 and BB' proteins (James and Harley, 1992; James et al., 1994a; Williams et al., 1990), proteins 70 kD, Λ and C of U1snRNP (James and Harley, 1995, 1996; James et al., 1994b) and proteinase-3 (Williams et al., 1994) were assayed in this manner.

Another method for systematically screening epitopes with short overlapping peptides was recently introduced to test autoimmune sera (Halimi et al., 1996). The method called spot synthesis has been introduced by Frank (Frank, 1992; Frank and Döring, 1988). It involves the simultaneous chemical synthesis of large numbers of different peptide sequences under continuous flow conditions by using cellulose paper as solid support. Depending on the conditions used about 50 nmol of each peptide are available for antibody testing. The SPOTscan method is exemplified below by the synthesis of 75 overlapping decapeptides of U1C protein (Fig. 7.1). In this particular example, each peptide differs from the previous one by four residues (two at the N-terminus and two at the C-terminus). The method was validated by using antipeptide rabbit antibodies (as internal positive controls) and sera from autoimmune patients. The results were compared with those obtained in parallel by ELISA with 15 overlapping peptides of 16–30 residues adsorbed to plastic surface and the antigenic maps obtained using the two approaches generally agreed (Halimi et al., 1996). The SPOTscan method was also used by Haaheim et al. (1996) to map epitopes on the SSB/La protein with sera from patients with systemic lupus erythematosus (SLE) and Sjögren's syndrome (SS) and Riemekasten et al. (1998) to study SmD1.

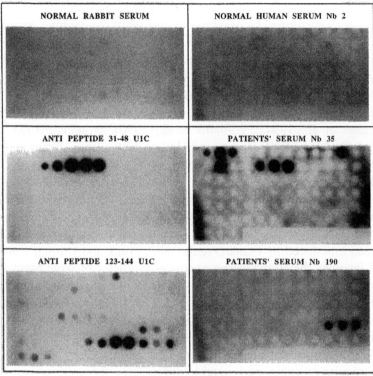

Figure 7.1. Analysis of a series of 75 overlapping decapeptides derived from the whole U1C sequence for binding to antipeptide rabbit antisera and patients' sera. Overlapping peptides were assembled using the spot-synthesis protocol described by Frank (1992). Antibody binding was identified by a standard protocol. The different steps of this assay are as follows: (1) saturation of paper sheet by incubation overnight at room temperature in casein-based blocking buffer (BB; Genosys, Cambridge, England); (2) incubation with rabbit antisera (1/500) or human sera (1/1000) during 90 min at 37°C; and (3) incubation with enzymatic conjugate (2 h at 20°C) followed by the addition of a standard chromogen or a chemiluminescent substrate (ECL, Amersham, or Super Signal CL-HRP, Pierce). Between each step, several washings with Tris-buffered saline pH 8.0 are repeated. Sheets can be reused more than 20 times. To improve multiple reuse of paper-bound peptides, particular attention has to be brought in the choice of system used for identifying reactive peptides (the method must be mild and produce nondestructive reaction) and for regenerating the membrane (adapted from Halimi et al., 1996).

7.2.2. Respective merits and limitations of the different approaches used to delineate epitopes recognized by autoantibodies

The most commonly used methods developed to map epitopes of autoantigens have been to test autoimmune sera with either successively truncated recombinant fragments of the autoantigen in ELISA, Western blot or immunoprecipitation assay, or to use overlapping synthetic peptides in ELISA. Immunoprecipitation has been claimed to be the only test able to reveal discontinuous epitopes in addition to continuous epitopes (Saitta et al., 1994). When comparing results obtained by independent investigators, the most striking observation is that although a number of important technical parameters differ between these studies (type of assay, type of antigen probe, selection of sera) in some cases, e.g. in the mapping of Ro52 and Ro60 epitopes, the position of major antigenic domains is consistent. For example, a dominant antigenic region in the middle part of Ro60 (within residues 155–326) has been identified in five of six studies published so far (Fig. 7.2) and peptides or recombinant fragments encompassing the zinc finger motif of Ro60 (residues 305–323) were found to be recognized by patients' antibodies in two of these studies. In Ro52 protein, a major antigenic region present in residues 136–292 has been identified in all studies reported to date (Fig. 7.2). This region contains a proposed coiled-coil domain and within this a putative leucine zipper motif (residues 211–232).

A number of discrepancies, however, exist between the results reported by different laboratories. In the SmD1 antigen, for example, one of the major epitopes identified by our group in residues 1–20 (Barakat et al., 1990; Dumortier et al., 1999a) using overlapping synthetic peptides in ELISA and also visualized using the SPOTscan method (Riemekasten et al., 1998) was not picked up by Sabbatini et al. (1993b) who used overlapping peptides in ELISA nor by Rokeach et al. (1992) who tested patients' sera with recombinant fragments of this antigen. In the case of the Ro52 protein, we observed that the peptide 191–208 was not recognized by patients'

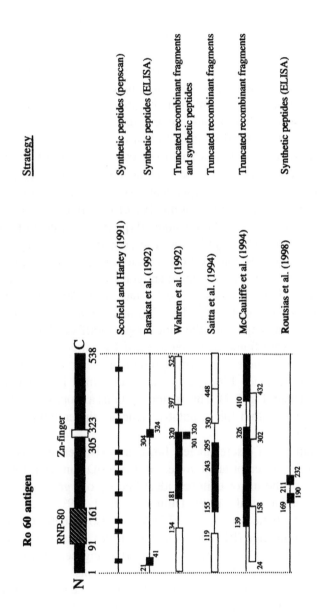

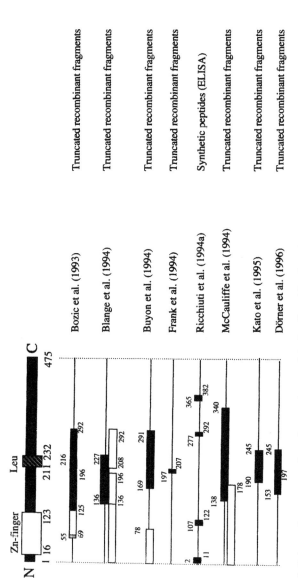

Fig. 7.2. Schematic representation of autoepitopes of the Ro60 and Ro52 antigens (adapted from Wahren-Herlenius et al., 1999). Structural features of the respective proteins are shown and the type of antigenic probe used to map epitopes of Ro antigens is indicated to the right. Solid blocks: major epitope region; open blocks: epitope of minor importance (i.e. recognized less frequently).

antibodies (Ricchiuti and Muller, 1994), whereas the peptide 197–207 was recognized by lupus sera in the study published by Frank et al. (1994) (Fig. 7.2). Such conflicting results may have several causes including the ethnic origin of the patients studied and their level of disease activity at the time of the bleed. The length of the fragment tested represents a critical parameter. Contrary to what is often claimed, the use of a longer peptide does not necessarily lead to a higher level of cross-reactivity. As pointed out by Hodges et al. (1988), short peptides of 4–11 residues can very efficiently mimic linear antigenic determinants present on the surface of native protein. This accords with our observation that antibodies induced against nucleosome particles react better with histone peptides than with intact histone molecules (Muller et al., 1989). In the same context, we also found that a long peptide can be devoid of antigenic activity while a shorter peptide situated within the long sequence (e.g. in our experience peptide 1–5 within fragment 1–39 of histone H2A) can be antigenically active (Muller et al., 1986). Such findings are somewhat disconcerting when one considers that the choice of peptide sequences tested is often the result of empirical decisions in the case of synthetic peptides, or is linked to the presence of restriction enzyme cleavage sites for recombinant antigens. Therefore serendipity affects the experiments. For example, peptide 91–129 of H2A was recognized by H2A antibodies while peptide 93–129 was not (Muller et al., 1986). Peptide 1–13 of Ro52 was strongly recognized by antibodies from patients with primary Sjögren's syndrome (pSS) which show very little reaction with peptide 2–11 of the same protein (Ricchiuti et al., 1994a; Ricchiuti and Muller, 1994).

It should be kept in mind that delineation of protein epitopes is rendered intrinsically difficult due to the fact that whatever its length, when a fragment is used instead of the full-length protein, conformational directives received from distal parts of the region studied are obviously lost. This feature has been discussed by Saitta et al. (1994) who showed that it may be misleading to deduce the location of an epitope simply by comparing the activity of truncated fragments of shorter and shorter length. In such cases, the position of the epitopes should be confirmed by using synthetic peptides covering the region which has been deduced as antigenically active as Wahren et al. (1992) and Frank et al. (1994) have done in the case of Ro60 and Ro52 antigens, respectively.

It is also important to realize that the presence of charged groups at the termini of peptides (recombinant or synthetic) can affect their reactivity when the peptides correspond to inner regions of the protein. In some cases, it can be advantageous to introduce an acetyl group at the N-terminal end and/or a carboxamide group at the C-terminus of the peptide to increase its reactivity with patients' autoantibodies. In our experience, we have observed that peptide 304–324 of Ro60 is much more reactive with lupus and SS sera when it is blocked (Briand et al., 1995). Conversely, depending on the position of the epitopes recognized by autoantibodies, the presence of the fusion partner of recombinant proteins (e.g. β-galactosidase) that blocks the free amino group at the N-terminus of the polypeptide may alter the antigenicity of peptides (Ou et al., 1997; Rokeach et al., 1990). Saitta et al. (1994) have discussed the importance of this possible problem when analysing the activity of recombinant Ro60 fragments containing the first residues of the protein.

As discussed in Chapter 1 and above, epitope mapping is largely affected by the type of strategy used (ELISA, Western blot, precipitation). In some cases, the free peptide used in solution as inhibitor is most active while in others, antibodies react preferentially with immobilized peptides adsorbed to a solid-phase or conjugated to a carrier (Muller et al., 1986; Ricchiuti et al., 1997). The level of conformational mimicry between peptide and protein can be increased by presenting the peptide in a particular way, for example after coupling to a carrier protein (Barakat et al., 1992). The microenvironment at the surface of the protein carrier can indeed induce a suitable conformation in the peptide (see Section 3.3.2.). The multipresentation of a reactive peptide (for example as a MAP, TASP or SOC, see Chapter 3) can also increase the sensitivity of a test (Briand et al., 1992a; Caponi et al., 1995; Petrovas et al.,

1998; Sabbatini et al., 1993b; Yiannaki et al., 1998). It is sometimes observed, however, that assays based on MAPs are slightly
less specific (Briand et al., 1992a; Petrovas et al., 1998).

The 'pepscan' method developed by Geysen and colleagues has
been adopted by a few investigators to characterize autoimmune
sera (see Section 7.2.1). This method is attractive because it enables
the testing of hundreds of peptides synthesized on polyethylene pins
assembled in such a way that they fit the wells of microtitre plates.
Unfortunately, this approach can present some limitations which
have been discussed by several groups (Hay et al., 1993; Pettersson,
1992; Van Regenmortel, 1992b). In this method, the peptides are
short (6–10 residues) and remain generally attached to the pins. This
can affect their antigenic activity and also prevents the quality of
peptides to be controlled. After each test, the pins have to be freed of
bound antibody by sonication and, in the particular case of sera from
patients with autoimmune diseases which can contain high levels of
immunoglobulin, the complete release of bound immunoglobulins
may be difficult to achieve. Finally, the high density of peptide on
the pins increases the detection of unwanted cross-reactions (Savoca et al., 1991; Trifilieff et al., 1991). All these problems obviously
limit the number of different sera which can be tested, thus making statistical evaluations more difficult. The recently introduced
strategy of mapping autoepitopes with gene-fragment phage display
libraries seems very promising and should allow the blind screening
of antibodies from patients' sera and synovial fluids (Blüthner et al.,
1996; Sioud et al., 1996).

7.2.3. Cross-reactivity of autoantibodies with synthetic peptides and the cognate protein

Some autoantibodies reveal a striking preference for conformational epitopes which are difficult to mimic with short synthetic
peptides. These autoantibodies are thought to be more pathogenic
than antibodies binding 'denatured' structures (e.g. by inhibiting

or stimulating enzymatic activities). Muro et al. (1994) have constructed compound peptides made up of short discontinuous regions
of the primary structure of the proliferating cell nuclear antigen
(PCNA) and showed that such constructs can mimic conformation-
dependent epitopes recognized by human PCNA autoantibodies.

Studies of several autoantigens have shown that in patients' sera,
antibodies reacting with peptides of a self-protein, but not with the
cognate protein itself, co-existed with antibodies reacting with the
whole parent protein. The presence of the former antibody population has long been ignored because in general, investigators select
sera reacting with a particular protein and only subsequently examine the reactivity of positive sera with peptides to delineate the
epitopes recognized in the parent protein. However, when sera are
tested systematically with peptides and the cognate protein, such
antibody subsets can be revealed. This phenomenon has been described in the case of histones (Stemmer et al., 1996; Tuaillon et al.,
1990), SmBB'N (Hines et al., 1991; Petrovas et al., 1998), SmD1
protein (Barakat et al., 1990; Riemekasten et al., 1998; Sabbatini
et al., 1993b), U1A protein (Dumortier et al., 1999a), Ro52 protein
(Ricchiuti et al., 1994b), and PARP (Decker et al., 1998; Muller
et al., 1994). It is difficult to know whether distinct antibody populations are effectively produced by the autoimmune patients and
animals. It could be argued that this observation only reflects the
fact that certain cross-reactions are better visualized when peptides
bearing a major epitope, rather than whole purified or recombinant
proteins, are assayed in different test conditions. We have recently
studied several monoclonal autoantibodies reacting with the peptide
83–100 of histone H3 presented as a dimer but not with the whole
H3 molecule in ELISA (Stemmer et al., 1996). These monoclonal
antibodies also reacted strongly with DNA and nucleosomes. This
study suggested that the cross-reactivity of these antibodies with
the H3 peptide and DNA was due to the fact that they recognized a
topographic determinant constituted by a segment of DNA associated with an epitope normally found in the $(H3H4)_2$ tetramer region
near the surface of the octamer core of the nucleosome. An oppos-

TABLE 7.1.

Examples of synthetic peptides mimicking B-cell epitopes recognized by antibodies from autoimmune patients[a]

Autoantigens[b]	Disease associations[c]	Peptides recognized by autoantibodies	References
Systemic autoimmune diseases			
Histones	SLE, RA, JCA		
H1		204–218	Stemmer and Muller (1996)
H2A		1–20, 65–85	Stemmer and Muller (1996)
H2B		1–25	Stemmer and Muller (1996)
H3		1–21, 40–55, 130–135	Stemmer and Muller (1996)
H4		1–29	Stemmer and Muller (1996)
UH2A		Branched octapeptide	Plaué et al. (1989)
SnRNPs	MCTD, SLE		
70-K		49–81, 57–76	Guldner et al. (1990); Query and Keene (1987)
A		1–11, 35–58, 258–282, 165–185, 232–256	Barakat et al. (1991); Habets et al. (1989b)
BB'N		29–36, 45–56, 142–151, PPGMRPP repeat (192–198, 217–223, 233–238)	James and Harley (1992); Williams et al. (1990)
C		119–125, other peptides (see Fig. 7.4)	Dumortier et al. (1999b); James and Harley (1995); Williams et al. (1990)
D1		1–20, 44–67, 95–119 (Fig. 7.3)	Barakat et al. (1990); Sabbatini et al. (1993b)
Ro/La proteins	SS, SLE		
Ro60		Multiple epitopes (see Fig. 7.2)	Barakat et al. (1992); Scofield and Harley (1991)
Ro52		1–13, 107–122, 277–292, 365–382 (Fig. 7.2)	Ricchiuti et al. (1994a)
La		145–164, 289–308, 301–320, 349–368, 381–390	Haaheim et al. (1996); Tzioufas et al. (1997)
Ribosomal P proteins (associated with the 60S subunit)	SLE	C-terminal 22 residues of P0, P1, P2	Elkon (1994)

PARP	SS, SLE, MCTD, CD	18–59 (Zn finger F1), 122–165 (Zn finger F2)	Decker et al. (1998); Muller et al. (1994)
PCNA	SLE	Construct 159–165: 255–261	Muro et al. (1994)
RNA polymerase I-II (large subunit)	Scleroderma	18 residue-long peptide construct in the C-terminus	Hirakata et al. (1996)
Topoisomerase I (Scl-70 antigen)	Scleroderma	737–753	Maul et al. (1989)
PM/Scl 100 antigen	Polymyositis/Scleroderma	229–244	Blüthner et al. (1996)
Proteinase-3	Wegener's disease	4–10, 8–14, 65–71, 108–114, 111–117, 118–124, 132–138, 154–160, 165–171, 173–179, 189–195	Williams et al. (1994)
Organ-specific autoimmune diseases			
Mitochondrial antigens:			
PDC-E2	PBC	40–52 LA, 167–184 LA	Briand et al. (1992b); Tuaillon et al. (1992)
Retinal antigens:			
Arrestin (S-antigen)	MS	290–309	Ohguro et al. (1993)
Skin antigens:			
230-kD BP protein	BP	Three 17–19 residue long peptides P1-1, P1-2, P3-1	Rico et al. (1990)
Membrane receptors:			
Thyrotropin (TSH) receptor	Graves' disease	181–200, 333–343, 376–394, 629–639	Mori et al. (1991); Morris et al. (1994)
β1-adrenergic receptor	Chagas' disease	201–205	Ferrari et al. (1995)
	Idiopathic dilated cardiomyopathy	206–212	Wallukat et al. (1995)
M2 muscarinic acetylcholine receptor	Chagas' disease	173–177	Elies et al. (1996)
Acetylcholine receptor	MG	195–212, 257–269, 310–327	Brocke et al. (1988)

[a] Autoepitopes identified by testing recombinant fragments are not listed.
[b] LA, peptides containing the cofactor lipoic acid; UH2A, ubiquinated histone H2A; PDC-E2, dihydrolipoamide acetyltransferase, the E2 subunit of pyruvate dehydrogenase.
[c] SLE, systemic lupus erythematosus; RA, rheumatoid arthritis; JCA, juvenile chronic arthritis; MCTD, mixed-connective tissue disease; SS, Sjögren's syndrome; PBC, primary biliary cirrhosis; MS, multiple sclerosis; BP, bullous pemphigus; MG, myasthenia gravis; CD, Crohn's disease.

ing view to explain the presence of high levels of specific peptide antibodies in the serum of autoimmune patients is that antibodies in certain autoimmune diseases show stronger reactivity with denatured, rather than native proteins. It is indeed possible that in these diseases, 'non-native' proteins may have pathogenic significance either in the initiation or propagation of the autoimmune response (Atanassov et al., 1991; Itoh et al., 1992; Rico et al., 1990; Williams et al., 1994).

7.3. Specific examples of autoepitope mapping data

It is generally accepted that solid-phase immunoassays based on the use of recombinant or synthetic fragments are among the most sensitive and specific assays currently available for antibody detection (Galperin et al., 1996). In particular, synthetic peptides have proved useful not only for the detection, but also in some cases for the discrimination of antibodies in patients with related autoimmune diseases. Examples of synthetic peptides mimicking B-cell epitopes recognized by antibodies from autoimmune patients are shown in Table 7.1. It is beyond the scope of this chapter to give a detailed account of epitope mapping data in autoimmune diseases. Several recent reviews are available which describe these results and summarize the approaches used to localize continuous and discontinuous epitopes in self-antigens obtained with truncated recombinant fragments and synthetic peptides (Klein Gunnewiek et al., 1997; Peter and Shoenfeld, 1996; van Venrooij and Maini, 1994; Wahren-Herlenius et al., 1999). However, some examples are discussed below. They were chosen because of the availability of results from different laboratories using both synthetic peptides and recombinant fragments. We deliberately selected different types of protein in order to illustrate a series of approaches rather than to present an exhaustive review.

7.3.7. B-cell epitopes of Ro60 protein

Autoantibodies directed against the protein components of the RoRNP are frequently found in patients with SLE and SS. They are associated with certain clinical features of SLE and/or SS including cutaneous vasculitis, photosensitivity, lymphopenia, the neonatal lupus syndrome and in those patients with an inherited complement factor C2 deficiency. Ro antibodies have been eluted from the kidney of patients with SLE and from an affected heart of a child dying with complete congenital heart block. Several Ro proteins are associated with the RoRNP particles including Ro60 and La. The presence of Ro52 in the particle is still a matter of controversy. Characteristics of the Ro antigen have been described recently (Chan and Buyon, 1994; Pruijn et al., 1997b). Autoepitopes of Ro60 have been described by several authors using different biochemical and molecular biology approaches:

> By using 531 overlapping octapeptides synthesized on derivatized polyethylene pins with four anti-Ro patient sera, Scofield and Harley (1991) identified 14 peptides which were antigenic (Fig. 7.2). Interestingly, the authors showed that among the 531 peptides synthesized, six shared sequence identity with the nucleocapsid (N) protein from the Indiana serotype of vesicular stomatitis virus, and that five of these six small peptides were bound by anti-Ro antibodies. Routsias et al. (1994), however, showed that this subset of antibodies only account for a minority of anti-Ro60 antibodies.

> Barakat et al. (1992) and Ricchiuti and Muller (1994) identified continuous epitopes of Ro60 using five synthetic peptides covering residues 1–23, 21–41, 304–324, 495–518 and 524–538 in ELISA. The peptide 21–41 was recognized by 57% of sera from patients with pSS but only by 7% of the unselected patients with SLE. Raised levels of IgG antibodies reacting with the peptide 304–324 which contain a zinc-finger motif were also observed in sera from patients with pSS. It is notable that the difference in reactivity between antibodies from

patients with pSS and SLE was not seen when the purified Ro60 protein was used as antigen in ELISA. This result was confirmed by Wahren et al. (1996) who showed differences between patients with pSS and secondary Sjögren's syndrome (sSS) with respect to autoantibody reactivity against Ro60 peptides, but not to full-length Ro60. In our studies we also noted heterogeneity in the Ro autoimmune response tested with Ro60 peptides according to the origin of patients' sera (Ricchiuti and Muller, 1994) and the HLA haplotype (Ricchiuti et al., 1994b).

By using recombinant Ro60 proteins encoded by both full-length and deletion clones in Western blotting, Wahren et al. (1992) identified a major antigenic domain located in residues 181–320 which was recognized by 85% of the sera tested and two other antigenic domains respectively located in residues 1–134 and 397–525 that were recognized by 20% of the sera (Fig. 7.2). These results were further confirmed in ELISA by using overlapping synthetic peptides from the immunodominant domain 181–320. At least six epitopes were characterized within the region 181–320 (residues 181–200, 201–210, 216–235, 226–245, 246–265 and 301–320). The sera tested in this study were selected on the basis of their anti-Ro reactivity established by counter immunoelectrophoresis (CIE).

Saitta et al. (1994) used 10 overlapping recombinant polypeptides of Ro60 to analyze the reactivity of serum from patients in an immunoprecipitation assay. Among the 12 sera tested, two reacted only with the full-length protein 1–538. The other 10 sera reacted with fragments of different lengths. Analysis of the reactivity of these sera suggested the position of at least five antigenic regions containing both continuous and discontinuous epitopes. They cover residues 1–119, 155–243, 243–295, 350–448 and 448–538 which is nearly the whole sequence of Ro60 (Fig. 7.2). Among these domains, the most frequently recognized region was located between residues 155 and 295. Evidence for the presence of a discontinuous epitope formed by residues 530–538 in the C-terminus associated to residues present in the NH$_2$-terminal one-third of the protein was obtained.

McCauliffe et al. (1994) used four recombinant fragments each covering approximately 1/4 of the Ro60 protein in ELISA and identified a major epitope contained within residues 139–326 (Fig. 7.2).

Routsias et al. (1996) identified Ro60 epitopes with synthetic peptides. In patients with pSS, antibodies to peptide 216–232 (or 211–232; Routsias et al., 1998) were detected, while antibodies from patients with SLE preferentially reacted with a sequence covering residues 175–184 (169–190; Routsias et al., 1998).

7.3.2. B-cell epitopes of SmD1 protein

SmD1 is one of the proteins forming the Sm core of spliceosomal snRNP particles. This Sm core includes the B'B, D1 (usually referred to as simply D), D2, D3, E, F and G proteins. Anti-Sm antibodies react with proteins B'B and D, sometimes with E and rarely with F and G (Hoch, 1994; Peng and Craft, 1996). Although there is no obvious primary sequence homology between B'B and D1, SmD1 is known to share at least one epitope with the Sm B'B proteins based on monoclonal antibodies that recognize all three antigens. SmD1 contains three characteristic domains in its C-terminal region: a lysine-rich hydrophilic region (residues 82–93), a ninefold repeated GR motif between residues 97–114 which is also found in a region of the Epstein-Barr EBNA-1 and -2 antigens as well as in the yeast transcription factor SNF-2 and a region with strong similarity to protamines in residues 114–119. This 119 residue-long protein presents no other particular structural features (Fig. 7.3).

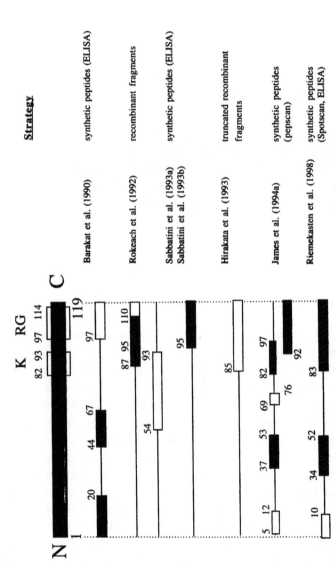

Fig. 7.3. B-cell epitopes of SmD1 autoantigen. Schematic representation of autoepitopes recognized by antibodies from autoimmune patients. Structural features of SmD1 are shown (for the legend, see Fig. 7.2). In the case of the pepscan study, certain bars represent antigenic regions covered by several contiguous octapeptides. B-cell epitopes recognized by several distinct SmD1-specific monoclonal antibodies have been recently characterized using in vitro translated SmD1 protein and deletion mutants of SmD1 in immunoprecipitation assays (Pruijn et al., 1997a).

TABLE 7.2.

Immunoreactivity of patients' sera with SmD1 peptides according to the selection of samples (adapted from Barakat et al., 1990).

	Serum selection			
	Clinically defined SLE n = 165		SLE sera reactive with the D1-band in Western blotting n = 18	
Peptides				
1–20	59%	($\overline{OD}$: 0.77)	67%	($\overline{OD}$: 0.47)
17–35	0		0	
33–51	0		0	
44–67	37%	($\overline{OD}$: 0.58)	89%	($\overline{OD}$: 0.57)
64–84	0		0	
77–96	0		0	
97–119	1%		33%	($\overline{OD}$: 0.46)

$\overline{OD}$, mean value of ODs measured with sera considered as positive (cutoff positive reaction = 0.3 OD unit).

Anti-Sm (or anti-Smith) autoantibodies are a marker of SLE. They occur in 5–10% of Caucasians but in up to 30% of Afro-Carribeans with lupus.

To study antigenic determinants of SmD1, Barakat et al. (1990) used seven overlapping peptides covering the whole sequence from SmD1 and tested the sera of two distinct populations of patients by ELISA. First the sera from a series of patients with different rheumatic diseases (SLE, SS, RA, JCA, scleroderma, etc.) were examined. IgG reactivity was found essentially in SLE sera in two peptides, spanning residues 1–20 and 44–67 (Fig. 7.3; Table 7.2). When SLE sera were selected based on their ability to react with SmD1 in Western blot, an additional peptide (residues 97–119) was found positive and the frequency of recognition of the other peptides was different

(Table 7.2). In an independent longitudinal study of 12 British SLE patients, 70% of the samples had antibodies binding peptide 1–20 (Muller et al., 1990a). The presence of antibodies reacting with peptides 1–20 and 44–67 in lupus patients has been shown to be related to particular HLA and T-cell receptor Vβ allele usage (Dumortier et al., 1999a; Youinou et al., 1997). The murine monoclonal anti-Sm autoantibody Y12 did not significantly recognize any of the seven SmD1 peptides tested. Using a competitive assay involving antibodies reacting with peptides 1–20, 44–67 and 97–119 adsorbed to the plastic microtitre plate and the D1 protein in solution as competitor, it was recently found that residues within the linear regions 44–67 and 97–119 (but not 1–20) of SmD1 are readily accessible at the surface of the free protein (Dumortier et al., 1999c).

Rokeach et al. (1992) tested patients' sera (all positive by Western blot against purified Sm snRNPs from HeLa cells or rabbit thymus) for their ability to recognize recombinant fusion proteins expressing various regions of the SmD1 protein. Most of the antigenicity was found in the C-terminus of the protein (distinct epitopes were found in fragments 54–93, 87–119, 95–119 and 110–119; Fig. 7.3). No reactivity was found in fragments 5–34, 25–54 and 34–87. Using an immunoprecipitation assay with peptides produced by *in vitro* translation, the authors confirmed that patients' antibodies reacted essentially with C- but not N-terminal residues of the protein. Ten out of 19 sera reacted in Western blot with the nearly full-length antigen (residues 5–119) but not (or very weakly) with recombinant fragments, suggesting that the sera contained antibodies directed against conformational or discontinuous epitopes.

Migliorini and colleagues (Sabbatini et al., 1993a, b) used seven overlapping synthetic peptides spanning residues 1–18, 15–34, 30–49, 45–64, 60–79, 75–94 and 95–119 of SmD1. The C-terminal peptide 95–119, tested as monomer or as MAP, was recognized by 25% of lupus sera while the other six peptides were recognized by 5–17% of sera. Less than 2% of sera from patients with other rheumatic diseases reacted with the C-terminal peptide. Interestingly out of the 20 sera tested, 4 sera contained detectable levels of antibodies reacting with SmD1 peptides but were negative with the SmD1 protein in Western immunoblotting.

Using truncated forms of SmD1 translated *in vitro* with 14 patients' sera, Hirakata et al. (1993) deduced the presence of a major epitope in the C-terminal domain 85–109 of the protein (Fig. 7.3). Other epitopes (not delineated using shorter fragments) are present in the fragment 1–84 which was recognized by 7/14 sera tested. In this study, the binding site recognized by the monoclonal antibody Y12 derived from an MRL lpr/lpr lupus mouse was suggested to involve residues 85 to 104.

Using overlapping octapeptides synthesized on polyethylene pins, James et al. (1994a) identified at least 5 regions (defined as epitopes 1–5) recognized by antibodies from lupus patients and MRL lpr/lpr autoimmune mice. They span regions 5–12, 37–53, 69–76, 82–97 and 92–113 (Fig. 7.3). The major antigenic region (residues 92–119) was bound by antibodies from 8/9 Sm precipitin-positive sera. Epitope 4 corresponding to octapeptides spanning the 82–97 region was recognized by 7/9 patients' sera and exhibited the highest average binding of the SmD1 peptides, 6 SD above the normal mean. None of the three sera tested from patients with other rheumatic diseases were positive with SmD1 octapeptides. Antibodies from lupus mice (positive with Sm proteins in Western immunoblotting) only bound octapeptides in the C-terminal region 92–119. Several murine monoclonal antibodies were included in this study: KSm2 specifically bound octapeptides in the region 84–98, KSm4 was mainly specific for peptides in the C-terminal region and Y12 was positive with peptides covering a broader region in the C-terminus (epitopes 4 and 5).

Riemekasten et al. (1998) tested 15 SLE sera with cellulose-bound 13-mer peptides overlapping 10 amino acid residues (SPOTscan). Four sera recognized more than five overlapping peptides of the SmD1 C-terminus. Five longer peptides (17–37 residues) from the positive regions were synthesized and tested for their ability to react with patients' sera in ELISA. Among these five peptides (residues 34–46, 83–99, 83–119, 95–119 and 105–119), peptide 83–119 was recognized by 70% of 167 SLE sera, by none of the sera from normal individuals and by only 8.3% of sera from 267 patients with other inflammatory diseases. The anti-SmD1$_{83\ 119}$ reactivity was correlated with disease activity.

7.3.3. B-cell epitopes of U1C protein

In contrast to SmD1 which is present in all spliceosomal snRNPs, the snRNP protein C is specifically found in the U1 snRNP. Two other U1 snRNP-specific proteins are present in U1 snRNPs, namely, U1-70K and U1A, and the three proteins U1-70K, U1A and U1C as well as U1 snRNA are frequent targets of anti-U1 snRNP autoantibodies from patients with SLE and MCTD. The U1C protein (159 residues) contains a zinc finger-like region at its N-terminus and a large C-terminal region rich in proline and methionine residues. In contrast to U1-70K and U1A, U1C lacks an RNP-80 motif also referred to as RNA-binding region or RNA-recognition motif common to many RNA-binding proteins (Klein Gunnewiek et al., 1997; Fig. 7.4).

Only few reports describing B-cell epitopes of U1C that are recognized by autoantibodies have been published.

Misaki et al. (1993) have shown that all anti-U1C positive sera tested reacted in Western blotting with truncated U1C fusion proteins containing residues 102–125. The presence of two epitopes was suggested in this region, in residues 102–112 and 112–125. The analysis of deleted mutants also permitted the identification of a minor epitope in residues 33–47 (Fig. 7.4).

James and Harley (1995) who used octapeptides tested by the pepscan method, showed that all twelve Sm/RNP precipitin

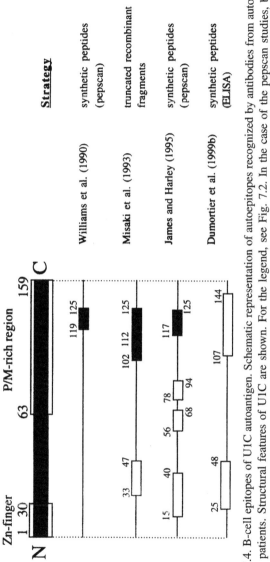

Fig. 7.4. B-cell epitopes of U1C autoantigen. Schematic representation of autoepitopes recognized by antibodies from autoimmune patients. Structural features of U1C are shown. For the legend, see Fig. 7.2. In the case of the pepscan studies, bars represent antigenic regions covered by several contiguous octapeptides.

positive sera reacted with peptides spanning residues 117–125. Ten other U1C epitopes primarily localized in the regions 15–40, 56–68 and 78–94 were also identified (Fig. 7.4). The immunodominant region 117-125 identified by Misaki et al. (1993) and James and Harley (1995) is interesting because it contains residues PAPGMRPP (residues 118–125). A similar region (PPPGMRPP) is repeated twice in SmB and three times in SmB′N. This proline rich sequence was shown to bear a dominant epitope of BB′N recognized by human and murine autoantibodies (Habets et al., 1989a; Hines et al., 1991; Hoet et al., 1998; James and Harley, 1996; Petrovas et al., 1998; Williams et al., 1990). In U1A, a similar sequence PPPG-MIPP, is found in residues 165–172. However, no antigenic activity was found in this region of U1A (Barakat et al., 1991; James and Harley, 1996). It is also notable that the segment 102–125 contains a GPPPPG (residues 106–111) which is also found in the herpes simplex virus type 1 ICP4 protein (residues 320–325).

Dumortier et al. (1999b) used a complete set of 15 U1C overlapping synthetic peptides (16–30 residue-long) in ELISA to identify linear B-cell epitopes of U1C that are recognized by antibodies from patients with SLE and MCTD. Respectively 51 and 77% of SLE and MCTD sera reacted in ELISA with the whole recombinant U1C protein and equally well with the truncated fragment 30–159. A weaker and less frequent reactivity was observed with the U1C mutant protein containing residues 1–60. Surprisingly when tested with the 15 overlapping peptides, it was found that very few sera (<16% of 58 SLE and MTCD sera) were positive with any of these peptides. Only a few sera reacted strongly with some of the peptides. These antigenically active peptides generally span regions located in the C-terminus of the molecule (residues 107–127 and 123–144) and segments in residues 25–40 and 31–48 (Fig. 7.4). These results were confirmed using the SPOTscan method (Halimi et al., 1996; Fig. 7.1). Using rabbit anti-U1C peptide antibodies in ELISA and immunoprecipitation, Du-mortier et al. (1998) identified the regions exposed at the surface of free and U1 snRNP-bound U1C. Epitopes within at least three regions spanning residues 31–62, 85–103 and 116–159 were recognized on free and plastic-coated recombinant human U1C expressed in *E. coli*, *in vitro* translated U1C protein and U1C bound to the U1 RNP particle present in HeLa extract.

7.4. *Prediction of epitopes recognized by autoantibodies*

In very few instances antigenicity prediction profiles have been used to anticipate putative autoantigen epitopes. Maul et al. (1989) used a prediction program to select two oligopeptides of topoisomerase I with high surface probability and flanking sequences with high amphipathic α-helical scores, and containing sequences similarities with viral and/or self proteins. One of these two peptides was recognized in ELISA by most of topoisomerase I-positive patients' sera. In their study of autoepitopes of bullous pemphigoid (BP) 200-kD protein recognized by the antibodies from patients with BP, Rico et al. (1990) selected six 17–19 residue-long peptides from the BP cDNA on the basis of hydrophilicity of the BP-deduced sequence. Three of the peptides were effectively recognized by the antibodies from autoimmune patients with BP. The prediction algorithms of Hopp (1986) were also successfully used by Muro et al. (1994) in the case of PCNA.

Using the two computer programs HYDRO 3 and ACRO developed by Hopp (1986), Pollard and Cohen (1990) predicted a number of epitopes of autoantigens, e.g. in histones, SnRNPs, SSB/La protein, PCNA, topoisomerase and HMG proteins. When the epitopes predicted by HYDRO 3 and ACRO in the U1A protein were compared with those subsequently identified in ELISA by the binding of autoantibodies to U1A synthetic peptides (Barakat et al., 1991), little agreement was observed. The region 35–58 identified experimentally encompassed the sequence 43–56 predicted by HYDRO 3 as containing a possible antigenic site of U1A (Table 7.3). This site was not predicted using the ACRO program, the mobility scale of Karplus and Schulz (1985) or the hydrophilicity scale of Parker et al. (1986). Although they do not correspond to major peaks in the prediction profiles (Fig. 7.5), antigenic sites could be predicted in the regions 1–11 and 258–282 by using the algorithms of Parker et al. (1986) and Karplus and Schulz (1985). However, these two antigenic sites could not be predicted using the programs HYDRO 3 and ACRO. The two U1A antigenic regions experimentally identified in residues 165–185 and 232–256 by Habets et al. (1989b) were not predicted by HYDRO 3 and ACRO, nor by the hydrophilicity algorithm of Parker et al. (1986) (Table 7.3; Fig. 7.5). The epitope in residues 165–185, but not the epitope in residues 232–256 was predicted using the mobility scale of Karplus and Schulz (1985). Nine potentially antigenic sequence regions predicted in residues 15-28, 83–96, 99–112, 106–119, 123–136, 134–147, 153–166, 199–211 and 212–225 by the programs HYDRO 3 and ACRO (Pollard and Cohen, 1990) were not found by Habets et al. (1989b) and Barakat et al. (1991) to be recognized by autoimmune sera.

Other examples showing a lack of agreement between the location of predicted and experimentally defined epitopes can be highlighted. Thus the dominant epitope of topoisomerase I in residues 737–753 (Maul et al., 1989) was not predicted by HYDRO 3 and ACRO (Pollard and Cohen, 1990). The epitope in residues 95–119 of SmD1 was correctly predicted with the algorithms of Hopp and Woods (1981), Karplus and Schulz (1985) and Parker et al. (1986) but the antigenic regions 1–20 and 44–67 were not predicted (Barakat et al., 1990). The major peak (around residue 90) in the Hopp and Woods' scale did not correspond to residues recognized by patients' antibodies (Barakat et al., 1990; Sabbatini et al., 1993b). The four epitopes of SSB/La antigen identified by Tzioufas et al. (1997) who screened patients' sera with 34 pin-bound 20-mer peptides and confirmed their finding with the four biotinylated soluble peptides synthesized by standard solid-phase methods,

TABLE 7.3.

Prediction of antigenic sites of snRNP U1A and position of continuous epitopes experimentally defined by the binding of autoantibodies to U1A synthetic fragments.

	U1A domains recognized by autoimmune sera				
	1–11[a]	35–58[a]	165–185[b]	232–256[b]	258–282[a]
Mobility scale[c]; Karplus and Schulz (1985)	+[e]	–	+	–	+
Hydrophilicity scale[c]; Parker et al. (1986)	–	–	–	–	+
Hydrophilicity scale HYDRO 3[d]; Hopp (1986)	–	+	–	–	–
Acrophilicity scale ACRO[d]; Hopp (1986)	–	–	–	–	–

[a] From Barakat et al. (1991).
[b] From Habets et al. (1989b).
[c] Antigenicity prediction profiles were obtained after normalizing the scales according to Pellequer et al. (1991). The plots were traced from the fourth residue onward and until the (n−3)th residue (not shown).
[d] From Pollard and Cohen (1990).
[e] + denotes presence of peak.

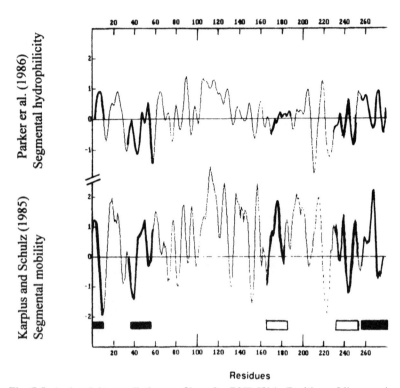

Fig. 7.5. Antigenicity prediction profiles of snRNP U1A. Position of linear epitopes experimentally defined by: □ Habets et al. (1989b), ■ Barakat et al. (1991).

were not predicted by the HYDRO 3 and ACRO programs. The epitope located in residues 381–390 of SSB/La by Haaheim et al. (1996) using the SPOTscan was correctly predicted by HYDRO 3 but not by ACRO. St. Clair et al. (1990) have tested six synthetic La peptides predicted to be antigenic on the basis of their hydrophilic properties determined with the scale of Kyte and Doolittle (1982). They found that mouse anti-La antibodies bound to five of the six 15-mer peptides while human anti-La antibodies failed to recognize any of these peptides. Finally, among the 10 potential La epitopes predicted by HYDRO 3 and ACRO (Pollard and Cohen, 1990), only one (in residues 382–395) was contained in a peptide which was effectively recognized by patients' antibodies (residues 381–390; Haaheim et al., 1996). It is notable, however, that other epitopes of autoantigens were correctly predicted either by HYDRO 3 or by ACRO or by both, e.g. regions 1–20 and 65–85 of H2A, 1–25 of H2B, 1–21, 40–55 and 130–135 of H3, 1–29 of H4, 94–115 of ribosomal protein P2 and 159–165 : 255–261 of PCNA. HYDRO 3 and ACRO predicted a number of other putative epitopes which were not characterized in the experimental studies.

These results illustrate the limited value of antigenicity prediction scales especially in the case of certain autoantigens, notably snRNP autoantigens. As stated in the beginning of this chapter, the antigens giving rise to autoantibody formation in patients with systemic autoimmune diseases are largely unknown. However, there is increasing evidence to show that autoantigens are components of larger intranuclear or intracytoplasmic particles which may be involved in the initiation of autoimmune response instead of the isolated protein itself. In the assembly or package of autoantigens into these macromolecular assemblies (snRNP particles, hnRNP complex, nucleosome, synthetase-tRNA complex, RoRNP complex), certain regions are buried whilst others are exposed. For these reasons and others (in particular, the possibility that altered antigens also play a role in the induction of autoantibodies), the prediction of autoepitopes based on the characteristics of residues in the primary structure of individual proteins remains unsatisfactory. Other parameters can further affect the prediction of putative epitopes in autoantigens. First, the autoimmune response can result from mimicry between foreign and self antigens. Second, the autoantibody response has been shown to diversify during the course of diseases such as SLE as a result of a phenomenon called epitope spreading (Atanassov et al., 1991; Craft and Fatenejad, 1997; James et al., 1995; McNeilage et al., 1990). Once immune tolerance to one component of a macromolecular particle is abrogated, antibodies directed against new peptides within the intact complex can appear. It seems likely that prediction techniques would be more successful if the autoantigens were injected into animals and tested with experimentally-induced antibodies rather than when fragments of these proteins are tested with autoimmune sera.

If it is difficult to predict the location of autoantigen epitopes, we can nevertheless conclude from the results described above that most autoepitopes are present at the N- and C-terminal ends of self-proteins, are rich in charged residues (Brendel et al., 1991) and often correspond to repetitive sequences (in the same protein or in different polypeptides associated in the same particle) which may contribute to the ability of certain proteins/particles to activate B-lymphocytes (see for example U1C, U1-70K, SmB'B and SmD1 antigens, histones, RNA polymerase II, ribosomal proteins P0, P1 and P2). Epitopes targeted by autoantibodies are also often located in active or functional sites of proteins, as evidenced by the ability of these antibodies to inhibit the enzymatic properties of certain target proteins or prevent their capacity to assemble in subcellular particles (see, for example, antibodies to enzymes such as the E2 subunit of pyruvate dehydrogenase, tRNA synthetases, topoisomerase 1, RNA polymerases I, II and III, and proteinase-3, or autoantibodies to the RNA binding sites of U1A and U1-70K proteins, and the DNA binding site of the Ku antigen and PARP). Finally, it has been observed that major epitopes are often highly conserved (as expected if they contain functional or active sites), although in some instances, patients' antibodies recognized sequences which are not conserved between species (Porges et al., 1990; Reichlin et al., 1989).

7.5. Peptides mimicking sites of post-translational modification recognized by autoantibodies

Besides the interest of synthetic peptides as antigenic probes which can be chemically controlled and produced in large amounts, peptides offer the possibility of introducing during synthesis modified residues and cofactors which are normally present in natural molecules or are added during certain stages of the cell cycle. The potential of this strategy is particularly attractive since several antigens targeted by autoantibodies contain such modified residues and cofactors, the presence of which is necessary to the antigen to be recognized by patients' antibodies. This is the case of the E2 subunit of pyruvate dehydrogenase (PDC-E2) which contains lipoyl cofactors, ubiquinated histone H2A, the p68 autoantigen characteristic of RA, citrullinated, filaggrin, and phosphorylated RNA polymerascs I and II (Bläss et al., 1998; Fussey et al., 1990; Girbal-Neuhauser et al., 1999; Plaué et al., 1989; Satoh et al., 1994; Schellekens et al., 1998; Stetler and Jacob, 1984). For examples of studies describing the reactivity of patients' antibodies with modified peptides, see Plaué et al. (1989), Tuaillon et al. (1992), Briand et al. (1992b), Schellekens et al. (1998) and Girbal-Neuhauser et al. (1999).

7.6. Concluding remarks

The analysis of epitopes recognized by antibodies in autoimmune sera has important fundamental and practical applications. A detailed description of specific autoepitopes should help to answer key questions notably what are the pathological events giving rise to the autoimmune response? Does the precise specificity of autoantibodies depend upon multiple variables such as the stage of the diseases, the treatment or the genetic predisposition of the patient?

The development of assays based on short peptide sequences makes it possible to study problems related to the mimicry of sequences in self antigens and infectious agents which seems to be of prime importance in the etiology of autoimmune disorders. Given that experimental transfer of appropriate autoantibodies can provoke disease in recipient animals (e.g. MG, autoimmune thyroïdis, diabetes mellitus of type I, idiopathic thrombocytopenic purpura or pemphigus), the careful analysis of these antibodies may also have an important biological significance. It should be stressed that epitope mapping data from patients with established autoantibody responses will certainly be unhelpful in elucidating early events which initiate autoimmunity since intramolecular spreading of the B-cell response during the disease seems to follow initiation of immunity to a single or a few self-components (Sercarz, 1998).

In this chapter, it was shown that conclusions reached regarding the antigenicity of a protein depend on the way test sera are selected (see Table 7.1, for example), on the Ig isotypes tested (see Wahren et al., 1994) and on the type of assay and antigenic probes chosen to identify epitopes recognized by autoantibodies. Furthermore, several authors have particularly emphasized the fact that the fine specificity of antibodies from autoimmune patients, those induced in experimental animals and of monoclonal (auto)antibodies differ in several aspects. Finally, it must be recognized that none of the methods applied to delineate an epitope is absolute and can lead to the 'complete' mapping of autoepitopes of a protein (Pettersson, 1992; Rokeach and Hoch, 1992; Van Regenmortel, 1992c; van Venrooij and van Gelder, 1994). The results obtained in the different epitope mapping studies published so far should thus be considered as complementary to each other, in an additive rather than in an exclusive manner.

CHAPTER 8

Synthetic peptides as vaccines

M. H. V. VAN REGENMORTEL

8.1. Introduction

The possibility of using synthetic peptides as vaccines has been recognized for over 30 years. Following the determination in 1960 of the amino acid sequence of the coat protein of tobacco mosaic virus, (Anderer, 1963) showed that short C-terminal peptides of the coat protein could elicit antibodies that recognized the virus and neutralized its infectivity. Anderer and his colleagues used both natural and synthetic peptides in their work (Anderer and Schlumberger, 1965a, b, 1966a, b; Anderer et al., 1967), and they should thus be credited with the discovery that synthetic peptides can elicit antibodies that neutralize viral infectivity. In some quarters, this work was not deemed relevant because it concerned a plant virus that replicates in hosts devoid of an immune system and not normally protected by antibodies. Sela and his colleagues used the same approach with MS2 bacteriophage and showed that this phage could be inactivated by antibodies raised to a 20-residue synthetic peptide of the viral coat protein (Langbeheim et al., 1976). As more viral protein sequences were determined and our knowledge of the antigenic structure of viruses progressed, it became possible to apply the same principles to the development of synthetic vaccines relevant to human and veterinary medicine (see reviews by Arnon, 1987; Arnon and Van Regenmortel, 1992; Milich, 1989; Nicholson, 1994b; Steward and Howard, 1987; Van Regenmortel and Neurath, 1985, 1990). It was found, for instance, that peptides of the VP1 protein of foot-and-mouth disease virus, when inoculated into guinea pigs, could elicit neutralizing antibodies and that protective immunity against this virus could be obtained by vaccinating cattle and pigs with synthetic peptides (Di Marchi et al., 1986). Antipeptide antibodies able to neutralize viral infectivity were also obtained in the case of several other viruses and these results led in the 1980s to a surge of interest in the potential of synthetic vaccines (Emini et al., 1983; Francis, 1994; Koolen et al., 1990; Lerner et al., 1981; Trudel et al., 1991)

In cases where a cellular immune response is important for conferring effective immunity against a pathogen, a synthetic peptide vaccine must contain T-helper and cytotoxic T-cell (CTL) epitopes in addition to B-cell epitopes. Immunization with synthetic peptides has been found to induce CTL responses although the low immunogenicity of peptides requires the use of efficient delivery systems such as lipopeptides (Deres et al., 1989), liposomes (Alving et al., 1995) or biodegradable microspheres (Partidos et al., 1994, 1997).

It is generally expected that a synthetic vaccine should possess the following advantages:

(a) Since a synthetic vaccine is a chemical rather than a biological product, it is not subject to biological variation and should be stable indefinitely. Its use does not require the maintenance of a cold chain as is the case with live attenuated vaccines.

(b) The burdensome containment procedures that are required when large amounts of infectious material are grown for producing classical vaccines are eliminated.

(c) The possibility of contamination with infectious agents or cellular products is eliminated as well as genetic reversion of live, attenuated vaccines or incomplete inactivation of killed vaccines. This should decrease the potential high liability costs associated with vaccine production.

(d) Synthetic vaccines are likely to be cheap to produce, partly because they are stable chemical products and completely safe.

(e) Synthetic peptide vaccines make it possible to direct the immune response of the vaccinated host against antigenic sites not normally expressed with classical vaccines. This may lead to the induction of a protective immune response not achievable with intact whole antigens and may overcome limitations encountered with agents not yet amenable to vaccination.

(f) It may be possible to avoid some unwanted immune responses such as the induction of enhancing antibodies, autoimmune responses or suppressor cells.

These potential advantages of synthetic peptides should, however, be measured against a number of limitations that have become more apparent as our knowledge of the immune system progressed over the years. Some authors have dismissed peptides as potential vaccine candidates for the following reasons:

(a) In most cases, the immune response induced by peptides is much lower than that evoked by the parent protein or intact virus particle. Several repeated injections of fairly large quantities of peptides are needed to produce the serum antibody titres that can be obtained with a single injection of intact virus.

(b) Most peptides are short-lived molecules that are rapidly degraded in vivo by proteases. This inherent instability of peptides is mainly responsible for their low immunogenicity.

(c) Most linear peptides do not mimic sufficiently well the conformation of the corresponding antigenic site in the intact, complete protein. As a result, most antibodies elicited against peptides react strongly with the homologous peptides but weakly or not at all with the intact infectious agents. In general, the antigenic cross-reactivity between peptides and the cognate intact protein is found to be low.

(d) Many antigenic sites involved in infectivity neutralization are of a discontinuous nature and it is usually impossible to mimic such sites by means of linear peptides.

(e) Peptides are sufficiently immunogenic only if they contain a T-helper epitope in addition to the B-cell epitope or if they are conjugated to a carrier molecule to provide T-cell help. This raises the problem of genetic restriction since T cell epitopes are only recognized in the context of genetically compatible MHC molecules. It is thus necessary to ensure that the T-cell epitopes are adequate for the particular host species targetted for vaccination. The problem of MHC polymorphism may require the use of clusters of T-helper and CTL epitopes.

(f) There is a lack of potent adjuvants required for peptide immunization that are acceptable for human use.

These limitations are probably responsible for the fact that no commercial peptide vaccine has yet reached the marketplace. However, the expected advantages of a successful synthetic vaccine are so considerable that there is still great scientific interest and research effort in this area. This chapter will review some of the systems that have been studied extensively in recent years. Because of their relatively simple structure compared to those of bacteria and parasites, viruses have received the most attention.

8.2. Antiviral vaccines

8.2.1. Foot-and-mouth disease virus

The particles of *Foot-and-mouth disease virus* (FMDV), which is a member of the family *Picornaviridae*, are 30 nm in diameter and are composed of one molecule of single-stranded RNA and 60 copies of each of four structural polypeptides, VP1–VP4 (Brown, 1985). Immunization with the individual proteins showed that only VP1 was able to stimulate the production of neutralizing antibodies (Bachrach et al., 1975; Kleid et al., 1981; Laporte et al., 1973). Studies with peptide fragments of VP1 indicated that the regions corresponding to residues 140–160 and 201–213 were dominant antigenic sites (Strohmaier et al., 1982). A synthetic peptide corresponding to residues 141–160, when coupled to KLH, was able to elicit antibodies that neutralized viral infectivity (Bittle et al., 1982; Pfaff et al., 1982). The C-terminal peptide 201–213 also elicited neutralizing antibodies but to a lower degree. A single inoculation with 200 μg of the peptide 141–160 conjugate was sufficient to protect guinea pigs against a subsequent challenge with the virus. The serum neutralizing titre induced by this peptide was about one order of magnitude lower than that obtained with inactivated virus but several orders of magnitude higher than that elicited by intact VP1 protein. Subsequently, it has been shown that protection could be achieved in cattle and pigs by immunizing them with synthetic peptides, although this was less effective than in the guinea pig model (Di Marchi et al., 1986; Morgan and Moore, 1990).

The structure of FMDV particles has been established by X-ray crystallography (Acharya et al., 1989). A characteristic feature of the virion structure is the presence of prominent loops corresponding to the residues 134–157 of each VP1 molecule. The sequence of this loop, known as the GH loop, is highly variable between the seven serotypes of the virus and is the immunodominant region of the virion (Rowlands et al., 1983). All GH loops of the different serotypes contain an Arg Gly Asp triplet involved in the attachment of virions to susceptible cells although additional attachment sites also exist.

The VP1 141–160 peptide is a particularly effective immunogen since it is able to induce in the serum of immunized animals a very high level of antipeptide antibodies that cross-react with virus particles (Parry et al., 1988). This very high cross-reactivity may be due to the fact that the GH loop is structurally disordered in the virus particle (Acharya et al., 1989). It is well known that regions of high mobility in proteins are better able to mimic the conformation of the corresponding free peptides, and that this leads to a strong antigenic cross-reactivity between peptide and intact protein (Tainer et al., 1985; Westhof et al., 1984). Since both peptides 141–160 and 200–213 of VP1 could be recognized by the same neutralizing Mab (Parry et al., 1989), it seems likely that these regions that were initially considered to be two distinct epitopes, can actually form a single neutralization neotope. The loop 141–160 of one protomeric subunit is in fact located very close to the C-terminal residues 200–213 of an adjacent subunit. This is a clear example of a discontinuous neutralization epitope corresponding to a neotope arising from the juxtaposition of residues from neighbouring subunits (Van Regenmortel, 1992a).

Guinea pigs immunized with chimeric peptides consisting of sites A and C from two different serotypes (A and O) were protected against infection with both serotypes (Doel et al., 1992). This result shows that by combining epitopes from different viral serotypes in a synthetic peptide, it may be possible to overcome one of the major limitations of viral vaccines, i.e. their narrow serotype specificity and concomitant ineffectiveness against multiple antigenic variants.

The unconjugated peptide 141–160 was also immunogenic when delivered in liposomes (Francis et al., 1985) or when allowed to form disulphide dimers via an additional cysteine residue added to the C-terminus (Francis et al., 1987a). A neutralizing antibody response capable of protecting guinea pigs against a challenge infection was obtained with a single inoculation of 1–4 μg of peptide 141–160 presented as a MAP construct (Tam, 1988) in octameric or tetrameric form, using the adjuvant aluminium hydroxide (Francis et al., 1991). This suggests that it may be possible to design a synthetic FMDV vaccine without using a carrier protein. The ability of these unconjugated peptides to induce neutralizing antibodies is probably due to the presence in the region 141–160 of VP1, of a T-helper epitope recognized by guinea pigs. The relatively low immunity induced in cattle and pigs by vaccination with VP1 synthetic peptides has been attributed to the lack of adequate T-cell epitopes effective in these animal species (Collen et al., 1991; Glass et al., 1991; Rodriguez et al., 1994; Van Lierop et al., 1995).

The amount of site A peptide that must be administered to guinea pigs to achieve protection ranges from 1 to 100 μg (Brown, 1994). This is much greater than the amount of inactivated virus (1 μg) needed to protect animals. An amount of 1 μg virus contains the equivalent of only 0.013 μg of peptide 141–160 distributed over the 60 VP1 copies present in a single virion. The difference in immunogenicity between peptide and virion relates more to the absence of neutralizing capacity of the antibodies than to the overall quantity of antibody produced. It has been shown that the neutralizing antibody response induced by peptide immunogens, as measured by in vitro assays, often does not correlate with protection of the host animals.

This lack of correlation is probably due to the high mutation rate of the replicating virus which leads to the appearance of neutralization escape mutants in the immunized animals (Domingo et al., 1990) but not during in vitro neutralization assays where no viral replication takes place.

The major reason for the relatively poor antiviral response induced by the peptides is the limited ability of most antipeptide antibodies to cross-react with epitopes of intact virions. Although site A in the virus is located on the highly accessible GH loop, this does not mean that its immunodominant conformation is necessarily the same as that in the corresponding free synthetic peptide. Depending on whether the peptide is conjugated to a carrier or is used as a free peptide, it will have one or both of its extremities free and it will therefore be able to adopt a greater variety of conformations than when it is part of the VP1 molecule and therefore constrained at both ends. Since the majority of peptide molecules used for immunization are likely to present conformations that cannot be adopted by the cognate region in the virus, it is not surprising that many of the antipeptide antibodies are unable to recognize the viral epitopes.

Another approach for presenting viral epitopes to the immune system in a more constrained manner is to express them as fusion proteins by means of recombinant technology (Hofnung and Charbit, 1993). FMDV peptides have been fused at one end of the vector protein (Broekhuijsen et al., 1986; Clarke et al., 1987; Giavedoni et al., 1991; Winther et al., 1986) and have also been inserted within the vector protein (Agterberg et al., 1990; Benito and Villaverde, 1994; Ruppert et al., 1994). When the peptide is inserted within the protein, both extremities are constrained and the number of formations that the peptide can display will be diminished. Provided the vector protein does not hinder the presentation of the viral epitope to the immune system, such constructions may possess a superior degree of conformational mimicry with the native viral protein and may lead to the induction of antibodies showing an improved level of cross-reactivity with the virus.

In a recent study, site A was inserted into three loops of the maltose-binding protein and its antigenicity was compared with site A presented as a conjugated synthetic peptide or inserted in β-galactosidase. The antigenic reactivity of each site A presentation format was assessed with a Biacore biosensor instrument by comparing the dissociation rate constants of two Mabs that recognized overlapping epitopes within site A (Benito and Van Regenmortel, 1998). It was found that site A inserted at three different positions in the maltose-binding protein was a slightly better mimic of the epitope present in the virus particle than the synthetic peptide alone or the β-galactosidase recombinant construct (Benito and Van Regenmortel, 1998). This result may be partly attributable to the fact that the three site-A regions had been fused within exposed loops of the maltose-binding protein which may have given them considerable mobility. The GH loop in FMDV is known to be very flexible (Acharya et al., 1989) and it has been suggested that it may be able to move in the native virus as a hinged unit endowed with significant internal stability (Curry et al., 1996; Lea et al., 1995). Little difference was observed in the average k_d values of the antisera raised against the different site A constructs. However, when the concentration of antisite A antibody in the different antisera was measured with Biacore under conditions of partial mass transport limitation (Richalet-Sécordel et al., 1997) it was found that the serum of animals immunized with peptide 141–160 coupled to ovalbumin contained about 10–30 times more antibody than the antisera to the recombinant proteins. Furthermore, antibodies raised against the conjugated synthetic peptide always reacted better with the peptide than with the recombinant proteins. Similarly, antibodies to the recombinant proteins usually reacted better with the site A inserted in the recombinant protein than with the free synthetic peptide. The immune system was thus clearly able to discriminate between the three site A presentation formats.

Various cyclization strategies of the GH loops of VP1 have been used in an attempt to improve the immunogenicity of the peptide but only some cyclic disulphide mimics were found to be better immunogens than the linear peptides (Camarero et al., 1993; Valero et al., 1995). However, an even more effective strategy for increasing the immunogenicity and stability of the synthetic GH loop of FMDV consisted in replacing classical L peptides by retro-all-D peptides. Retro-all-D peptides, also called retro-inverso peptides, are peptide analogues in which the direction of the sequence is reversed and the chirality of each residue is inverted (Chorev and Goodman, 1995). This leads to a peptide analogue in which the side chains are oriented in the same way as in the original L peptide, although there is an interconversion of the CO and NH atom pairs in the backbone and of the amino and carboxyl end groups. The ability of retro-inverso peptides to mimic the antigenic activity of L peptides was first demonstrated in a study of the C-terminal hexapeptide of histone H3. The retro-all-D analogue of this peptide was shown to be antigenically closely related to the parent peptide (Guichard et al., 1994).

The relationship between a retro-all-D peptide and its corresponding L peptide is illustrated in Fig. 8.1 using a four residue peptide as a model (Van Regenmortel, 1997). In this representation, residue 4 is glycine which has no L- or D-form. The similarity in side chain orientation in the L peptide and the retro-all-D form is readily seen when the L peptide drawn with its amino terminal residue to the left (line 1, Fig. 8.1) is compared with the retro-all-D peptide drawn from the back with its amino terminal residue to the right (line 8, Fig. 8.1). This similarity is responsible for the fact that L and retro-all-D peptides cross-react antigenically (Guichard et al., 1994; Muller et al., 1995; Van Regenmortel and Muller, 1998). This cross-reaction occurs in spite of the fact that in relation to the side chain orientation in the L peptide, both the direction of the peptide bonds and the location of the charged end groups are reversed in the retro-inverso peptide. Apparently side chain atoms contribute more to antigenic specificity than do main chain atoms, a conclusion that is confirmed by the presence of antigenic cross-reactivity between the retro and the D analogues (lines 4 and 5, Fig. 8.1) of a peptide (Benkirane et al., 1996a; Guichard et al., 1994).

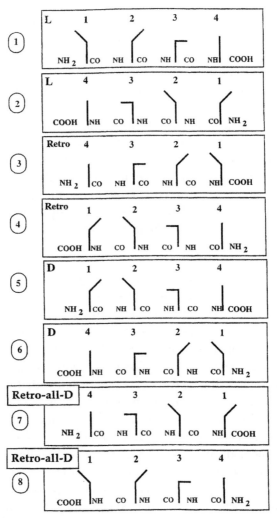

Fig. 8.1. Schematic representation of the results of various transformations of an L peptide (retro, D peptide and combined retro-all-D) on the orientation of side chains in a model tetrapeptide. Residue 4 is glycine. Note the similarity in side chain orientation in lines 1 and 8, and in lines 4 and 5 respectively. Note also the reversal of end groups and of backbone direction (Van Regenmortel 1997).

In some cases the reversal of the charged groups at both ends of the peptide hampers the detection of any potential cross-reactivity between the L and retro-all-D peptides or between the retro-all-D peptides and the cognate protein. Sometimes it is sufficient to remove the charges by acetylation and carboxamidation (Briand et al., 1995), but in other cases, blocking both extremities may be detrimental to antigenic activity. In some cases, it is necessary to replace the amino terminal residue of the retro-all-D peptide by a C-2-substituted malonic acid in order to closely mimic the carboxy terminus of the L peptide (Briand et al., 1997). This malonyl residue which is incorporated as a racemate generates a pairs of diastereoisomers that must be separated by HPLC since their antigenic reactivity can be vastly different (Briand et al., 1997; Muller et al., 1995). The amino terminus of the L peptide can be mimicked in the retro-all-D peptide by introducing a gem-diaminoalkyl residue at its carboxy terminus (Chorev and Goodman, 1995). Since there are no rules about the best strategy for solving the end-group problem in retro-inverso peptides, the optimal solution for each peptide must be determined by trial and error (Briand et al., 1995).

Retro-inverso peptide analogues of the region 141–159 of VP1 of two variants of FMDV of serotype A, subtype 12, have been synthesized and tested as possible candidate vaccines against foot-and-mouth disease. The various peptides used in these studies are shown in Table 8.1. They include a blocked L peptide (Ac–141–159(C)–NH$_2$), a blocked retro-all-D peptide (NH$_2$–141–159(C)–Ac), a NH$_2$ carboxyamidated retro-all-D peptide (NH$_2$–(C) 141–159–OH) and an acetylated L peptide (Ac–(C) 141–159–OH). Cysteine residues were added to the FMDV sequence to allow conjugation of the peptides to liposomes or to carrier proteins. The N-terminus of the carboxyamidated retro-all-D peptide was replaced by a C-2 substituted malonic acid.

The retro-all-D peptide (NH$_2$(C) 141–159–OH) coupled to liposomes containing the adjuvant monophosphoryl lipid A was found to induce in rabbits a higher peptide-specific IgG response than the L peptide (Benkirane et al., 1996a; Muller et al., 1995). The

TABLE 8.1

Amino acid sequences and nomenclature of the parent peptides and retro-inverso analogues of the 141–159 region of FMDV, FP variant

L-peptide
H-141-159(C)-OH
H-G→S→S→G→V→R→G→D→F→G→S→L→A→P→R→V→A→R→Q→L→C-*OH*

L-peptide
H-(C)141-159-OH
H-C→G→S→S→G→V→R→G→D→F→G→S→L→A→P→R→V→A→R→Q→L-*OH*

L-peptide
H-141-159(C)-NH₂
H-G→S→S→G→V→R→G→D→F→G→S→L→A→P→R→V→A→R→Q→L→C- *NH₂*

L-peptide
Ac-141-159(C)-NH₂
CH₃CO-G→S→S→G→V→R→G→D→F→G→S→L→A→P→R→V→A→R→Q→L→C-*NH₂*

RI-peptide
NH₂-141-159(C)-Ac
H₂N-G←s←G←v←r←G←d←f←G←s←l←a←p←r←v←a←r←q←l←c-*COCH₃*

L-peptide
Ac-(C)141-159-OH
CH₃CO-C→G→S→S→G→V→R→G→D→F→G→S→L→A→P→R→V→A→R→Q→L-*OH*

RI-peptide
NH₂-(C)141-159-OH
H₂N-c←c←G←s←G←v←r←G←d←f←G←s←l←a←p←r←v←a←r←q←(R,S)mL-*OH*

RI, retro-inverso; the arrows (→, ←) indicate the sense of the CO–NH bond in the peptide backbone. For conventional reasons, the numbering of resides was maintained in L and RI-peptides regardless of the orientation of the peptide bonds. Lower case letters indicate D-amino acid residues. m, malonate; Ac, acetyl; R, Rectus diastereoisomer; S, Sinister diastereoisomer.

response also appeared earlier after the start of immunization and lasted longer compared to what was observed with the L peptide. Antibodies to the retro-inverso peptide cross-reacted strongly with the L peptide and with virus particles, and guinea pig antisera to VP1 and to FMDV particles cross-reacted strongly with the retro-inverso peptide (Benkirane et al., 1996b).

It was also found that a single inoculation of the retro-all-D peptide (NH_2–(C) 141–159–OH) in guinea pigs (10–70 μg of KLH-conjugated peptide per animal in the presence of aluminium hydroxide gel) elicited high levels of neutralizing antibodies that persisted longer than those induced against the corresponding L peptide. The guinea pigs were protected when challenged with the cognate virus (Briand et al., 1997). A single injection of 100 μg of the retro-all-D peptide conjugated to KLH protected 8 out of 9 animals against the disease when they were challenged by contact with donor pigs showing full clinical signs. These results demonstrate that retro-inverso peptidomimetics have considerable potential as synthetic vaccines (Muller et al., 1998).

In the crystal structure of the virus in which the disulphide bond between Cys 134 of VP1 and Cys 130 of VP2 has been reduced, the region 148–155 of VP1 was found to possess a helical conformation (Logan et al., 1993) which had not been observed in the earlier crystallographic analysis of the virus (Acharya et al., 1989). This finding is of interest in view of the prediction of Guptasarma (1996) that retro-inverso analogues of L peptides are likely to possess the same right-handed helices as the natural L peptides.

In a comparative NMR study of the L- and retro-inverso 141–159 peptides, this prediction could not be corroborated. It was found that in trifluoroethanol, the retro-all-D peptide took on a lefthanded helix conformation whereas the L peptide took on the classical right-handed helix conformation (Carver et al., 1997). Since the structural mimicry achieved with the retro-all-D peptide did not extend to the handedness of the helix, it seems likely that the functional antigenic mimicry was obtained because of the absence of the helical conformation under the solvent conditions used for measuring antigenic activity (Guichard et al., 1996).

When the L and retro-all-D peptides were submitted to trypsin digestion, the half-life of the retro-all-D peptide was found to be more than 20-fold longer than that of the L peptide.

The introduction of D-amino acids in peptides is known to make them much more resistant to proteolytic degradation (Sela and Zisman, 1997; Van Regenmortel and Muller, 1998). The results obtained with the retro-all-D peptides of FMDV indicate that their superior stability gives them considerable potential as synthetic vaccines. It seems likely, however, that additional epitopes of FMDV will need to be incorporated in a synthetic vaccine in order to obtain a really effective peptide vaccine (Mateu, 1995; McCahon et al., 1989).

8.2.2. Poliovirus

Poliovirus is a member of the *Picornaviridae* virus family characterized by small isometric particles, 30 nm in diameter, containing a single molecule of single stranded RNA. The virus occurs as three serotypes, 1, 2 and 3, each serotype being neutralized by its own antibodies but not by antibodies specific for other serotypes. Poliovirus particles consist of four proteins, VP1 to VP4, that are post translationally cleaved from the same polyprotein strand. The three-dimensional structure of poliovirus has been determined by X-ray crystallography (Hogle et al., 1985). The secondary and tertiary structures of VP1, VP2 and VP3 are similar despite the lack of sequence homology. The conformational homology is based on the sheet-like alignment of eight antiparallel β strands. The strands are connected by loops, some of which protrude from the virion surface and harbour major epitopes of the virus (Fig. 8.2).

The antigenic structure of poliovirus has been reviewed by Hogle and Filman (1989) and by Van der Werf (1994). The four structural proteins assemble to produce the smallest structural sub-

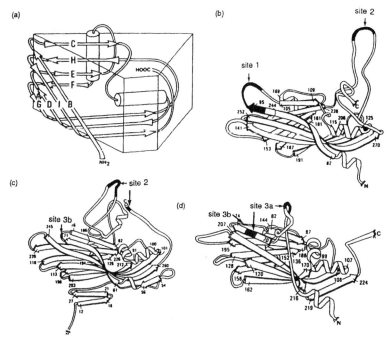

Fig. 8.2. (a) Schematic representation of the general folding pattern of the major poliovirus structural proteins. Eight antiparallel β-strands, the connecting loops and two α-helices are shown; (b) ribbon diagram of the VP1 protein of poliovirus showing antigenic site 1 (residues 89–101) and part of antigenic site 2; (c) diagram of the VP2 protein of poliovirus showing parts of antigenic site 2 and antigenic site 3; and (d) diagram of the VP3 protein showing parts of antigenic site 3. (From Wiley et al., 1994).

unit of the virion, the protomer. Five protomeric subunits, in turn, assemble to produce a pentameric subunit. In the virion, there are 12 pentameric subunits and thus 60 copies of each of the structural proteins (Rueckert, 1990). Antigenic site 1 is composed of residues 89–101 of VP1 present on a loop-linking two β strands (Fig. 8.2). Site 1 is immunodominant in poliovirus types 2 and 3, a feature attributed to the greater surface exposure of the loop compared to the situation in poliovirus type 1 (Minor et al., 1986; Patel et al.,

1993). Antigenic site 2 is a neotope which in serotypes 1 and 3 comprises residues 221–226 of VP1 as well as residues 164–172 and 270 of VP2 (Boeyé and Rombaut 1992). Antigenic site 3 is even more complex and has been subdivided into subsites according to serotype (Patel et al., 1993; Rombaut et al., 1990).

Various neutralization epitopes of the virus have been identified through the isolation and sequencing of mutants resistant to neutralization (Van der Werf, 1994). A number of neutralization epitopes were also located by measuring the ability of various synthetic peptides to bind to neutralizing Mabs. In addition, several T-helper cell epitopes were found to be adjacent to, or overlapping with, known B-cell epitopes (Kutubuddin et al., 1992a, b; Leclerc et al., 1991).

Various synthetic peptides of VP1 and VP2 have been shown to be able to elicit neutralizing antibodies in rabbits, rats and mice, but most studies have concentrated on the continuous epitope corresponding to antigenic site 1. Peptide 93–103 of VP1, conjugated to BSA, was found to elicit a significant serotype-specific level of neutralizing antibodies in rabbits (Emini et al., 1983). The same group reported that after a priming injection with the peptide, a single inoculation of a sub-immunogenic dose of virus was able to induce a neutralizing response (Emini et al., 1983, 1984; Jameson et al., 1985) while others failed to obtain any priming effect (Horaud et al., 1987)

In general, only about a quarter of all animals immunized with synthetic peptides were found to elicit a neutralizing antibody response. This low success rate could be due to the absence of T-cell help effective in the particular animal tested or to the fact that the conformation of the linear peptide encompassing the region 93–104 was not sufficiently similar to that of the same region in the intact virus particle and was not immunogenic in certain animals. Attempts to improve the level of conformational mimicry between peptide and virion by using longer peptides were unsuccessful (Chow et al., 1985; Horaud et al., 1987).

Since cyclization of peptides sometimes enhances their immunogenicity and ability to induce antibodies cross-reactive with the parent protein (Dreesman et al., 1982; Ferguson et al., 1985; Friede et al., 1993 a; Vuilleumier and Mutter, 1992) a number of different cyclization strategies have been tested to assess if the immunogenicity of the region 93–104 could be enhanced (Van der Werf et al., 1994). In these experiments, the antipeptide antibodies were tested for their ability to react with the linear peptide 95–104 and with infectious viral particles as well as for their capacity to neutralize viral infectivity in vitro. The peptides that induced a neutralizing antibody response in the highest number of immunized animals contained residues 104–115 in addition to antigenic site 1. This result may be due to the presence of a T-helper epitope in residues 103–115 (Leclerc et al., 1991).

One of the peptides was cyclized via an amide bond between Asp 93 and Lys 103 using the approach described by Plaue (1990). Three of the five animals immunized with this peptide in unconjugated form, produced a strong antibody response and in one animal there was a high neutralizing antibody titre (Van der Werf et al., 1994). Similar results were obtained in animals immunized with the same cyclized peptide conjugated to BSA. The extensive variations observed in the response of different animals were probably due to the ability of the cyclic peptide to adopt a variety of conformations which are not recognized equally well by all animals.

Studies with other viruses have shown that cyclization of an epitope corresponding to a loop in the native protein does not necessarily constrain the structure or increase the level of conformational mimicry between peptide and protein (Joisson et al., 1993). It would be interesting to establish if conjugation of peptide 93–103 to liposomes, which ensures a uniform chemical environment for each coupled peptide moiety, would succeed in reducing the heterogeneity in immune response, as was recently observed in the case of a cyclic peptide of influenza virus haemagglutinin (Friede et al., 1994). It is noteworthy that the addition of the T-cell epitope located in residues 103–115 of VP1 was not a prerequisite for rendering the cyclic peptide 93–103 immunogenic and capable of inducing neutralizing antibodies. In spite of our considerable knowledge of the

structure and antigenic properties of poliovirus attempts to develop
a synthetic vaccine have met with little success. Some of the reasons
for the lack of success in the so-called rational design of synthetic
vaccines are discussed in Section 8.11.

8.2.3. Influenza virus

Influenza virus A is a member of the family *Orthomyxoviridae*. The
virus particles are enclosed by a lipid envelope containing several
hundred copies of two oligomeric transmembrane glycoproteins,
the haemagglutinin (HA) and neuraminidase. Both proteins possess
globular heads mounted on a fibrous stalk that projects from the
virion membrane. The haemagglutinin is a trimeric structure, anchored in the membrane lipid bilayer by its C-terminal end, which
is responsible for attachment and fusion of the viral envelope to susceptible cells. Following the elucidation of the three-dimensional
structure of HA by X-ray crystallography, five antigenic sites were
identified at the surface of the molecule by the selection of escape
mutants using neutralizing Mabs (Air and Laver, 1990; Wiley et al.,
1981; Wilson et al., 1981).

Although antibodies to the HA neutralize virus infectivity, they
do not protect the host against recurrent outbreaks of influenza.
This is due to the fact that the HA undergoes continuous antigenic variation which takes two different forms. The first type of
variation, known as antigenic drift, is produced by the gradual accumulation of single amino acid substitutions in any one of the five
major antigenic sites of the HA molecule. Antigenic drift can be
mimicked in the laboratory by growing the virus in the presence
of neutralizing Mabs. This allows neutralization escape mutants to
be selected which generally contain a single substitution in any one
of the antigenic sites (Caton et al., 1982; Wilson et al., 1981). The
infectivity of such mutants can still be neutralized by antibodies
specific for one of the nonmutated antigenic sites. It seems that it is
the cumulative effect of mutations in each of the neutralizable sites

that eventually produces new successful epidemic variants capable of infecting individuals immune to viruses previously in circulation.

The second type of antigenic variation occurring in influenza virus is known as antigenic shift. This is generated by genetic reassortment in a mixed infection involving a human influenza virus and an avian strain of the virus. This may lead to the sudden emergence of a completely new human HA subtype, possessing many alterations in all the antigenic sites. Such abrupt changes were responsible for the influenza pandemics of 1957 and 1968.

In view of our extensive knowledge of the antigenic structure of influenza HA, this system has been studied extensively for assessing the potential usefulness of synthetic peptides for vaccination. Since influenza virus also infects mice, it is possible to evaluate the immune response to peptides and to study antigenic cross-reactivity as well as active and passive protection in this animal species.

Several groups have attempted to mimic HA epitopes with synthetic peptides. Green et al. (1982) synthesized 20 partially overlapping peptides representing over 75% of the HA sequence, coupled them to KLH and used the conjugates to immunize rabbits. Of the 20 peptides, 18 were found to elicit antibodies that reacted in ELISA with HA and with the virus, although none of the peptides reacted with anti-HA antibodies present in influenza virus antisera. It is likely that the high frequency with which the antipeptide antibodies reacted with HA in ELISA was due to the denaturation of the HA molecules following their adsorption to the solid-phase. In another study, linear peptides corresponding to residues 123–151, 128–148, 139–146 and 140–150 of HA failed to induce antibodies that cross-reacted with the virus (Schulze-Gahmen et al., 1986). When the peptide 140–146 was cyclized by a disulphide bond, it was able to elicit antibodies that cross-reacted weakly with the virus.

Some authors have succeeded in inducing protective immunity against influenza by immunization with peptides. A peptide corresponding to residues 91–108 of HA, after conjugation to tetanus toxoid, was found to elicit in rabbits and mice antibodies that reacted with influenza A virus and inhibited both the haemag-glutinating activity and the in vitro growth of the virus in tissue culture (Muller et al., 1982a). Furthermore, mice immunized with the peptide-toxoid conjugate were partially protected against fur-ther challenge infection with the virus. The region 91–101 which is conserved in the HA of several influenza strains was not identi-fied as one of the antigenic sites by Wilson et al. (1981), although antibodies to this region were found to elicit protection against sev-eral different viral strains. This result indicates that peptides may induce a broader cross-reactive protection against influenza than conventional vaccines. The findings of Muller et al. (1982a) were confirmed by Wilson et al. (1984) who showed that peptide 75–110 of HA could induce Mabs reacting with HA. The major activity within this peptide was located in the sequence 98–106 contained within the 91–108 peptide studied by Muller et al. (1982b). Since the sequence 98–106 is relatively inaccessible in the trimer HA in-terface (Wilson et al., 1984), the results imply that a conformational change occurs in the trimeric structure prior to antibody binding.

Antigenic site A (residues 139–46) which corresponds to a pro-truding loop at the surface of the trimeric HA structure has been studied by several groups. Immunization with peptides 139–146 and 123–151 did not induce antibodies cross-reacting with the virus (Jackson et al., 1982; Shapira et al., 1984). However, immunization with the longer peptide 138–164 led to the induction of antibodies that recognized the virus and provided partial protection against challenge infection. Schulze-Gahmen et al. (1986) cyclized peptide 140–146 by prolonging the sequence with Thr and Val residues fol-lowed by two Cys residues to form a disulphide bridge. However, the level of mimicry of the site A loop achieved in this manner was still insufficient since antibodies to haemagglutinin were not able to recognize the cyclic peptide. In order to mimic more precisely the conformation of site A, two cyclic peptides corresponding to residues 139–147 of HA, called the K loop and the D loop, were synthesized (Muller et al., 1990b). These peptides were obtained by cyclization of the 139–147 peptide by insertion of an amide bond between the N-terminus (Cys 139) and an additional C-terminal Asp for the D loop, or an additional Lys for the K loop. An additional Tyr was added at the C-terminus end of the peptides to allow them to be conjugated. When these peptide conjugates were administered with Freund's adjuvant, 80% of immunized mice were protected against an intranasal challenge with infectious virus. Antibodies to influenza virus reacted with both conjugated D and K loops adsorbed to the wells of ELISA plates. However, only the D loop in solution was recognized by antivirus antibodies and was able to inhibit the binding of these antibodies to the virus, presumably because it mimicked the site A loop more closely than the K loop (Muller et al., 1990b). When the two peptides were analyzed by nuclear magnetic resonance, the D loop was found to have a more compact conformation than the K loop (Kieffer et al., 1993). The greater flexibility of the K loop may allow the peptide, after it is conjugated to a protein carrier, to adopt a D loop-like structure and hence to confer protection.

In order to obviate the need for Freund's adjuvant, the two cyclic peptides were conjugated to unilamellar liposomes containing monophosphoryl lipid A as adjuvant (Friede et al., 1994). In contrast to the results obtained with protein carriers where both D and K loops conferred protection, only the D loop had a protective effect in the case of the peptide-liposome conjugates. As shown in Fig. 8.3, there was a difference in the cross-reactive potential of antibodies to the two peptides depending on whether they were raised against the peptide conjugated to a protein carrier or conjugated to liposomes. The higher cross-reactivity observed with the protein conjugates may account for the fact that both peptides conferred protection. On liposomes, the two loops presumably have a different conformation which mimimizes the cross-reactivity between them. Since the surface of liposomes is homogeneous, all conjugated peptide moieties are in the same micro-environment and probably adopt the same conformation. On a protein carrier, on the other hand, the environment at each point of attachment of the peptide to the protein is likely to be different and this may induce various conformations in the peptide moieties. These results indicate that the constrained conformation of cyclic peptides can be altered when they are conjugated to carrier proteins and that this may influence their antigenic properties and capacity to induce protection. On the other hand, when the peptides are conjugated to liposomes containing monophosphoryl lipid A as carrier, they assume a uniform conformation which may improve their immunizing activity as a synthetic vaccine. The importance of anchoring another HA peptide (residues 317–329) to liposomes for achieving a suitable conformation of the epitope has been demonstrated in a recent study (Laczko et al., 1998). The advantages of liposomes as carriers of peptide antigens and as vehicles for vaccines have been reviewed by Alving et al. (1995).

8.2.4. Canine parvovirus

Canine parvovirus (CPV) is a member of the *Parvoviridae* family of viruses characterized by small isometric particles containing a single stranded DNA genome. The three dimensional structure of CPV has been determined by X-ray crystallography (Tsao et al., 1991). Neutralization antigenic sites have been identified on the CPV surface, using escape mutant analysis and peptide mapping (Langeveld et al., 1993; Lopez de Turisto et al., 1991; Rimmelzwaan et al., 1990; Strassheim et al., 1994).

The viral capsid is formed by structural proteins VP1, VP2 and VP3, with VP2 being predominant. VP3 is a proteolytic product formed by removal of part of the amino terminus of VP2. This N-terminus contains a neutralization site conserved in different viral isolates which in the form of synthetic peptides is able to induce neutralizing antibodies and protection in the host (Langeveld et al., 1994a; Langeveld et al., 1994b).

Two overlapping 15-residue peptides of the VP2 protein (residues 1–15 and 7–21), after conjugation to KLH, were injected together into dogs in the presence of adjuvants Quil A and

OVALBUMIN-CONJUGATE

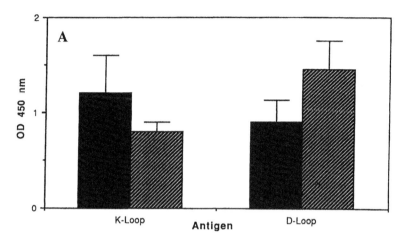

LIPOSOME-CONJUGATE

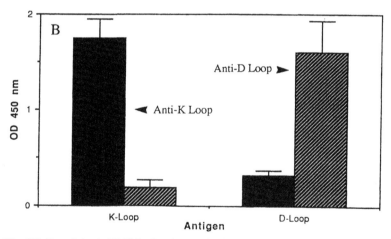

Fig. 8.3. Reactivity in ELISA of antisera raised against the D loop (shaded blocks) and K loop (solid blocks) peptides corresponding to residues 139–147 of influenza virus haemagglutinin synthesized with an additional Asp (D loop) and Lys residue (K loop). The peptides were conjugated to ovalbumin (A) or to liposomes (B). Antisera were tested at a dilution of 1/2000 against the K loop or D loop conjugated to BSA. Bars represent the standard deviation of 10 sera tested individually (Friede et al., 1994).

aluminium hydroxyde gel. Two vaccine doses of 1 mg of each peptide were administered to the animals on day 1 and 30. The vaccinated dogs were challenged 40 days later with a faecal CPV preparation and remained clinically healthy without any sign of disease (Langeveld et al., 1994a). All inoculated control animals which had not been vaccinated succumbed as a result of infection. These results represent the first example of a synthetic peptide vaccine inducing protection in target animals that complies with the requirements for practical application.

The protective mechanism appeared to be mediated by antipeptide antibodies aided by T-helper epitopes contained in the carrier protein used for peptide coupling. One factor that may have contributed to the success of this peptide vaccine is the fact that the N-terminal domain of VP2 to which the antibodies were directed is a flexible region of the protein, a feature which could facilitate the cross-reactivity between peptide and intact virus particles. However, the molecular details of the mechanism of antibody neutralization remain as obscure in this case as in other instances of virus infectivity neutralization by antibodies (Dimmock, 1993). In an independent study of the neutralization of CPV by a monoclonal antibody using image reconstruction of electron micrographs, it was suggested that the mechanism of neutralization was not by crosslinking of antigenic sites but more likely by interference with cell attachment, cell entry or uncoating (Wikoff et al., 1994).

The CPV peptide vaccine was also found to be highly effective in minks for preventing infection with mink enteritis virus (MEV). This virus is antigenically closely related to CPV and shares with it more than 98% sequence identity in the capsid proteins (Parrish, 1994; Parrish et al., 1988). A single injection of the CPV VP2 peptide in the presence of a defined adjuvant ISCOM matrix (Lövgren and Morein, 1988) was found to fully protect minks against a challenge infection with MEV (Langeveld et al., 1995). It is noteworthy that protection was obtained in the absence of any detectable antiviral antibodies or MEV neutralizing activity in the serum of vaccinated animals. The same situation was found in the vaccinated dogs which also developed only antipeptide antibodies in their serum (Langeveld et al., 1994a). The presence in the serum of vaccinated animals of detectable antibodies reacting with virus particles is therefore not a prerequisite or predictor for the efficacy of a synthetic peptide vaccine.

8.2.5. Measles virus

Measles virus (MV) is a member of the *Morbillivirus* genus of the *Paramyxoviridae* family. The enveloped virions are about 150 nm in diameter and contain one molecule of single stranded RNA. The virus has two surface glycoproteins, the haemagglutinin (H) and the fusion (F) proteins which are responsible for the attachment and fusion of virus particles to host cells. Antibody responses to the H and F proteins have been shown to play a key role in protection against measles (Drillien et al., 1988; Malvoisin and Wild, 1990). Despite the widespread and successful use of live attenuated measles vaccine in developed countries, the virus still remains a major cause of infant mortality in many parts of the world. It is generally accepted that there is a need to develop a better measles vaccine, in particular for overcoming the neutralizing effect of maternal antibodies in young vaccinated recipients (Obeid and Steward, 1994).

Both antibodies and CTL are important in the prevention of MV infection (Van Binnendijk et al., 1989). Several B- and T-cell epitopes from the H and F proteins have been identified as potential components of a synthetic vaccine (Partidos et al., 1992a, b; Partidos and Steward, 1992) A chimeric peptide (known as TTB peptide) representing two copies of a T-cell epitope from the F protein (residues 288–304) and one copy of a B-cell epitope also from the F protein (sequence 404–414) has been shown to be immunogenic in several inbred strains of mice (Partidos et al., 1991). The TTB peptide was also found to induce a protective immune response against challenge with a neuro-adapted MV in three inbred strains of mice (Obeid et al., 1995). The protection conferred by the TTB chimeric peptide was shown to correlate with the presence of antibodies of high affinity for the B-cell epitope 404–414. The critical role played by the antibody response to the TTB peptide in protection against MV-induced encephalitis was demonstrated by the fact that passive transfer of anti-TTB sera provided protection against disease.

A CTL epitope present in residues 52–60 of the MV nucleo-protein (Beauverger et al., 1994) has been covalently linked to the promiscuous T-helper epitope corresponding to residues 288–302 of the F protein of MV. The presence of two copies of the T-helper epitope at the N-terminus of the CTL epitope (TT-CTL) resulted in the induction of strong CTL responses in mice after administration in saline (Partidos et al., 1997). The importance of peptide structure for the induction of CTL responses was assessed by the analysis of circular dichroism spectra of the chimeric peptides. The results suggest that the amphipathic character of the TT-CTL chimeric construct favours its interaction with the cell membrane of antigen presenting cells, thereby facilitating its cytosolic delivery for class I presentation (Partidos et al., 1997).

The nature of the adjuvant used as well as the route of immu-nization was found to play an important role in the induction of a protective anti-TTB peptide antibody response. Protection against MV-induced encephalitis was obtained only when the TTB peptide was administered in Freund's complete or incomplete adjuvant or in alum (Obeid et al., 1996). When the TTB peptide was admin-istered in phosphate buffered saline or with the cytokine IL-2, no protection was observed. Furthermore, the subcutaneous route of immunization was found to be superior to the intraperitoneal route for inducing protection (Obeid et al., 1996). These results show that the best adjuvant and optimum route of immunization for use with a synthetic vaccine can only be determined in an empirical, trial-and-error manner.

A set of six mimotopes of an epitope recognized by a Mab to the F protein of MV has been generated by the use of a solid-phase combinatorial synthetic peptide library (Steward et al., 1995). The sequences of these mimotopes did not correspond to any region of the F protein. The anti-MV Mab did not bind to the mimotope peptides adsorbed to an ELISA plate, and the binding of the mimotopes to the Mab could only be demonstrated by the ability of the mimotopes to inhibit the binding of the Mab to MV in ELISA. Mimotopes 2 (NIIRTKKQ) and 4 (TRRAGPMQ) possessed the highest inhibitory capacity in such assay. When mice were immunized with the individual mimotopes together with a T-helper epitope peptide from the F protein (residues 258–277), only antibodies from mice injected with mimotope 2 cross-reacted with MV in ELISA and inhibited MV plaque formation. Mice immunized with mimotope 2 induced an antibody response which conferred protection against fatal encephalitis induced following challenge with MV and with the related canine distemper virus (Steward et al., 1995).

8.2.6. Human immunodeficiency virus

Human immunodeficiency virus 1 (HIV-1), a member of the *Lentivirus* genus of the family *Retroviridae*, is the causative agent of AIDS. Two envelope (env) glycoproteins are expressed on the surface of the virion, the surface glycoprotein gp 120 and the transmembrane glycoprotein gp 41. These two glycoproteins are gene products of a single gene and are synthesized as a precursor gp 160 which is proteolytically cleaved into gp 120 and gp 41. Several hundred copies of each glycoprotein are present on each virion surface, in the form of trimers. There are more than 20 glycosylation sites on gp 120 and about half of its mass is contributed by carbohydrate. There is considerable sequence variability among the envelope glycoproteins. The third variable region of gp 120 known as the V3 domain is the principal neutralization domain and is considered to be immunodominant (Norrby, 1993). It consists of about 35 amino acid residues flanked by two cysteines that form a disulphide bridge (LaRosa et al., 1990).

Classical vaccine approaches based on live attenuated virus or chemically inactivated virus have not been actively pursued in the case of HIV because of safety concerns. Most efforts have concentrated on subunit envelope vaccines using recombinant forms of the HIV-1 gp 120 envelope glycoprotein, as well as on a variety of synthetic peptides. More recently, live recombinant canary pox vectors that include HIV-1 antigens and naked DNA vectors that also express these antigens have given some promising results (Letvin, 1998).

The development of an HIV vaccine is a particularly difficult task because of factors such as considerable antigenic variation, a rapid viral replication rate, the poor immunogenicity of the envelope glycoproteins and the fact that HIV infects and destroys the CD4+ target cells that are crucial for an immune response. Another complicating factor is the ability of the viral nucleic acid to integrate into host DNA, which means that some of the infecting virus will remain invisible to humoral and cellular immune responses (Burton and Moore, 1998; Hilleman, 1995). Since a natural HIV infection does not lead to recovery and long-lasting protection, there is no reason to expect that mimicking natural infection with a vaccine will necessarily achieve protection (Hilleman, 1995). It seems that a successful vaccine would have to elicit an immune response that is stronger or qualitatively different from the immune response elicited by the natural infection with a single serotype.

The recently solved X-ray crystallographic structure of a ternary complex containing a portion of HIV-1 gp 120 bound to CD4 and to a neutralizing Mab has provided valuable information that may help in the design of novel epitopes able to induce neutralizing epitopes or protective CTL responses (Kwong et al., 1998; Wyatt et al., 1998).

In view of the enormous literature on HIV synthetic vaccines, it is not possible in this chapter to review the subject in an exhaustive manner. The interested reader should consult some of the extensive reviews devoted to the subject (Berzofsky and Berkover, 1995; Burton, 1997; Burton and Moore, 1998; Cease and Berzofsky, 1994;

Letvin, 1998; Norrby, 1993; Rowland-Jones et al., 1997). Initial studies on a synthetic peptide vaccine against HIV-1 concentrated on the V3 loop region of gp 120 (Neurath, 1993) but since this region is highly variable, the neutralizing antibodies obtained were mostly type-specific (Berzofsky and Berkover, 1995). In addition to B-cell epitopes, the V3 loop also contains an immunodominant epitope (called P18) for $CD8^+$ CTL in mice and humans. Covalent linkage between this CTL epitope and a T-helper epitope was important for optimal in vivo induction of CTL (Ahlers et al., 1993; Shirai et al., 1994). Furthermore, a single adjuvant formulation with a cluster peptide P18 vaccine construct elicited type-1 helper T cells, CTL and neutralizing antibody (Ahlers et al., 1996).

Since mucosal tissues are major sites of HIV-1 entry and initial infection, the induction of a mucosal CTL response is an important element for an effective HIV vaccine. This has been achieved with a synthetic multideterminant peptide vaccine which protected mice against mucosal challenge with HIV-1 (Belyakov et al., 1998). There is increasing emphasis on vaccines inducing mucosal immunity for a variety of viral infections (Levi et al., 1995; Londono et al., 1996; McGhee et al., 1992).

By replacing amino acids at certain positions of CTL or T-helper epitopes, it is possible to increase peptide immunogenicity, either by improving binding to MHC molecules or T-cell recognition (Lipford et al., 1995; Pogue et al., 1995). Such a process which has been called epitope enhancement, has been used successfully in the case of an HIV peptide vaccine construct (Ahlers et al., 1997). The enhancement mechanism operates by the removal of an adverse binding reaction in the natural peptide sequence caused by a bulky or charged side chain. The substitution of such a residue then leads to a more potent antigen and immunogen.

In spite of considerable research efforts, synthetic peptide formulations have so far proved disappointing in their ability to elicit CTLs in limited human trials. However, peptides may in future find a place as one element in a combination HIV vaccine strategy utilizing several different components.

8.2.7. Other viruses

Experimental peptide vaccines are also under development for several other viral diseases. These are based either on continuous neutralization epitopes of one of the structural virion proteins or on mimotopes of discontinuous epitopes defined by phage-displayed random peptide libraries (Folgori et al., 1994; Meola et al., 1995), or chemical combinatorial libraries (Sloostra et al., 1995). Promising results have been obtained with the following viruses: hepatitis B virus (Gerin et al., 1983; Itoh et al., 1986; Meola et al., 1995; Neurath and Kent, 1985), respiratory syncytial virus (Chargelegue et al., 1998; Simard et al,, 1997), human papillomaviruses (Feltkamp et al., 1993; Lipford et al., 1995), bovine leukemia virus (Kabeya et al., 1996; Ohishi et al., 1996), feline immunodeficiency virus (Rigby et al., 1996) and hepatitis C virus (Sarobe et al., 1998).

8.3. Vaccines against bacterial infections

One of the first uses of synthetic peptides for eliciting protection against a bacterial infection was the study of Beachy et al. (1981) who showed that a synthetic 35-residue peptide of the M protein of *Streptococcus pyogenes* could induce type-specific protective antibodies. Most work on bacterial synthetic vaccines has been concerned with bacterial toxins. The first demonstration that a synthetic peptide could elicit antitoxin activity was provided by Audibert et al. (1981) who showed that a 14-residue peptide corresponding to the N-terminal region of diphtheria toxin could induce protective antibodies when administered to guinea pigs. A protective antitoxin response could be obtained without the use of adjuvant by attaching the peptide to a synthetic polymer that included N-acetyl-muramyl-L-alanyl-D-isoglutamine (MDP), the active adjuvant ingredient of mycobacteria (Audibert et al., 1982; Chedid, 1987).

A similar approach was used with the B subunit of *Vibrio cholerae* toxin (CT). Antibodies induced against regions 8–20 and

50–64 of CT were found to inhibit the biological activity of the cholera toxin (Jacob et al., 1983) as well as that of the related heat-labile toxin of pathogenic strains of *E. coli* (Jacob et al., 1985; Jacob et al., 1984). These results indicate that it may be feasible to develop a synthetic vaccine suitable for protection against various forms of bacterial diarrhoeal diseases.

Several peptides of the B subunit of the *Shigella dysenteriae* toxin were also found to elicit antibodies that neutralized the entero-toxic and neurotoxic activity of the Shiga toxin (Harari et al., 1988). In shigellosis, as in all enteric diseases, the gut is the organ into which the toxin is secreted and where it exerts its detrimental effect. For this reason, attempts have been made to develop local immunity by intragastric immunization that could lead to neutralization of the toxin in situ. Oral immunization of rats with the peptide conjugates of Shiga toxin has been shown to induce high levels of specific IgA antibodies. Furthermore, the immunized rats were protected against the intestinal fluid secretion induced by injection of Shiga toxin (Arnon et al., 1990).

Peptides from the fimbriae of *Porphyromonas gingivalis*, respon-sible for periodontal disease, have been shown to induce a protective immune response in guinea pigs (Ogawa, 1994). These various studies show that synthetic peptides have considerable potential for inducing both systemic and local immunity against bacterial infections.

8.4. Vaccines against parasites

Malaria is the most important parasitic disease. The World Health Organization estimates that up to 300 million cases of malaria and 3 million deaths occur worldwide each year. Despite considerable research efforts, the development of malaria vaccines has met with little success. In view of the antigenic complexity of the *Plas-modium* organism that causes malaria, it has been very difficult to select appropriate targets for vaccine-induced immunity (Good and Miller, 1994). Different life cycle stages of the organism express novel, polymorphic surface antigens, while antigens inserted by the parasite into the surface membrane of infected erythrocytes undergo clonal antigenic variation. Furthermore, antigens that are immunodominant in natural infections tend not to induce protective immunity while the absence of a good animal model for evaluating the efficacy of putative vaccines has made the scientific assessment of a malaria vaccine extremely difficult (Riley, 1995). Only one synthetic peptide vaccine has undergone field trials and the results regarding its efficacy have been highly controversial (Maurice, 1995; Moreno and Patarroyo, 1995).

The major surface circumsporozoite protein contains a repeating tetrapeptide sequence $(NANP)_n$ which has been used in an experimental vaccine (Zavala et al., 1985). In spite of the many candidate synthetic peptide vaccines that have been tested in recent years (Calvo-Calle et al., 1993; Deoliveira et al., 1994; Herrera et al., 1997; Migliorini et al., 1993; Patarroyo et al., 1992; Tam et al., 1990; Wang et al., 1995) it is still uncertain whether this approach will eventually provide the long-awaited vaccine against malaria.

Schistosomiasis is a serious parasitic disease caused by the helminth *Schistosoma mansoni* which infects over 200 million people worldwide (Arnon and Sela, 1969). There is no vaccine available against schistosomiasis (Bergquist, 1995) and synthetic peptide vaccines are one strategy that is being actively pursued. B-cell and T-helper epitopes have been identified in *S. mansoni* antigens and used as candidate vaccines (Reynolds et al., 1994; Reynolds et al., 1992) and a CTL epitope has been used in the form of a lipopeptide (Pancre et al., 1996) and a MAP (Ferru et al., 1997). A 14-residue peptide corresponding to the N-terminal region of the 45 kDa subunit of the 9 B antigen of *S. mansoni* has been shown to induce a significant level of protection against challenge infection (Tarrab-Hazdai et al., 1998). Since the parasite does not reproduce in the mammalian host, the observed 50% reduction in worm burden brought about by vaccination with this peptide may be sufficient for the purpose of developing a practical vaccine.

8.5. Are molecular design strategies applicable to the development of synthetic vaccines?

Our increased understanding of the molecular basis of immunological recognition has given rise in some quarters to the expectation that it may be possible to apply molecular design strategies to the development of peptide based vaccines. This belief is based on the misconception that vaccine development is somehow similar to the development of new drugs by what has been called rational design. In the case of structure-based drug design, many molecular biologists endorse the viewpoint of Amzel (1998) according to which 'one of the goals of biotechnology is to transform the process of developing a drug from a trial-and-error, empirical operation into a rational, structure-based process'. Such statements tend to accredit the view that empiricism and rationality are two separate approaches to problem solving and that the rational approach is to be preferred. That such a view is mistaken is demonstrated by the historical fact that modern science blossomed after the seventeenth century because of the primacy of empirical observations over purely rational analysis. Although logic and rationality are needed to set up a research project, it is not deductive thinking but the unpredictable outcome of experiments that leads to novel findings and scientific discoveries (Van Regenmortel, 1999b).

In recent years it has become fashionable to give the label 'rational' to any biological research that makes extensive use of molecular data. For instance, in research on peptide-based viral vaccines, the commonsense decision to focus on known antigenic regions of a viral protein as primary targets for investigation has been hailed as a rational approach (Obeid et al., 1995). It seems that the term rational is meant to convey that the approach that is used is based on recently acquired scientific knowledge rather than on empirical, trial and error investigations

A scientific procedure can be said to be rational if it is based on reason, logic and scientific theory. A rational design implies that it is possible to predict the outcome of an experiment on the basis of logic and theoretical principles. In contrast, an empirical approach implies that the outcome cannot be predicted from pre-existing knowledge and must be derived from the experimental observations themselves. Opposing rational and empirical approaches in the practice of experimental science is actually misleading since all scientific knowledge is derived from empirical observations gathered in the course of experiments that must be designed and analyzed in a rational manner.

Although it could be argued that it may be possible, using a molecular design approach, to improve the antigenic reactivity of a molecule with respect to a single monoclonal antibody, such an attempt is bound to fail for improving the molecule's immunogenicity. The reason for this is that immunogenicity depends not only on intrinsic properties of the antigen but also on the potentialities of the host being immunized such as its immunoglobulin gene repertoire, self-tolerance and various cellular and regulatory mechanisms. These immunological parameters cannot be optimized following molecular design principles. Optimizing the binding properties of a peptide with respect to one neutralizing monoclonal antibody does not insure that the same antibody will be elicited when the peptide is used as vaccine immunogen.

8.6. Empirical discovery rather than molecular design will bring about new synthetic vaccines

There are many reasons why the molecular design of synthetic vaccines is not a realistic scientific enterprise (Van Regenmortel, 1999b).

1. The shape and electrostatic complementarity of antigen-antibody interfaces is poorer than that of other protein ligand interfaces (Braden and Poljak, 1995). This is due to the conserved architecture of the antibody-combining site and to the absence of optimization of individual epitope-paratope pairs through evolution.

2. Immune recognition is mediated by multispecific binding sites. A single immunoglobulin molecule harbours many different combining sites or paratopes, each one consisting of only about one third of the CDR residues of the molecule. This leads to many potential antigenic cross-reactivities between related as well as unrelated antigenic determinants or epitopes.

3. Whereas the lock-and-key model has been successful for the molecular docking of drugs (Gschwend et al., 1996) it fails in the case of antigen-antibody docking (Carneiro and Steward, 1994) because the induced fit and solvent effects that occur during epitope-paratope interactions cannot be modelled satisfactorily (Doniach, 1997).

4. It is not possible to translate the atomic coordinates of an antigen-antibody complex into interaction binding energy (Janin, 1997). Although higher equilibrium affinity constants or slower dissociation rate constants of antibodies could be useful for increasing the capacity of antibodies to neutralize infectivity (Van Cott et al., 1994), such constants cannot be engineered at will.

5. Epitopes and paratopes are relational entities that cannot be defined by intrinsic features existing independently of this relationship. It is impossible to visualize the structure of the binding site in the absence of a particular, individual interaction (see Chapter 1).

6. Structural analysis of an immune complex involves a single epitope-paratope pair. However, neutralization antigenic sites consist of several overlapping or nonoverlapping epitopes that are functionally active in a collective manner. Cooperativity effects in infectivity neutralization by antibodies cannot be dissected at the molecular level in terms of individual structures.

7. Infectivity neutralization by antibody involves a ternary interaction between the pathogen, the antibody and the host cell. Mechanisms of neutralization and of escape from neutralization are poorly understood (Dimmock, 1993). None of the exist-

ing successful vaccines has had its mechanism of action fully elucidated.

8. Modifying binding sites by mutagenesis does not amount to a molecular design strategy. The effects of site-directed mutagenesis on binding activity are not predictable, partly because of nonadditivity (cooperativity) between individual mutations (Rauffer-Bruyére et al., 1997) Residue substitutions tend to produce small structural shifts that cannot be detected at the current resolution of structural data although they affect binding activity (Sturtevant, 1994).

9. The recognition between epitopes and paratopes does not take place at the level of whole residues but at the level of individual atoms. Peptides showing little sequence similarity may cross-react with the same antibody because only a minority of the atoms of any residue actually participate in the interaction. Site-directed mutagenesis, therefore, cannot increase the level of atomic complementarity in a predictable manner.

10. There are no general rules for designing peptide immunogens that elicit neutralizing rather than nonneutralizing antibody. For instance, it is customary to block the unnatural charges present at the termini of peptides which are absent in the cognate protein, but this does not guarantee that such blocked peptides will be able to elicit neutralizing antibodies. In the case of retro-all-D peptide analogues of an immunodominant epitope of foot-and-mouth disease virus, it was found that only some of the methods used for removing the charges of the peptides were successful and led to peptides able to induce neutralizing antibodies (Briand et al., 1997). When immunodominant epitopes of influenza virus and of poliovirus were cyclized in order to improve the level of conformational mimicry between peptide and intact protein, it was found that conjugation of the peptides to a carrier affected the induction of neutralizing antibodies in an unpredictable manner (Friede et al., 1994; Van der Werf et al., 1994). It is a sobering fact that the best results obtained with synthetic peptide vaccines so far concern epitopes located in

disordered regions of viral proteins which cannot be designed to have the correct conformation (Brown, 1994; Langeveld et al., 1994a).

11. The optimal size of a peptide and the need to incorporate helper T-cell and cytotoxic T-cell epitopes in the construction of a synthetic peptide vaccine can only be established empirically (Partidos and Steward, 1992).

12. MHC polymorphism dictates the use of several peptide epitopes of the pathogen for effective memory response (Berzofsky et al., 1991). Clinical trials are needed to assess the efficacy of each particular combination of peptides (Ahlers et al., 1996). The titre of neutralizing antibody in the serum of vaccinated subjects is not necessarily correlated with protection against infection (Obeid and Steward, 1994).

13. The best adjuvant and delivery route for each vaccine cannot be predicted and must be established by trial and error (Obeid et al., 1996).

Since the capacity of a synthetic peptide to induce a protective immune response depends on many extrinsic factors and regulatory mechanisms in the recipient host, the immunogenic effectiveness and vaccine potential of peptides cannot be predicted. It seems safe to predict that rational design strategies based on the optimization of the structural complementarity of single epitope-paratope pairs will be of little use for the development of synthetic vaccines. Efforts to develop peptide-based vaccines will therefore continue to rely on empirical discovery rather than on so-called rational molecular design. However, all scientific knowledge and applications are ultimately derived from empirical observations and the need to rely on empiricism in no way diminishes the potential usefulness of synthetic vaccines.

References

Aaskov, J. G., Geysen, H. M. and Mason, T. J. (1989) Arch. Virol. *105*, 209.

Absolom, D. and Van Regenmortel, M. H. V. (1977) FEBS Lett. *81*, 419.

Acharya, R., Fry, E., Stuart, D., Fox, G., Rowlands, D. and Brown, F. (1989) Nature *337*, 709.

Adam, A. and Lederer, E. (1988) ISI atlas of science. Immunology *1*, 205.

Adam, A. and Souvannavong, V. (1992) In: Structure of Antigens, Vol. 1 (Van Regenmortel, M. H. V., ed.). CRC Press, Boca Raton, p. 159.

Adler, S., Frank, R., Lanzavecchia, A. and Weiss, S. (1994) FEBS Lett. *352*, 167.

Agterberg, M., Adriaanse, H., Lankhof, H., Meloen, R. and Tommassen, J. (1990) Vaccine *8*, 85.

Ahlhorg, N., Anderson, R., Perlmann, P. and Berzins, K. (1996) Immunology *88*, 630.

Ahlers, J. D., Dunlop, N., Pendleton, C. D., Newman, M., Nara, P. L. and Berzofsky, J. A. (1996) Aids Res. Hum. Retroviruses *12*, 259.

Ahlers, J. D., Pendleton, C. D., Dunlop, N., Minassian, A., Nara, P. L. and Berzofsky, J. A. (1993) J. Immunol. *150*, 5647.

Ahlers, J. D., Takeshita, T., Pendleton, C. D. and Berzofsky, J. A. (1997) Proc. Natl. Acad. Sci. USA *94*, 10856.

Air, G. M. and Laver, W. G. (1990) In: Immunochemistry of Viruses II. The Basis for Serodiagnosis and Vaccines (Van Regenmortel, M. H. V. and Neurath, A. R., eds.). Elsevier, Amsterdam, p. 171.

Aithal, H. N., Knigge, K. M., Kartha, S., Czyzewski, E. A. and Toback, F. G. (1988) J. Immunol. Meth. *112*, 63.

Akhmanova, A., Miedema, K., Wang, Y., Van Bruggen, M., Berden, J. H. M., Moudrianakis, E. N. and Hennig, W. (1997) Chromosoma *106*, 335.

Al Moudallal, Z., Altschuh, D., Briand, J. P. and Van Regenmortel, M. H. V. (1984) J. Immunol. Meth. *68*, 35.

Al Moudallal, Z., Briand, J. P. and Van Regenmortel, M. H. V. (1982) EMBO J. *1*, 1005.

Al Moudallal, Z., Briand, J. P. and Van Regenmortel, M. H. V. (1985) EMBO J. *4*, 1231.

Albericio, F., Andreu, D., Giralt, E., Navalpotro, C., Pedroso, E., Ponsati, B. and Ruiz-Gayo, M. (1989) Int. J. Pept. Prot. Res. *34*, 124.

319

Albrecht, H., Geldreich, A., Menissier de Murcia, J., Kirchheer, D., Mesnard, J. M. and Lebeurier, G. (1988) Virology *163*, 503.

Alexander, H., Alexander, S., Getzoff, E. D., Tainer, J. A., Geysen, H. M. and Lerner, R. A. (1992) Proc. Natl. Acad. Sci. USA. *89*, 3352.

Alexander, J., Snoke, K., Ruppert, J., Sidney, J., Wall, M., Southwood, S., Oseroff, C., Arrhenius, T., Gaeta, F. C. A., Colon, S. M., Grey, H. M. and Sette, A. (1993) J. Immunol. *150*, 1.

Allauzen, S., Joly, S., Granier, C., Molina, F., Bouix, O., Pau, B. and Bouanani, M. (1995) Mol. Immunol. *32*, 27.

Allison, A. C. and Byars, N.E. (1986) J. Immunol. Meth. *95*, 157.

Allison, A. C. and Byars, N.E. (1991) Molec. Immunol. *28*, 279.

Altschuh, D., Al Moudallal, Z., Briand, J. P. and Van Regenmortel, M. H. V. (1985) Molec. Immunol. *22*, 329.

Altschuh, D., Dubs, M. C., Weiss, E., Zeder-Lutz, G. and Van Regenmortel, M. H. V. (1992) Biochemistry *31*, 6298.

Altschuh, D., Hartman, D., Reinbolt, J. and Van Regenmortel, M. H. V. (1983) Molec. Immunol. *20*, 271.

Altschuh, D. and Van Regenmortel, M. H. V. (1982) J. Immunol. Meth. *50*, 99.

Alving, C. R. (1991) J. Immunol. Meth. *140*, 1.

Alving, C. R., Koulchin, V., Glenn, G. M. and Rao, M. (1995) Immunol. Rev. *145*, 5.

Alving, C. R. and Richards, R. L. (1983) In: Liposomes (Ostro, M. J., ed.). Marcel Dekker, New York, p. 209.

Alving, C. R., Richards, R. L., Moss, J., Alving, L. I., Clements, J. D., Shiba, T., Kotani, S., Wirtz, R. A. and Hockmeyer, W. T. (1986) Vaccine *4*, 166.

Amit, A. G., Mariuzza, R. A., Phillips, S. E. V. and Poljak, R. J. (1986) Science *233*, 747.

Amzel, L. M. (1998) Cur. Opin. Biotech. *9*, 366.

Anderer, F. A. (1963) Adv. Protein Chem. *18*, 1.

Anderer, F. A. and Schlumberger, H. D. (1965a) Z. Naturforsch. *20B*, 564.

Anderer, F. A. and Schlumberger, H. D. (1965b) Biochem. Biophys. Acta *97*, 503.

Anderer, F. A. and Schlumberger, H. D. (1966a) Biochem. Biophys. Acta *115*, 222.

Anderer, F. A. and Schlumberger, H. D. (1966b) Z. Naturforsch. *21B*, 602.

Anderer, F. A., Schlumberger, H. D. and Frank, M. (1967) Biochem. Biophys. Acta *140*, 80.

Antoni, G., Mariani, M., Presentini, R., Lafata, M., Neri, P., Bracci, L. and Cianfriglia, M. (1985) Mol. Immunol. *22*, 1237.

Apostolopoulos, V., Pietersz, G. A., Loveland, B. E. and Sandrin, M. S. (1995) Proc. Natl. Acad. Sci. USA *92*, 10128.

Appel, J. R., Muller, S., Benkirane, N., Houghten, R. A. and Pinilla, C. (1996) Peptide Res. *9*, 174–182.

Arnon, R. (1987) Synthetic Vaccines, Vols. 1 and 2, CRC Press, Boca Raton.

Arnon, R., Harari, I. and Keusch, G. T. (1990) In: New Generation Vaccines (Woodrow, G. C. and Levine, M. M., eds.), Marcel Dekker, New York, p. 688.

Arnon, R., Maron, E., Sela, M. and Anfinsen, C. B. (1971) Proc. Natl. Acad. Sci. USA *68*, 1450.

Arnon, R. and Sela, M. (1969) Proc. Natl. Acad. Sci. USA *62*, 163.

Arnon, R., Sela, M., Parant, M. and Chedid, L. (1980) Proc. Natl. Acad. Sci. USA *77*, 6769.

Arnon, R., Shapira, M. and Jacob, C. O. (1983) J. Immunol. Meth. *61*, 261.

Arnon, R. and Van Regenmortel, M. H. V. (1992) FASEB J. *6*, 3265.

Atanassov, C., Briand, J. P., Bonnier, D., Van Regenmortel, M. H. V. and Muller, S. (1991) Clin. Exp. Immunol. *86*, 124.

Atassi, M. Z. (1975) Immunochemistry *12*, 423.

Atassi, M. Z. (1977a) In: Immunochemistry of Proteins, Vol 1 (Atassi, M. Z., ed.). Plenum Press, New York, p. 1.

Atassi, M. Z. (1977b) Immunochemistry of Proteins, Vol. 1. Plenum Press, New York.

Atassi, M. Z. (1984) Eur. J. Biochem. *145*, 1.

Atassi, M. Z., Dolimbek, B. Z. and Manshouri, T. (1995) Molec. Immunol. *32*, 919.

Atassi, M. Z. and Habeeb, A. F. S. A. (1972) Meth. Enzymol. *25*, 546.

Atassi, M. Z. and Habeeb, A. F. S. A. (1977) In: Immunochemistry of Proteins, Vol. 2 (Atassi, M. Z., ed.). Plenum Press, New York, p. 177.

Atassi, M. Z., Habeeb, A. F. S. A. and Ando, K. (1973) Biochem. Biophys. Acta *303*, 203.

Atassi, M. Z. and Lee, C. (1978) Biochem. J. *171*, 429.

Atassi, M. Z. and Smith, J. A. (1978) Immunochemistry *15*, 609.

Atassi, M. Z. and Young, J. A. (1985) CRC Crit. Rev. Immunol. *5*, 387.

Atherton, E. and Sheppard, R. C. (1989) Solid Phase Peptide Synthesis. A Practical Approach. IRL Press, Oxford, p. 203.

Audhya, T. (1988) In: Macromolecular Sequencing and Synthesis. Selected Methods and Applications, Alan R. Liss, New York, p. 101.

Audibert, F. (1987) In: Synthetic Vaccines, Vol. II (Arnon, R., ed.). CRC Press, Boca Raton.

Audibert, F., Jolivet, M., Chedid, L., Alouf, J. E., Boquet, P., Rivaille, P. and Siffert, O. (1981) Nature *289*, 593.

Audibert, F., Jolivet, M., Chedid, L., Arnon, R. and Sela, M. (1982) Proc. Natl. Acad. Sci. USA *79*, 5042.

Ausubel, F. M., Brent, R., Kingston, R. E., Moore, D. D., Seidman, J. G., Smith, J. A. and Struhl, K. (1994–1997) In: Current Protocols in Molecular Biology (Ausubel, F. M., Brent, R., Kingston, R. E., Moore, D. D., Seidman, J. G., Smith, J. A. and Struhl, K., eds.). John Wiley, New York.

Bachrach, H. L., Moore, D. M., McKercher, P. D. and Polatnick, J. (1975) J. Immunol. *115*, 1636.

Bahraoui, E., El Ayeb, M., Granier, C. and Rochat, H. (1987) Eur. J. Biochem. *167*, 371.

Bahraoui, E., El Ayeb, M., Van Rietschoten, J., Rochat, H. and Granier, C. (1986a) Mol. Immunol. *23*, 357.

Bahraoui, E. M., Granier, C., Van Rietschoten, J., Rochat, H. and El Ayeb, M. (1986b) J. Immunol. *136*, 3371.

Ball, J. M., Henry, N. L., Montelaro, R. C. and Newman, M. J. (1994) J. Immunol. Meth. *171*, 37.

Ban, N., Escobar, C., Garcia, R., Hasel, K., Day, J., Greenwood, A. and McPherson, A. (1994) Proc. Natl. Acad. Sci. USA *91*, 1604.

Ban, N., Escobar, C., Hasel, K., Day, J., Greenwood, A. and McPherson, A. (1995) FASEB J. *9*, 107.

Barakat, S., Briand, J. P., Abuaf, N., Van Regenmortel, M. H. V. and Muller, S. (1991) Clin. Exp. Immunol. *86*, 71.

Barakat, S., Briand, J. P., Weber, J. C., Van Regenmortel, M. H. V. and Muller, S. (1990) Clin. Exp. Immunol. *81*, 256.

Barakat, S., Meyer, O., Torterotot, F., Youinou, P., Briand, J. P., Kahn, M. F. and Muller, S. (1992) Clin. Exp. Immunol. *89*, 38.

Barbara, D. J. and Clark, M. F. (1982) J. Gen. Virol. *58*, 315.

Baron, M. H. and Baltimore, D. (1982a) Cell *28*, 395.

Baron, M. H. and Baltimore, D. (1982b) J. Virol. *43*, 969.

Bauminger, S. and Wilcher, M. (1980) Meth. Enzymol. *70.*, 151.

Bayer, E. and Rapp, W. (1992) In: Poly(Ethylene Glycol) Chemistry: Biotechnical and Biomedical Applications (Harris, J. M., ed.). Plenum Press, New York, p. 325.

Beachy, E. A., Seyer, J. M., Dale, J. B., Simpson, W. A. and Kang, A. (1981) Nature *289*, 457.

Beauverger, P., Chadwick, J., Buckland, R. and Wild, T. F. (1994) Virology *203*, 172.

Becker, J., Leser, U., Langford, A., Jilg. W., Reichart, P., Gelderblom, H. and Wolf, H. (1989) In: Epstein-Barr Virus and Human Disease II (Ablashi et al. Eds.), Humana Press, New-Jersey, p. 267.

Beesley, K. M., Francis, M. J., Clarke, B. E., Beesley, J. E., Dopping-Hepenstal, P. J. C., Clare, J. J., Brown, F. and Romanos, M. A. (1990) Biotechnology *8*, 644.

Bellet, D., Bidart, J. M., Jolivet, M., Tartar, A., Caillaud, J. M., Ozturk, M., Strugo, M. C., Audibert, F., Gras-Masse, H., Assicot, M. and Bohuon, C. (1984) Endocrinology *115*, 330.

Belyakov, I. M., Derby, M. A., Ahlers, J. D., Kelsall, B. L., Earl, P., Moss, B., Strober, W and Berzofsky, J. A. (1998) Proc. Natl. Acad. Sci. USA *95*, 1709.

Benito, A. and Van Regenmortel, M. H. V. (1998) FEMS Immun. Med. Microbiol. *21*, 101.

Benito, A. and Villaverde, A. (1994) FEMS Microbiol. Lett. *123*, 107.

Benjamin, D. C., Berzofsky, J. A., East, I. J., Gurd, F. R. N., Hannum, C., Leach, S. J., Margoliash, E., Michael, J. G., Miller, A., Prager, E. M., Reichlin, M., Sercaz, E. E., Smith-Gill, S. J., Todd, P. E. and Wilson, A. C. (1984) Annu. Rev. Immunol. *2*, 67.

Benjamin, D. C. and Perdue, S. (1996) Methods *9*, 508.

Benjamin, D. C., Williams, D. C., Smith-Gill, S. J. and Rule, G.S. (1992) Biochemistry *31*, 9539.

Benjamini, E. (1977) In: Immunochemistry of Proteins, Vol. 2 (Atassi, M. Z., ed.). Plenum Press, New York, p. 265.

Benjamini, E., Shimizu, M., Young, J. D. and Leung, C. Y. (1968a) Biochemistry *7*, 1253.

Benjamini, E., Shimizu, M., Young, J. D. and Leung, C. Y. (1968b) Biochemistry *7*, 1261.

Benjamini, E., Young, J. D., Peterson, W. J., Leung, C. Y. and Shimizu, M. (1965) Biochemistry *4*, 2081.

Benjamini, E., Young, J. D., Shimizu, VI. and Leung, C. Y. (1964) Biochemistry *3*, 1115.

Benkirane, N., Briand, J. P. and Muller, S. (1996a) Unpublished.

Benkirane, N., Friede, M., Guichard, G., Briand, J. P., Van Regenmortel, M. H. V. and Muller, S. (1993) J. Biol. Chem. *268*, 26279.

Benkirane, N., Guichard, G., Briand, J. P., Muller, S., Brown, F. and Van Regenmortel, M. H. V. (1996b) In: New Approaches to Stabilisation of Vaccines Potency, Vol. 87 (Brown, F., ed.). Karger; Dev. Biol. Stand., Basel, p. 281.

Benkirane, N., Guichard, G., Van Regenmortel, M. H. V., Briand, J.-P. and Muller, S. (1995) J. Biol. Chem. *270*, 11921.

BenMohamed, L., Gras-Masse, H., Tartar, A., Daubersies, P., Brahimi, K., Bossus, M., Thomas, A. and Druilhe, P. (1 997) Eur. J. Immunol. *27*, 1242.

Bennet, B., Check, I. J., Olsen, M. R. and Hunter, R. L. (1992) J. Immunol. Meth. *153*, 31.

Bentley, G. A., Boulot, G., Karjalainen, K. and Mariuzza, R. A. (1995) Science *267*, 1984.

Bentley, G. A., Boulot, G., Riottot, M. M. and Poljak, R. J. (1990) Nature *348*, 254.

Bergquist, N. R. (1995) Parasitol. Today *11*, 191.

Berna, A., Briand, J. P., Stussi-Garaud, C. and Godefroy-Colburn, T. (1986) J. Gen. Virol. *67*, 1135.

Berna, A., Gafny, R., Wolf, S., Lucas, W. J., Holt, C. A. and Beachy, R. N. (1991) Virology *182*, 682.

Bernatowicz, M. S. and Matsueda, G. R. (1986) Anal. Biochem. *155*, 95.

Berzins, K., Perlmann, H., Wahlin, B., Carlsson, J., Wahlgren, M., Udomsang-petch, R., Bjorkman, A, Patarroyo, M. E. and Perlmann, P. (1986) Proc. Natl. Acad. Sci. USA *83*, 1065.

Berzofsky, J. A. (1985) Science *229*, 932.

Berzofsky, J. A. and Berkover, J. (1995) AIDS *9*, S143.

Berzofsky, J. A., Buckenmeyer, G. K., Hicks, G., Gurd, F. R. N., Feldmann, R. J. and Minna, J. (1982) J. Biol. Chem. *257*, 3189.

Berzofsky, J. A., Pendleton, C. D., Clerici, M., Ahlers, J., Lucey, D. R., Putney, S. D. and Shearer, G. M. (1991) J. Clin. Invest *88*, 876.

Bessler, W. G. (1992) Develop. Biol. Standard *77*, 49.

Bhat, T. N., Bentley, G. A., Boulot, G., Greene, M. I., Tello, D., Dallacqua, W., Souchon, H., Schwarz, F. P., Mariuzza, R. A. and Poljak, R. J. (1994) Proc. Natl. Acad. Sci. USA *91*, 1089.

Bhat, T. N., Bentley, G. A., Fischmann, T. O., Boulot, G. and Poljak, R. J. (1990) Nature *347*, 483.

Bhatnagar, P. K., Mao, S. J. T., Gotto, A. M., Sparrow, J. T., Jr. and Sparrow, J. T. (1983) Peptides *4*, 343.

Bhatnager, P. K., Papes, E., Blum, H. E., Milich, D. R., Nitecki, D., Karels, M. J. and Vyas, G. N. (1982) Proc. Natl. Acad. Sci. USA *79*, 4400.

Bhattacharjee, A. K. and Glaudemans, C. P. J. (1978) J. Immunol. *120*, 411.

Bittle, J. L., Houghten, R. A., Alexander, H., Shinnick, T., Sutcliffe, J. G., Lerner, R. A., Rowlands, D. J. and Brown, F. (1982) Nature *298*, 30.

Bizebard, T., Gigant, B., Rigolet, P., Rasmussen, B., Diat, O., Bösecke, P., Wharton, S. A., Skehel, J. J. and Knossow, M. (1995) Nature *376*, 92.

Bizzini, B., Blass, J., Turpin, A. and Raynaud, M. (1970) Eur. J. Biochem. *17*, 100.

Björkman, P. J., Saper, M. A., Samraoui, B., Bannett, W. S., Strominger, J. L. and Wiley, D. C. (1987) Nature *329*, 506.

Blange, I., Ringertz, N. R. and Pettersson, I. (1994) J. Autoimmun. *7*, 263.

Bläss, S., Meier, C., Vohr, H. W., Schwochau, M., Specker, C. and Burmester, G. R. (1998) Ann. Rheum. Dis. *57*, 220.

Blondel, B., Crainic, R., Fichot, O., Dufraisse, G., Candrea, A., Diamond, D., Girard, M. and Horaud, F. (1986) J. Virol. *57*, 81.

Bloomer, A. C. and Butler, P. J. G. (1986) In: The Plant Viruses. The Rod-Shaped Plant Viruses (Van Regenmortel, M. H. V. and Fraenkel-Conrat, H., eds.). Plenum Press, New York, p. 19.

Bloomer, A. C., Champness, J. N., Bricogne, G., Staden, R. and Klug, A. (1978) Nature *276*, 362.

Blüthner, M., Bautz, E. K. F. and Bautz, F. A. (1996) J. Immunol. Meth. *198*, 187.

Böcher, M., Böldicke, T., Kiess, M. and Bilitewski, U. (1997) J. Immun. Meth. *208*, 191.

Boeckler, C., Frisch, B., Muller, S. and Schuber, F. (1996) J. Immunol. Meth. *191*, 1.

Boersma, W. J. A., Claassen, E., Deen, C., Gerritse, K., Haaijman, J. J. and Zegers, N. D. (1988) Anal. Chim. Acta *213*, 187.

Boersma, W. J. A., Haaijman, J. J. and Claassen, E. (1993) In: Immunochemistry II (Cuello, A. C., ed.). John Wiley, Chichester, p. 1.

Bomford, R. (1980) Clin. Exp. Immunol. *39*, 435.

Borras-Cuesta, F., Fedon, Y. and Petit-Camurdan, A. (1988) Eur. J. Immunol. *18*, 199.

Boudet, F., Thèze J. and Zouali, M. (1991) J. Immunol. Meth. *142*, 73.

Boulain, J.-C. Ménez, A., Couderc, J., Faure, G., Liacopoulos, P. and Fromageot, P. (1982) Biochemistry *21*, 2910.

Boyle, W. J., Reddy, E. P., Baluda, M. A. and Lipsick, J. S. (1983) Proc. Natl. Acad. Sci. USA *80*, 2834.

Bozic, B., Pruijn, G. J. M., Rozman, B. and van Venrooij, W. J. (1993) Clin. Exp. Immunol. *94*, 227.

Braden, B. C., Fields, B. A. and Poljak, R. J. (1995) J. Mol. Recog. *8*, 317.

Braden, B. C., Fields, B. A., Ysern, X., Goldbaum, F. A., Dall'Acqua, W., Schwarz, F. P., Poljak, R. J. and Mariuzza, R. A. (1996) J. Mol. Biol. *257*, 889.

Braden, B. C. and Poljak, R. J. (1995) FASEB J. *9*, 9.

Braden, B. C., Souchon, H., Eisele, J. L., Bentley, G. A., Bhat, T. N., Navaza, J. and Poljak, R. J. (1994) J. Mol. Biol. *243*, 767.

Brahm, J., Vento, S. Rondanelli, E. G., Rameri, S., Fagan, E. A., Williams, R. and Eddleston, L. W. F. (1988) J. Med. Virol. *24*, 205.

Brandtzaeg, P. (1998) J. Immunol. Meth. *216*, 49.

Brandtzaeg, P., Halstensen, T. S., Huitfeldt, H. S. and Valnes, K. N. (1997) In: Immunochemistry 2—A Practical Approach (Johnstone, A. P. and Turner, M. W., eds.). IRL Press, Oxford, p. 71.

Brendel, V., Dohlman, J., Blaisdell, B. E. and Karlin, S. (1991) Proc. Natl. Acad. Sci. USA *88*, 1536.

Brennand, D. M., Danson, M. J. and Hough D. W. (1986) J. Immunol. Meth. *93*, 9.

Briand, J.-P., André, C., Tuaillon, N., Hervé, L., Neimark, J. and Muller, S. (1992a) Hepatology *16*, 1395.

Briand, J.-P., Barin, C., Van Regenmortel, M. H. V. and Muller, S. (1992b) J. Immunol. Meth. *156*, 255.

Briand, J.-P., Benkirane, N., Guichard, G., Newman, J. F. E., Van Regenmortel, M. H. V., Brown, F. and Muller, S. (1997) Proc. Natl. Acad. Sci. USA *94*, 12545.

Briand, J.-P., Guichard, G., Dumortier, H and Muller, S. (1995) J. Biol. Chem. *270*, 20686.

Briand, J.-P., Muller, S. and Van Regenmortel, M. H. V. (1985) J. Immunol. Meth. *78*, 59.

Brocke, S., Brautbar, C., Steinman, L., Abramsky, O., Rothbard, J., Neumann, D., Fuchs, S. and Mozes, E. (1988) J. Clin. Invest. *82*, 1894.

Broekhuijsen, M. P., Blom, T., Kottenhagen, M., Pouwels, P. H., Meloen, R. H., Barteling, S. J. and Enger-Valk, B. E. (1986) Vaccine *4*, 119.

Broekhuijsen, M. P., Van Rijn, J. N.M., Blom, A. J. M., Pouwels, P. H., Enger-Valk, B. E., Brown, F. and Francis, M. J. (1987) J. Gen. Virol. *68*, 3137.

Brown, F. (1985) In: Immunochemistry of Viruses. The Basis for Serodiagnosis and Vaccines (Van Regenmortel, M. H. V. and Neurath, A. R., eds.). Elsevier Science, North-Holland, p. 265.

Brown, F. (1994) In: Synthetic Vaccines (Nicholson, B. H., ed.). Blackwell Scientific, Oxford, p. 416.

Brown, J. H., Jardetzky, T. S., Gorga, J. C., Stern, L. J., Urban, R. G., Strominger, J. L. and Wiley, D. C. (1993) Nature *364*, 33.

Brown, L., Westby, M., Souberbielle, B. E., Szawlowski, P. W. S., Kemp, G., Hay, P. and Dalgleish (1997) J. Immunol. Meth. *200*, 79.

Buiting, A., Van Rooijen, N. and Claasen, E. (1992) Res. Immunol. *143*, 471.

Burnens, A., Demotz, S., Corradin, G., Binz, H. and Bosshard, H. R. (1987) Science *235*, 780.

Burnette, W. N. (1981) Anal. Biochem. *112*, 195.

Burton, D. R. (1997) Proc. Natl. Acad. Sci. USA *94*, 10018.

Burton, D. R. and Moore, J. P. (1998) Nature Medicine Vaccine Supplement *4*, 495.

Butler, J. E. (1991) Immunochemistry of Solid-Phase Immunoassay., CRC Press, Boca Raton, p. 352.

Butler, J. E. (1992) In: Structure of Antigens, Vol. 1 (Van Regenmortel, M.H.V., ed.). CRC Press, Boca Raton, p. 209.

Butler, J. E. (1996) In: Immunoassay (Diamandis, E. P. and Christopoulos, T. K., eds.). Academic Press, San Diego, p. 205.

Butler, J. E., Spradling, J. E., Suter, M., Dierks, S. E., Heyermann, H. and Peterman, J. H. (1986) Mol. Immunol. *23*, 971.

Butler, V. P. and Beiser, S. M. (1973) Adv. Immunol. *17*, 255.

Butz, S., Rawer, S., Rapp, W. and Birsner, U. (1994) Peptide Res. *7*, 20.

Buyon, J. P., Slade, S. G., Reveille, J. D., Hamel, J. C. and Chan, E. K. L. (1994) J. Immunol. *152*, 3675.

Callebaut, C., Jacotot, E., Guichard, G., Krust, B., Rey-Cuille, M.-A., Cointe, D., Benkirane, N., Blanco, J., Muller, S., Briand, J. P. and Hovanessian, A. G. (1996) Virology *218*, 181.

Calvo-Calle, J. M., De Oliveira, G. A., Clavijo, P., Maracic, M., Tam, J. P., Lu, Y. A., Nardin, E. H., Nussenzweig, R. S. and Cochrane, A. H. (1993) J. Immunol. *150*, 1403.

Camarero, J. A., Andreu, D., Cairo, J. J., Mateu, M. G., Domingo, E. and Giralt, E. (1993) FEBS Lett *328*, 159.

Cameron, D. J. and Erlanger, B. F. (1977) Nature *268*, 763.

Caponi, L., Pegoraro, S., Di Bartolo, V., Rovero, P., Revoltella, R. and Bombardieri, S. (1995) J. Immunol. Meth. *179*, 193.

Caraux, J., Chichehian, B., Gestin, C., Longhi, B., Lee, A. C., Powell, J. E., Stevens, V. C. and Pourquier, A. (1985) J. Immuriol. *134*, 835.

Carlsson, J., Drevin, H. and Axen, R. (1978) Biochem. J. *173*, 723.

Carneiro, J. and Stewart, J. (1994) J. Theor. Biol. *169*, 391.

Carver, J. A., Esposito, G., Viglino, P., Fogolari, F., Guichard, G., Briand, J. P., Van Regenmortel, M. H. V., Brown, F. and Mascagni, P. (1997) Biopolymers *41*, 569.

Caton, A. J., Brownlee, G.G., Yewdell, J. W. and Gerhard, W. (1982) Cell *31*, 417.

Cease, K. B. and Berzofsky, J. A. (1994) Annu. Rev. Immunol. *12*, 923.

Cello, J., Samuelson, A., Stalhandske, P., Svennerholm, B., Jeansson, S. and Forsgren, M. (1993) J. Clin. Microbiol. *31*, 911.

Chacko, S., Silverton, E., Kam-Morgan, L., Smith-Gill, S., Cohen, G. and Davies, D. (1995) J. Mol. Biol. *245*, 261.

Chacko, S., Silverton, E. W., Smith-Gill, S. J., Davies, D. R., Shick, K. A., Xavier, K. A., Willson, R. C., Jeffrey, P. D., Chang, C. Y. Y., Sieker, L. C. and Sheriff, S. (1996) Proteins *26*, 55.

Chai, S. K., Clavijo, P., Tam, J. P. and Zavala, F. (1992) J. Immunol. *149*, 2385.

Champion, A. B., Soderberg, K. L., Wilson, A. C. and Ambler, R. P. (1975) J. Mol. Evol. *5*, 291.

Chan, E. K. L. and Buyon, J. P. (1994) In: Manual of Biological Markers of Disease, Vol. B4.1 (van Venrooij, W. J. and Maini, R. N., eds.). Kluwer Academic, Dordrecht, p. 1.

Chappey, O., Debray, M., Niel, E. and Scherrmann, J. M. (1994) J. Immunol. Meth. *172*, 219.

Charbit, A., Sobczak, E., Michel, M. L., Molla, A., Tiollais, P. and Hofnung, M. (1987) J. Immunol. *139*, 1658.

Chard, T. (1996) In: Immunoassay (Diamandis, E. P. and Christopoulos, T. K., eds.). Academic Press, San Diego, p. 270.

Chargelegue, D., Obeid, O. E., Hsu, S. C., Shaw, M. D., Denbury, A. N., Taylor, G. and Steward, M. W.(1998) J. Virol. 72, 2040.

Chatellier, J., Rauffer-Bruyère, N., Van Regenmortel, M. H. V., Altschuh, D. and Weiss, E. (1996) J. Mol. Recog. 9, 39.

Chatterjee, S., Sharma, P., Kumar, S. and Chauhan, V. S. (1995) Vaccine 13, 1474.

Chedid, L. (1987) In: Synthetic Vaccines, Vol. 1 (Arnon, R., ed.). CRC Press, Boca Raton, p. 93.

Chen, Y. C. J., Delbrook, K., Dealwis, C., Mimms, L., Mushahwar, I. K. and Mandecki, W. (1996) Proc. Natl. Acad. Sci. USA 93, 1997.

Chersi, A., Ruocco, E. and Muratti, E. (1989) J. Immunol. Meth. 122, 285.

Chitarra, V., Alzari, P. M., Bentley, G. A., Bhat, T. N., Eisele, J. L., Houdusse, A., Lescar, J., Souchon, H. and Poljak, R. J. (1993) Proc. Natl. Acad. Sci. USA 90, 7711.

Chomyn, A., Mariottini, P., Gonzalez-Cadavid, N., Attardy, G., Strong, D. D., Trovato, D., Riley, M. and Doolittle, R. F. (1983) Proc. Natl. Acad. Sci. USA 80, 5535.

Chong, P., Sydor, M., Wu, E. and Klein, M. (1992) Mol. Immunol. 29, 443.

Chong, P., Sydor, M., Wu, E., Zobrist, G., Boux, H. and Klein, M. (1991) Mol. Immunol. 28, 239.

Choppin, J. (1988) Personal communication.

Choppin, J., Metzger, J. J., Bouillot, M., Briand, J. P., Connan, F., Van Regenmortel, M. H. V. and Levy, J. P. (1986) J. Immunol. 136, 1738.

Chorev, M. and Goodman, M. (1995) Trends Biotechnol. 13, 438.

Chothia, C. (1976) J. Mol. Biol. 105, 1.

Chothia, C. (1984) Annu. Rev. Biochem. 53, 537.

Chou, P. Y. and Fasman, G. D. (1974) Biochemistry 13, 211.

Chou, P. Y. and Fasman, G. D. (1978) Adv. Enzymol. Relat. Subj. Biochem. 47, 45.

Chow, M., Yabrov, R., Bittle, J., Hogle, J. and Baltimore, D. (1985) Proc. Natl. Acad. Sci. USA 82, 910.

Christian, R. B., Zuckermann, R. N., Kerr, J. M., Wang, L. and Malcolm, B. A. (1992) J. Mol. Biol. 227, 711.

Churchill, M. E. A., Stura, E. A., Pinilla, C., Appel, J. R., Houghten, R. A., Kono, D. H., Balderas, R. S., Fieser, G.G., Schulze-Gahmen, U. and Wilson, I. A. (1994) J. Mol. Biol. 241, 534.

Clark, R., Wong, G., Arnheim, N., Nitecki, D. and McCormick, F. (1985) Proc. Natl. Acad. Sci. USA 82, 5280.

Clarke, B. E., Newton, S. E., Carroll, A. R., Francis, M. J., Appleyard, G., Syred, A. D., Highfield, P. E., Rowlands, D. J. and Brown, F. (1987) Nature 330, 381.

Clausen, J. (1981) Immunochemical Techniques for the Identification and Estimation of Macromolecules, 2nd edition. Elsevier, Amsterdam, p. 387.

Cleland, J. L. (1998) Biotechnol. Prog. *14*, 102.

Clemens, M. J. (1984) In: Transcription and Translation: A Practical Approach (Hames, B. D. and Higgins, S. J., eds.). IRL Press., Oxford.

Clough, E. R., Jolivet, M., Audibert, F., Barnwell, J. W., Schlessinger, D. H. and Chedid, L. (1985) Biochem. Biophys. Res. Commun. *131*, 70.

Cochet, O. (1998) In: Immunological Techniques Made Easy (Cochet, O., Teillaud, J. L. and Sautes, C., eds.). John Wiley, Chichester, p. 42.

Cole, S. R., Ashman, L. K. and Ey, P. L. (1987) Mol. Immunol. *24*, 699.

Collawn, J F., Wallace, C. J. A., Proudfoot, A. E. I. and Paterson, Y. (1988) J. Biol. Chem. *263*, 8625.

Collen, T., Di Marchi, R. and Doel, T. R. (1991) J. Immunol. *146*, 749.

Colman, P. M. (1988) Adv. Immunol. *43*, 99

Commandeur, U., Koenig, R., Manteuffel, R., Torrance, I., Lüddecke, P. and Frank, R. (1994) Virology *198*, 282.

Cooper, H. M. and Paterson, Y. (1987) In: Protides of Biological Fluids (Peeters, H., ed.). Vol. 35. Pergamon Press, Oxford, p. 523.

Coppel, R. L., Cowman, A. F., Lingelbach, K. R., Brown, G. V., Saint, R. B., Kemp, D. J. and Anders, R. F. (1983) Nature *306*, 751.

Cornette, J. L., Cease, K. B., Margalit, F., Spouge, J. L., Berzofsky, J. A. and DeLisi, C. (1987) J. Mol. Biol. *195*, 659.

Corthier, G. and Franz, J. (1981) Infect. Immunol. *31*, 833.

Coursaget, P., Barres, J. L., Chiron, J. P. and Adamovicz, P. (1985) Lancet *i*, 1152.

Coursaget, P., Deprie, N., Buisson, Y., Molinie, C. and Roue, R. (1994) Res. Virol. *145*, 51.

Cox, J. C. and Coulter, A. R. (1997) Vaccine *15*, 248.

Cox, J. H., Ivanyi, J., Young, D. B., Lamb, J. R., Syred, A. D. and Francis, M. J. (1988) Eur. J. Immunol. *18*, 2015.

Craft, J. and Fatenejad, S. (1997) Arthritis Rheum. *40*, 1374.

Crescenzi, A., d'Aquino, L., Nuzzaci, M., Ostuni, A., Bavoso, A., Comes, S., De Stradis, A. and Piazzolla, P. (1997) J. Virol. Meth. *69*, 181.

Crewther, P. E., Bianco, A. E., Brown, G. V., Coppel, R. L., Stahl, H. D., Kemp, D. J. and Anders, R. F. (1986) J. Immunol. Meth *86*, 257.

Crowther, J. R. (1995) ELISA: Theory and Practice, Humana Press Inc., Totowa, New Jersey, p. 223.

Crumpton, M. J. (1974) In: The Antigens (Sela, M., ed.). Vol. II. Academic Press, New York, p. 1.

Crumpton, M. J. (1986) Ciba Found. Symp. *119*, 93.

Cuniasse, P., Thomas, A., Smith, J. C., Thanh, H. L., Leonetti, M. and Ménez, A. (1995) Biochemistry *34*, 12782.

Cunningham, B. C. and Wells, J. A. (1989) Science *244*, 1081.

Curry, S., Fry., E., Blakemore, W., Albughazaleh, R., Jackson, T., King, A., Lea, S., Newman, J., Rowlands, D. and Stuart, D. (1996) Structure *4*, 135.

Cwirla, S. E., Peters, E. A., Barrett, R. W. and Dower, W. J. (1990) Proc. Natl. Acad. Sci. USA *87*, 6378.

Dagenais, P., Desprez, B., Albert, J. and Escher, E. (1994) Anal. Biochem. *222*, 149.

Daiss, J. L. and Scalice, E. R. (1994) Methods *6*, 143.

Daniels, D. A. and Lane, D. P. (1996) Methods *9*, 494.

Darcy, F., Maes, P., Gras-Masse, H., Auriault, C., Bossus, M., Deslee, D., Godard, I., Cesbron, M. F., Tartar, A. and Capron, A. (1992) J. Immunol. *149*, 3636.

Darsley, M. J. and Rees, A. R. (1985) EMBO J. *4*, 383.

Darst, S. A., Robertson, C. R. and Berzofsky, J. A. (1988) Biophys. J. *53*, 533.

Davenport, M. P., Shon, I. A. P. H. and Hill, A. V. S. (1995) Immunogenetics *42*, 392.

Davies, D. R. and Cohen, G. H. (1996) Proc. Natl. Acad. Sci. USA *93*, 7.

Davies, D. R., Padlan, E. A. and Sheriff, S. (1990) Annu. Rev. Biochem. *59*, 439

Day, E. D. (1990) Advanced Immunochemistry, 2nd edition, Wiley-Liss, New York, p. 693.

Dayhoff, M. O. (1976) Atlas of Protein Sequence and Structure. National Biomedical Research Foundation, Washington, DC.

Dayhoff, M. O. (1978) In: Atlas of Protein Sequence and Structure, Vol. 5. National Biomedical Research Foundation, Washington, DC.

De Boer, M., Ossendorp, F. A., Al, B. Jr. M., Hilgers, J., de Vijlder, J. J. M. and Tager, J. M. (1987) Mol. Immunol. *24*, 1081.

De Groot, A. S., Meister, G. E., Cornette, J. L., Margalit, H., DeLisi, C. and Berzofsky, J. A. (1997) In: New Generation Vaccines (Levine, M. M., Woodrow, G. C., Kaper, J. B. and Cohen, G. S., eds.). Marcel Dekker, New York, p. 127.

De Koster, H. S., Amons, R., Benckhuijsen, W. E., Feijlbrief, M., Schellekens, G. A. and Drijfhout, J. W. (1995) J. Immunol. Meth. *187*, 179.

De Weck, A. L. (1974) In: The Antigens Vol. 2 (Sela, M., ed.). Academic Press, New York, p. 142.

Dean, P. D. E., Johnson, W. S. and Middle, F. A. (1985) In: Affinity Chromatography. A Practical Approach, IRL Press, Oxford.

Decker, P., Briand, J. P., De Murcia, G., Pero, R. W., Isenberg, D. A. and Muller, S. (1998) Arthritis Rheum. *41*, 918,

Deeb, B. J., DiGiacomo, R. F., Kunz, L. L. and Stewart, J. L. (1992) J. Immunol. Meth. *152*, 105.

Deen, C., Claassen, E., Gerritse, K., Zegers, N. D. and Boersma, W. J. A. (1990) J. Immunol. Meth. *129*, 119.

Defoort, J.-P., Nardelli, B., Huang, W., Ho, D. D. and Tam, J. P. (1992) Proc. Natl. Acad. Sci. USA *89*, 3879.

Delmas, A., Muhaud, G., Raulais, D. and Rivaille, P. (1985) Mol. Immunol. *22*, 675.

Delmastro, P., Meola, A., Monaci, P., Cortese, R. and Galfré, G. (1997) Vaccine *15*, 1276.

Delorme, B., Dahl, E., Jarry-Guichard, T., Briand, J. P., Willecke, K., Gros, D. and Théveniau-Ruissy, M. (1997) Circ. Res. *81*, 423.

Demangeat, G., Greif, C., Hemmer, O. and Fritsch, C. (1990) J. Gen. Virol. *71*, 1649.

Demangeat, G., Hemmer, O., Fritsch, C., Le Gall, O. and Candresse, T. (1991) J. Gen. Virol. *72*, 247.

Demangeat, G., Hemmer, O., Reinbolt, J., Mayo, M. A. and Fritsch, C. (1992) J. Gen. Virol. *73*, 1609.

Denery-Papini, S., Briand, J.-P., Quillien, L., Popineau, Y. and Van Regenmortel, M. H. V. (1994) J. Cereal Sci. *20*, 1.

Denton, G., Hudecz, F., Kajtar, J., Murray, A., Tendler, S. J. B. and Price, M. R. (1994) Peptide Res. *7*, 258.

Deodhar, S. D. (1960) J. Exp. Med. *111*, 419.

Deoliveira, G. A., Clavijo, P., Nussenzweig, R. S. and Nardin, E. H. (1994) Vaccine *12*, 1012.

Deprez, B., Sauzet, J.-P., Boutillon, C., Martinon, F., Tartar, A., Sergheraert, C., Guillet, J.-G., Gomard, E. and Gras-Masse, H. (1996) Vaccine *14*, 375.

Deres, K., Schild, H., Wiesmüller, K.-H., Jung, G. and Rammensee, H.-G. (1989) Nature *342*, 561.

Derksen, J. T. P. and Scherphof, G. L. (1985) Biochem. Biophys. Acta *814*, 151.

Desaymard, C. and Howard, J. C. (1975) Eur. J. Immunol. *5*, 541.

Devare, S. G., Reddy, E. P., Law, J. D., Robbins, K. C. and Aaronson, S. A. (1983) Proc. Natl. Acad. Sci. USA *80*, 731.

Devereux, J., Haeberli, P. and Smithies, O. (1984) Nucleic Acids Res. *12*, 387.

Devlin, J. J., Panganiban, J. J. and Devlin, J. J. (1990) Science *249*, 404.

Di Marchi, R., Brooke, G., Gale, C., Cracknell, V., Doel, T. and Mowat, N. (1986) Science *232*, 639.

Diamandis, E. P. and Christopoulos, T. K. (1996) Immunoassay. Academic Press, San Diego, 579 pp.

Dierks, S. E., Butler, J. E. and Richerson, H. B. (1986) Mol. Immunol. *23*, 403.

Dietrich, J. B. (1985) Biosci. Rep. *5*, 137.

Dietzgen, R. G. and Zaitlin, M. (1986) Virology *155*, 262.

Dighiero, G., Lymberi, P., Holmberg, D., Lundquist, I., Coutinho, A. and Avrameas, S. (1985) J. Immunol. *134*, 765.

Dillner, J., Dillner, L., Robb, J., Willems, J., Jones, I., Lancaster, W., Smith, R. and Lerner, R. (1989) Proc. Natl. Acad. Sci. USA *86*, 3838.

Dimmock, N. J. (1993) Neutralization of Animal Viruses. Springer-Verlag, Berlin, 149 pp.

Doel, T. R., Doel, C. M. F. A., Staple, R. F. and Di Marchi, R. (1992) J. Virol. *66*, 2187.

Domingo, E., Mateu, M. G., Martinez, M. A., Dopazo, J., Moya, A. and Sobrino, F. (1990) In: Applied Virology Research, Vol. 2 (Kurstak, E., Marusyk, R. G., Murphy, F. A. and Van Regenmortel, M. H. V., eds.). Plenum Press, New York, p. 233.

Doniach (1997) In: Weir's Handbook of Experimental Immunology, 5th edition. (Herzenberg, L. A., Weir, D. M., Herzenberg, L. A. and Blackwell, C., eds.). Blackwell Science, Cambridge (USA), 12.1.

Dore, I., Ruhlmann, P., Oudet, P., Cahoon, M., Caspar, D. L. D. and Van Regenmortel, M. H. V. (1990) Virology *176*, 25.

Dore, I., Weiss, E., Altschuh, D. and Van Regenmortel, M. H. V. (1988) Virology *162*, 279.

Dörner, T., Feist, B. Wagenmann, A., Kato, T., Yamamoto, K., Nishioka, K., Burmester, G. R. and Hiepe, F. (1996) J. Rheumatol. *23*, 462.

Dorow, D. S., Shi, P. T., Carbone, F. R., Minasian, E., Todd, P. E. E. and Leach, S. J. (1985) Mol. Immunol. *22*, 1255.

Dower, S. K., DeLisi, C., Titus, J. A. and Segal, D. M. (1981) Biochemistry *20*, 6326.

Dreesman, G. R., Sanchez, Y., Ionescu-Matiu, I., Sparrow, J. T., Six, H. R., Peterson, D. L., Hollinger, F. B. and Melnick, J. L. (1982) Nature *295*, 158.

Dresser, D. W. (1986) In: Handbook of Experimental Immunology, Vol. 1 (Weir, D. M., Herzenberg, L. A, Blackwell, C. and Herzenberg, L. A., eds.). Blackwell, Oxford, 8.1.

Drillien, R., Spehner, D., Kirn, A., Giraudon, P., Buckland, R., Wild, F. and Lecocq, J. P. (1988) Proc. Natl. Acad. Sci. USA *85*, 1252.

Dubs, M. C., Altschuh, D. and Van Regenmortel, M. H. V. (1992) J. Chromatogr. *597*, 127.

Dumortier, H., Abbal, M., Fort., M., Briand, J, P., Cantagrel, A. and Muller, S. (1999a) Int. Immunol. *11*, 249.

Dumortier, H., Klein-Gunnewiek, J., Roussel, J.-P., van Aarssen, Y., Briand, J.-P., van Venrooij, W. J. and Muller, S. (1998) Nucl. Acids Res. *26*, 5486.

Dumortier, H., Klein-Gunnewick, J., van Venrooij, W. J. and Muller, S. (1999b) unpublished.

Dumortier, H., Pruijn, G. and Muller, S. (1999c) unpublished.

Duncan, R. J. S., Weston, P. D. and Wrigglesworth, R. (1983) Anal. Biochem. *132*, 68.

Dussossoy, D., Carayon, P., Feraut, D., Belugou, S., Combes, T., Canat, X., Vidal, H. and Casellas, P. (1996) Cytometry *24*, 39.

Dyrberg, T. and Oldstone, M. B. A. (1986) J. Exp. Med. *164*, 1344.

Dyson, H. J., Cross, K. J., Houghten, R. A., Wilson, I. A., Wright, P. E. and Lerner, R. A. (1985) Nature *318*, 480.

Dyson, H. J., Rance, M., Houghten, R. A., Lerner, R. A. and Wright, P. E. (1988) J. Mol. Biol. *201*, 161.

Dyson, H. J., Satterthwait, A. C., Lerner, R. A. and Wright, P. E. (1990) Biochemistry *29*, 7828.

East, I. J., Hurrell, J. G. R., Todd, P E. E. and Leach, S. J. (1982) J. Biol. Chem. *257*, 3199.

East, I. J., Todd, P. E. and Leach, S. J. (1980) Mol. Immunol. *17*, 519.

Edelman, R. (1992) AIDS Res. Hum. Retroviruses *8*, 1409.

Edwards, R. J., Singleton, A. M., Boobis, A. R. and Davies, D. S. (1989) J. Immunol. Meth. *117*, 215.

Eisen, H. N. and Siskind, G. W. (1964) Biochemistry *3*, 996.

Elies, R., Ferrari, I., Wallukat, G., Lebesgue, D., Chiale, P., Elizari, M., Rosenbaum, M., Hoebeke, J. and Levin, M. (1996) J. Immunol. *157*, 4203.

Elkon, K. B. (1992) Mol. Biol. Rep. *16*, 207.

Elkon, K. B. (1994) In: Manual of Biological Markers of Disease, Vol. B2.5 (van Venrooij, W. J. and Maini, R. N., eds.). Kluwer Academic, Dordrecht, p. 1.

Elliot, W. L., Stille, C. J., Thomas, L. J. and Humphreys, R. E. (1987) J. Immunol. *138*, 2949.

Emini, E. A., Hughes, J. V., Perlow, D. S. and Boger, J. (1985) J. Virol. *55*, 836.

Emini, E. A., Jameson, B. A. and Wimmer, E. (1983) Nature *304*, 699.

Emini, E. A., Jameson, B. A. and Wimmer, E. (1984) J. Virol. *52*, 719.

Endoh, H., Suzuki, Y and Hashimoto, Y. (1981) J. Immunol. Meth. *44*, 79.

Engelhard, V. H. (1994a) Annu. Rev. Immunol. *12*, 181.

Engelhard, V. H. (1994b) Curr. Opin. Immunol. *6*, 13.

Engelman, D. M., Steitz, T. A. and Goldman, A. (1986) Annu. Rev. Biophys. Biophys. Chem. *15*, 321.

Eppstein, D. A. and Longenecker, J. P. (1988) In: Critical Reviews in Therapeutic Drug Carrier Systems, Vol. 5. CRC Press, Boca Raton, p. 99.

Erlanger, B. F. (1980) Meth. Enzymol. *70*, 85.

Escribano, M. J. (1974) Eur. J. Immunol. *4*, 793.

Evans, S. V., Rose, D. R., To, R., Young, N. M. and Bundle, D. R. (1994) J. Mol. Biol. *241*, 691.

Fägerstam, L. G., Frostell, A., Karlsson, R., Kullman, M., Larsson, A., Malmqvist, M. and Butt, H. (1990) J. Mol. Recogn. *3*, 208.

Fägerstam, L. G. and Karlsson, R. (1994) In: Immunochemistry (Van Oss, C. J. and Van Regenmortel, M. H. V., eds.). Marcel Dekker, New York, p. 949.

Feeney, R. E., Yamasaki, R. B. and Geoghegan, K. F. (1982) In: Advances in Chemistry, Series 198 (Feeney, R. E. and Whitaker, J. R., eds.). American Chemical Society, Washington, DC.

Feltkamp, M. C., Smits, H. L., Vierboom, M. P., Minnaar, R. P., De, J. B., Drijfhout, J. W., Ter, S. J., Melief, C. J. and Kast, W. M. (1993) Eur. J. Immunol. 23, 2242.

Ferguson, M., Evans, D. M. A., Magrath, D. I., Minor, P. D., Almond, J. W. and Schild, G. C. (1985) Virology 143, 505.

Fernandes, I., Frisch, B., Muller, S. and Schuber, F. (1997) Mol. Immunol. 34, 569.

Fernando, G. J. P., Stenzel, D. J., Tindle, R. W., Merza, M. S., Morein, B. and Frazer, I. H. (1995) Vaccine 13, 1460.

Ferrari, I., Levin, M. J., Wallukat, G., Elies, R., Lebesgue, D., Chiale, P., Elizari, M., Rosenbaum, M. and Hoebeke, J. (1995) J. Exp. Med. 182, 59.

Ferru, I., Georges B., Bossus, M., Estaquier, Delacre, M., Ham, D. A., Tartar, A., Capron, A., Gras-Masse, H. and Auriault, C. (1997) Parasite Immunol. 19, 1.

Fields, B. A., Goldbaum, F. A., Ysern, X., Poljak, R. J. and Mariuzza, R. A. (1995) Nature 374, 739.

Fields, G. B. (1997) Meth. Enzym. 289, 2376.

Fieser, T. M., Tainer, J. A., Geysen, H. M. and Houghten, R. A. (1987) Proc. Natl. Acad. Sci. USA 84, 8568.

Fischer, P. M. and Howden, E. H. (1990) J. Immunoassay 11, 311.

Fischmann, T. O., Bentley, G. A., Bhat, T. N., Boulot, G., Mariuzza, R. A., Phillips, S. E. V., Tello, D. and Poljak, R. J. (1991) J. Biol. Chem. 266, 12915.

Fitzmaurice, C. J., Brown, L. E., McInerney, T. L. and Jackson, D. C. (1996) Vaccine 14, 553.

Fleet, G. W. J., Porter, R. R. and Krowles, J. R. (1969) Nature 224, 511.

Fok, K. F., Ohga, K., Incefy, G. S. and Erickson, B. W. (1982) Mol. Immunol. 19, 1667.

Folgori, A., Tafi, R., Meola, A., Felici, F., Galfrè, G., Cortese, R., Monaci, P. and Nicosia, A. (1994) EMBO J. 13, 2236.

Fourquet, P., Bahraoui, E., Fontecilla-Camps, J. C., Van Rietschoten, J., Rochat, H. and Granier, C. (1988) Int. J. Pept. Prot. Res. 32, 81.

Fraker, P. J. and Speck, J. C. (1978) Biochem. Biophys. Res. Commun. 80, 849.

Francis, M. J. (1994) In: Immunochemistry (Van Oss, C. J. and Van Regenmortel, M. H. V., eds.). Marcel Dekker, New York, p. 533.

Francis, M. J., Clarke, B. E., Hastings, G. Z., Brown, A. L., Rowlands, D. J. and Brown, F. (1990) In: Vaccines 90. Modern Approaches to New Vaccines including Prevention of AIDS (Brown, F., Chanock, R. M., Ginsberg, H. S. and Lerner, R. A., eds.). Cold Spring Harbor Laboratory Press, New York, p. 179.

Francis, M. J., Fry, C. M., Rowlands, D. J., Bittle, J. L., Houghten, R. A., Lerner, R. A. and Brown, F. (1987a) Immunology 61, 1.

Francis, M. J., Fry, C. M., Rowlands, D. J., Brown, F., Bittle, J. L., Houghten, R. A. and Lerner, R. A. (1985) J. Gen. Virol. *66*, 2347.

Francis, M. J., Hastings, G. Z., Brown, F., McDermed, J., Lu, Y.-A. and Tam, J. P. (1991) Immunology *73*, 249.

Francis, M. J., Hastings, G. Z., Syred, A. D., McGinn, B., Brown, F. and Rowlands, D. J. (1987b) Nature *300*, 168.

Frank, M. B., Itoh, K. and McCubbin, V. (1994) Clin. Exp. Immunol. *95*, 390.

Frank, R. (1992) Tetradedron *48*, 9217.

Frank, R. (1995) J. Biotechnol. *41*, 259.

Frank, R. and Döring, R. (1988) Tetrahedron *44*, 6031.

Frank, R. and Overwin, H. (1996) In: Epitope Mapping Protocols (Morris, G. E., ed.). Humana Press, Totowa, New Jersey, p. 149.

Frankenburg, S., Axelrod, O., Kutner, S., Greenblatt, C. L., Klaus, S. N., Pirak, E. A., McMaster, R. and Lowell, G. H. (1996) Vaccine 14, 923.

Fremont, D. H., Matsumura, V., Stura, E. A., Peterson, P. A. and Wilson, I. A. (1992) Science *257*, 919.

Fridkin, M. and Najjar, V. A. (1989) Crit. Rev. Biochem. Mol. Biol. *24*, 1.

Friede, M. (1995) In: Liposomes as Tools in Basic Research and Industry (Philippot, J. R. and Schuber, F., eds.). CRC Press, Boca Raton, p. 189.

Friede, M., Muller, S., Briand, J. P., Plaue, S., Fernandes, I., Frisch, B., Schuber, F. and Van Regenmortel, M. H. V. (1994) Vaccine *12*, 791.

Friede, M., Muller, S., Briand, J. P., Schuber, F. and Van Regenmortel, M. H. V. (1993a) In: Immunotechnology (Gosling, J. P. and Reen, D. J., eds.). Portland Press, London, p. 1.

Friede, M., Muller, S., Briand, J. P., Van Regenmortel, M. H. V. and Schuber, F. (1993b) Mol. Immunol. *30*, 539.

Friede, M., Van Regenmortel, M. H. V. and Schuber, F. (1993c) Anal. Biochem. *211*, 117.

Friguet, B., Djavadi-Ohaniance, L. and Goldberg, M. E. (1984) Mol. Immunol. *21*, 673.

Frisch, B., Muller, S., Briand, J. P., Van Regenmortel, M. H. V. and Schuber, F. (1991) Eur. J. Immunol. *21*, 185.

Fujio, H., Imanishi, M., Nishioka, K. and Amano, T. (1959) Biken J. *2*, 56.

Fujio, H., Imanishi, M., Nishioka, K. and Amano, T. (1968) Biken J. *11*, 219.

Fujio, H., Martin, R. E., Ha, Y.-M., Sakato, N. and Amano, T. (1974) Biken J. *17*, 73.

Fujio, H., Sakato, N. and Amano, T. (1971) Biken J. *14*, 395.

Fujio, H., Takagaki, Y., Ha, Y.-M., Doi, E. M., Soebandrio, A. and Sakato, N. (1985) J. Biochem. *98*, 949.

Furuta, A., Rothstein, J. D. and Martin, L. J. (1997) J. Neurosc. *17*, 8363.

Fussey, S. P. M., Ali, S. T., Guest, J. R., James, O. F. W., Bassendine, M. F. and Yeaman, S. J. (1990) Proc. Natl. Acad. Sci. USA *87*, 3987.

Gaertner, H. F., Rose, K., Cotton, R., Timms, D., Camble, R. and Offord, R. E. (1992) Bioconjugate Chem. *3*, 262.

Gaire, F., Schmitt, C., Pinck, L. and Ritzenthaler, C. (1999) Virology, in press.

Gaither, K. K., Fox, O. F., Yamagata, H., Mamula, M. J., Reichlin, M. and Harley, J. B. (1987) J. Clin. Invest. *79*, , 841.

Galardy, R. E., Craig, L. C. and Printz, M. P (1973) Nature *242*, 127.

Galperin, C., Coppel, R. L. and Gershwin, M. E. (1996) Int. Arch. Allergy Immunol. *111*, 337.

Garboczi, D. N., Ghosh, P., Utz, U., Fan, Q. R., Biddison, W. E. and Wiley, D. C. (1996) Nature *384*, 134.

Garcia, K. C., Degano, M., Pease, L. R., Huang, M., Peterson, P. A., Teyton, L. and Wilson, I. A. (1998) Science *279*, 1166.

Garcia, K. C., Degano, M., Stanfield, R. L., Brunmark, A., Jackson, M. R., Peterson, P. A., Teyton, L. and Wilson, I. A. (1996) Science *274*, 209.

Garcon, N. M. J. and Six, H. R. (1991) J. Immunol. *146*, 3697.

Garnier, J., Osguthorpe, D. J. and Robson, B. (1978) J. Mol. Biol. *120*, 97.

Gazin, C., Rigolet, M., Briand, J. P., Van Regenmortel, M. H. V. and Galibert, F. (1986) EMBO J. *5*, 2241.

Geerligs, H. J., Weijer, W. J., Bloemhoff, W., Welling, G. W. and Welling-Wester, S. (1988) J. Immunol. Meth. *106*, 239.

Geerligs, H. J., Weijer, W. J., Welling, G. W. and Welling-Wester, S. (1989) J. Immunol. Meth. *124*, 95.

Gegg, C. V. and Etzler, M. E. (1993) Anal. Biochem. *210*, 309.

Gendloff, E. H., Casale, W. L., Ram, B. P., Tai, J. H., Pestka, J. J. and Hart, L. P. (1986) J. Immunol. Meth. *92*, 15

Gentry, L. E., Rohrschneider, L. R., Casnellie, J. E. and Krebs, E.G. (1983) J. Biol. Chem. *258*, 11219.

Geoghegan, K. F., Emery, M. J., Martin, W. H., McColl, A. S. and Daumy, G. O. (1993) Bioconjugate Chem. *4*, 537

Geoghegan, K. F. and Stroh, J. G. (1992) Bioconjugate Chem. *3*, 138.

Gerhard, W. and Webster, R. G. (1978) J. Exp. Med. *148*, 382.

Gerin, J. L., Alexander, H., Shih, J. W., Purcell, R. H., Dapolito, T., Engje, R., Green, R., Sutcliffe, J.G., Shinnick, T. M. and Lerner, R. A. (1983) Proc. Natl. Acad. Sci. USA *80*, 2365.

Gerritse, K. (1995) In: Immunological Recognition of Peptides in Medicine and Biology (Zegers, N. D., Boersma, W. J. A. and Claassen, E., eds.). CRC Press, Boca Raton, p. 269.

Gerritse, K., Fasbender, M., Boersma, W. J. A. and Claassen, E. (1991) J. Histochem. Cytochem. *39*, 987.

Getzoff, E. D., Geysen, H. M., Rodda, S. J., Alexander, H., Tainer, J. A. and Lerner, R. A. (1987) Science *235*, 1191.

Getzoff, E. D., Tainer, J. A., Lerner, R. A. and Geysen, H. M. (1988) Adv. Immunol. *43*, 1.

Geysen, H. M. (1985) Immunol. Today *6*, 364.

Geysen, H. M., Barteling, S. J. and Meloen, R. H. (1985a) Proc. Natl. Acad. Sci. USA *82*, 178.

Geysen, H. M., Mason, T. J. and Rodda, S. J. (1988) J. Mol. Recognit. *1*, 32.

Geysen, H. M., Mason, T. J., Rodda, S. J., Meloen, R. H. and Barteling, S. J. (1985b) In: Vaccines (Lerner, R. A., Channock, R. M. and Brown, F., eds.). Cold Spring Harbor Laboratory, New York, p. 133.

Geysen, H. M., Meloen, R. H. and Barteling, S. J. (1984) Proc. Natl. Acad. Sci. USA *81*, 3998.

Geysen, H. M., Rodda, S. J. and Mason, T. J. (1986) Mol. Immunol. *23*, 709.

Geysen, H. M., Rodda, S. J., Mason, T. J., Tribbick, G. and Schoofs, P. G. (1987) J. Immunol. Meth. *102*, 259.

Ghiara, J. B., Stura, E. A., Stanfield, R. L., Profy, A. T. and Wilson, I. A. (1994) Science *264*, 82.

Ghose, A. C. and Karush, F. (1985) Mol. Immunol. *22*, 1145.

Giavedoni, L. D., Kaplan, G., Marcovecchio, F., Piccone, M. E. and Palma, E. (1991) J. Gen. Virol. *72*, 967.

Gilliland, D. G. and Collier, R. J. (1980) Cancer Research *40*, 3564.

Girbal-Neuhauser, E., Durieux, J. J., Arnaud, M., Dalbon, P., Sebbag, M., Vincent, C., Simon, , M., Senshu, T., Masson-Bessière, C., Jolivet-Reynaud, C., Jolivet, M. and Serre, G. (1999) J. Immunol. *162*, 585.

Glass, E. J., Oliver, R. A., Collen, T., Doel, T. R., Di Marchi, R. and Spooner, R. L. (1991) Immunology *74*, 594.

Glazer, A. N., Delange, R. J. and Sigman, D. S. (1975) In: Chemical Modification of Proteins (Work, T. S. and Work, E., eds.). Elsevier/North Holland, Amsterdam, p. 205.

Glover, D. M., (ed.) (1985) DNA Cloning Techniques: A Practical Approach, Vol. 1. IRL Press, Oxford, p. 394.

Glück, R., Mischler, R., Finkelm, B., Que, J. U., Scarpa, B. and Cryz, S. J. J. (1994) Lancet *344*, 160.

Gnann, J. W., McCormick, J. B., Mitchell, S., Nelson, J. A. and Oldstone, M. B. A. (1987a) Science *237*, 1346.

Gnann, J. W., Nelson, J. A. and Oldstone, M. B. A. (1987b) J. Virol. *61*, 2639.

Godefroy-Colburn, T., Gagey, M. J., Berna, A. and Stussi-Garaud, C. (1986) J. Gen. Virol. *67*, 2233.

Godefroy-Colburn, T., Thivent, C. and Pinck, L. (1985) Eur. J. Biochem. *147*, 541.

Goding, J. W. (1983) In: Monoclonal Antibodies: Principles and Practice (Goding, J. W., ed.). Academic Press, London, p. 56.

Goldbaum, F. A., Schwarz, F. P., Eisenstein, E., Cauerhff, A., Mariuzza, R. A. and Poljak, R. J. (1996) J. Mol. Recogn. *9*, 6.

Goldfarb, D. S., Gariepy, J., Schoolnik, G. and Kornberg, R. D. (1986) Nature *322*, 641.

Goldmacher, V. S. (1983) Biochem. Pharmacol. *32*, 1207.

Golvano, J., Lasarte, J. J., Sarobe, P., Gullon, A., Prieto, J. and Borras-Cuesta, F. (1990) Eur. J. Immunol. *20*, 2363.

Gomez, C. E., Lopez-Campistrous, A. E. and Duarte, C. A. (1998) J. Virol. Meth. *71*, 7.

Gonda, M. A. (1994) In: Immunochemistry (Van Oss, C. J. and Van Regenmortel, M. H. V., eds.). Marcel Dekker, New York, p. 867.

Good, M. F., Maloy, W. L., Lunde, M. N., Margalit, H., Cornette, J. L., Smith, G. L., Moss, B., Miller, L. H. and Berzofsky, J. A. (1987) Science *235*, 1059.

Good, M. F. and Miller, L. H. (1994) In: Synthetic Vaccines (Nicholson, B. H., ed.). Blackwell Scientific, Oxford, p. 394.

Goodfriend, T. L., Levine, L. and Fasman, G. D. (1964) Science *144*, 1344.

Gosling, J. P. (1996) In: Immunoassay (Diamandis, E.P. and Christopoulos, T. K., eds.). Academic Press, San Diego, p. 287.

Grant, G. A. (1992) Synthetic Peptides: A User's Guide, W.H. Freeman and Company, New York.

Granzow, R. (1994) Methods *6*, 95.

Gras-Masse, H., Gomard, E., Deprez, B., Venet, A., Boutillon, C., Guillet, J.-G., Levy, J.-P. and Tartar, A. (1996) In: Peptides in Immunology (Schneider, C. H., ed.). John Wiley, New York, p. 75.

Gras-Masse, H., Jolivet, M., Drobecq, H., Aubert, J. P., Beachey, E. H., Audibert, F., Chedid, L. and Tartar, A. (1988) Mol. Immunol. *25*, 673.

Grassetti, D. R. and Murray, J. F., Jr. (1967) Arch. Biochem. Biophys. *119*, 41.

Green, M., Brackmann, K. H., Lucher, L. A., Symington, J. S. and Kramer, T. A. (1983) J. Virol. *48*, 604.

Green, N., Alexander, H., Olson, A., Alexander, S., Shinnick, T. M., Sutcliffe, J. G. and Lerner, R. A. (1982) Cell *28*, 477.

Green, N., Shinnick, T. M., Witte, O., Ponticelli, A., Sutcliffe, J. G. and Lerner, R. A. (1981) Proc. Natl. Acad. Sci. USA 78, 6023.

Greenspan, N. S. (1992) Bull. Inst. Pasteur *90*, 267.

Greenwood, F., Hunter, W. and Glower, J. (1963) Biochem. J. *89*, 114.

Greenwood, J., Willis, A. E. and Perham, R. N. (1991) J. Mol. Biol. *220*, 821.

Gregoriadis, G. (1990) Immunol. Today *11*, 89.

Gregoriadis, G. (1995) Trends Biotech, *13*, 527.

Gregoriadis, G., Davis, D., Garcon, N., Tan, L., Weissig, V. and Xiao, Q. (1989) In: Liposomes in the Therapy of Infectious Diseases and Cancer, Alan R. Liss, New York, p. 35.

Gregoriadis, G., Wang, Z., Barenholz, Y. and Francis, M. J. (1993) Immunology 80, 535.

Gregorius, K., Mouritsen, S. and Elsner, H. (1995) J. Immunol. Meth. 181, 65.

Grihalde, N. D., Chen, Y. C. J., Golden, A., Gubbins, E. and Mandecki, W. (1995) Gene 166, 187.

Grivel, J.-C. and Smith-Gill, S. J. (1996) In: Structure of Antigens, Vol. 3 (Van Regenmortel, M. H. V., ed.). CRC Press, Boca Raton, p. 91.

Gschwend, D. A., Good, A. C. and Kuntz, I. D. (1996) J. Mol. Recogn. 9, 175.

Guichard, G., Benkirane, N., Zeder-Lutz, G., Van Regenmortel, M. H. V., Briand, J. P. and Muller, S. (1994) Proc. Natl. Acad. Sci. USA 91, 9765.

Guichard, G., Muller, S., Van Regenmortel, M. H. V., Briand, J. P., Mascagni, P. and Giralt, E. (1996) Trends Biotech. 14, 44.

Guldner, H. H., Netter, H. J., Szostecki, C., Jaeger, E. and Will, H. (1990) J. Exp. Med. 171, 819.

Guo, H. C., Jardetzky, T. S., Garrett, T. P. J., Lane, W. S., Strominger, J. L. and Wiley, D. C. (1992) Nature 360, 364.

Gupta, R. K., Chang, A. C. and Siber, G. R. (1998) Dev. Biol. Stand. 92, 63.

Gupta, R. K. and Siber, G. R. (1995) Vaccine 13, 1263.

Guptasarma, P. (1996) Trends Biotech 14, 42.

Gurd, F. R. N. (1967) Meth. Enzymol, 11, 532.

Haack, T., Camarero, J. A., Roig, X., Mateu, M. G., Domingo, E., Andreu, D. and Giralt, E. (1997) Int. J. Biol. Macromol. 20, 209.

Haaheim, L. R., Halse, A.-K., Kvakestad, R., Stern, B., Normann, O. and Jonsson, R. (1996) Scand. J. Immunol. 43, 115.

Habeeb, A. F. S. A. and Hiramoto, R. (1968) Arch. Biochem. Biophys. 126, 16.

Habets, W. J., Hoet, M. H., De Jong, B. A. W., van der Kemp, A. and van Venrooij, W. J. (1989a) J. Immunol. 143, 2560.

Habets, W. J., Sillekens, P. T. G., Hoet, M. H., McAllister, G., Lerner, M. R. and van Venrooij, W. J. (1989b) Proc. Natl. Acad. Sci. USA 86, 4674.

Hagg, P. M., Hagg, P.O., Peltonen, S., Autio-Harmainen, H. and Pihlajaniemi, T. (1997) Am. J. Pathol. 150, 2075.

Halimi, H., Dumortier, H., Briand, J. P. and Muller, S. (1996) J. Immunol. Meth. 199, 77.

Hall, R., Hyde, J. E., Goman, M., Simmons, D. L., Hope, I. A., Machay, M. and Scaife, J. (1984) Nature 311, 379.

Hammer, J., Bono, E., Gallazzi, F., Belunis, C., Nagy, Z. and Sinigaglia, F. (1994) J. Exp. Med. 180, 2353.

Han, K. K., Richard, C. and Delacourte, A. (1984) Int. J. Biochem. 16, 129.

Hann, S. F., Abrams, H. D., Rohrschneider, L. R. and Eisenman, R. N. (1983) Cell *34*, 789.

Hannum, C. H. and Margoliash, E. (1985) J. Immunol. *135*, 3303.

Harari, I., Donohue-Rolf, A. G., Keusch, G. and Arnon, R. (1988) Infec. Immun. *56*, 1618.

Harlow, E. and Lane, D. (1989) Antibodies. A Laboratory Manual, Cold Spring Harbor Laboratory, New York.

Harper, M., Lema. F., Boulot, G. and Poljak, R. J. (1987) Mol. Immunol. *24*, 97.

Hartman, F. C. and Wold, F. (1966) J. Am. Chem. Soc. *88*, 3890.

Harvey, R., Faulkes, R., Gillett, P., Lindsay, N., Paucha, E., Bradbury, A. and Smith, A. E. (1982) EMBO J. *1*, 473.

Hathaway, L. J., Partidos, C. D., Vohra, P. and Steward, M. W. (1995) Vaccine *13*, 1495.

Hattori, S., Kiyokawa, T., Imagawa, K., Shimizu, F., Hashimura, E., Seiki, M. and Yoshida, M. (1984) Virology *136*, 338.

Hay, F. C., Jones, M. G., Soltys, A. and Horsfall, A. (1993) Immunol. Today *14*, 102.

Heath, T. D., Macher, B. A. and Papahadjopoulos, D. (1981) Biochim. Biophys. Acta *640*, 66.

Heath, T. D. and Martin, F. J. (1986) Chem. Phys. Lipids *40*, 347.

Herbert, W. J. and Kristensen, F. (1986) In: Handbook of Experimental Immunology. Applications of Immunological Methods in Biomedical Sciences, Vol. 4 (Weir, D. M., ed.). Blackwell Scientific, Oxford, p. 1.

Hermanson, G. T. (1996) Bioconjugate Techniques. Academic Press, San Diego, 785 pp.

Herrera, S., De Plata, C., Gonzalez, J. M., Perlaza, B. L., Bettens, F., Corradin, G. and Arevalo-Herrera, M. (1997) Parasite Immunol. *19*, 161.

Herzenberg, L. A. and Tokuhisha, T. (1980) Nature *285*, 664.

Herzenberg, L. A., Weir, D. M., Herzenberg, L. A. and Blackwell, C. (1997) Weir's Handbook of Experimental Immunology, 5th edition, Blackwell Science, Malden, MA.

Hiernaux, J. R., Stashak, P. W., Cantrell, J. L., Rudbach, J. A. and Baker, P. J. (1989) Infect. Immunity *57*, 1483.

Hilbert, A., Hudecz, F., Mezo, G., Mucsi, I., Kajtar, J., Kurucz, I., Rajnavolgyi, E. and Gergely, J. (1994) Scand. J. Immunol. *40*, 609.

Hilleman, M. R. (1995) Vaccine *13*, 1733.

Hines, J. J., Danho, W. and Elkon, K. B. (1991) Arthritis Rheum. *34*, 572.

Hioe, C. E., Qiu, H., Chend, P.-D., Bian, Z., Li, M.-L., Li, J., Singh, M., Kuebler, P., McGee, P., O'Hagan, [)., Zamb, T., Koff, W., Allsopp, C., Wang, C. Y. and Nixon, D. F. (1996) Vaccine *14*, 412.

Hirabayashi, Y., Fukuda, H., Kimura, J., Miyamoto, M. and Yasui, K. (1996) J. Virol. Meth. *61*, 23.

Hirakata, M., Craft, J. and Hardin, J. A. (1993) J. Immunol. *150*, 3592.

Hirakata, M., Kanungo, J., Suwa, A., Takeda, Y., Craft, J. and Hardin, J. A. (1996) Arthritis Rheum. *39*, 1886.

Hobbs, R. N. (1989) J. Immunol. Meth. *117*, 257.

Hoch, S. O (1994) In: Manual of Biological Markers of Disease, Vol. B2.4 (van Venrooij, W. J. and Maini, R. N., eds.). Kluwer Academic, Dordrecht, p. 1.

Hodges, R. S., Heaton, R. J., Parker, J. M., Molday, L. and Molday, R. S. (1988) J. Biol. Chem. *263*, 11768.

Hodgson, J. (1994) BioTechniques *12*, 31, 35.

Hoet, R. M. A., Raats, J., de Wildt, R., Dumortier, H., Muller, S., van den Hoogen, F. and van Venrooij, W. J. (1998) Mol. Immunol. *35*, 1045.

Hofnung, M. (1991) In: Methods in Cell Biology, Vol. 34 (Tartakoff, A. M., ed.). Academic Press, New York, p. 77.

Hofnung, M. and Charbit, A. (1993) In: Structure of Antigens, Vol. 2 (Van Regenmortel, M. H. V., ed.). CRC Press, Boca Raton, p. 79.

Hogle, J. M., Chow, M. and Filman, D. J. (1985) Science *229*, 1358.

Hogle, J. M. and Filman, D. J. (1989) Phil. Trans. R. Soc. Lond. *B323*, 467.

Hopp, T. M. (1993) Peptide Res. *6*, 183.

Hopp, T. P. (1984a) Mol. Immunol. *21*, 13.

Hopp, T. P. (1984b) Ann. Sclavo *2*, 47.

Hopp, T. P. (1986) J. Immunol. Meth. *88*, 1.

Hopp, T. P. (1994) Pept. Res. *7*, 229.

Hopp, T. P. and Woods, K. R. (1981) Proc. Natl. Acad. Sci. USA *78*, 3824.

Hopp, T. P. and Woods, K. R. (1983) Mol. Immunol. *20*, 483.

Horaud, F., Crainic, R., Blondel, B., Akacem, O., Couillin, P., Van der Werf, S., Wychowski, C., Bruneau, P., Siffert, O. and Girard, M. (1987) Prog. Med. Virol. *34*, 129.

Hornbeck, P. V. and Wilson, A. C. (1984) Biochemistry *23*, 998.

Houen, G., Jakobsen, M. H., Svaerke, C., Koch, C. and Barkholt, V. (1997) J. Immunol. Meth. *206*, 125.

Houghten, R. A. (1985) Proc. Natl. Acad. Sci. USA *82*, 5131.

Houghten, R. A., Appel, J. R., Blondelle, S. E., Cuervo, J. H., Dooley, C. T. and Pinilla, C. (1992) Peptide Res. *5*, 351.

Houghten, R. A., Pinilla, C., Blondelle, S. E., Appel, J. R., Dooley, C. T. and Cuervo, J. H. (1991) Nature *354*, 84.

Hovi, T. and Roivainen, M. (1993) J. Clin. Microbiol. *31*, 1083.

Huang, A., Huang, L. and Kennel, S. J. (1980) J. Biol. Chem. *255*, 8015.

Huang, J. H., Wey, J. J., Lee, H. F., Tsou, T. L., Wu, C. S., Wu, J. R., Chen, H. M., Chin, C., Chien, L. J., Chen, L. K., Wu, Y. C., Pan, M. J. and Wang, T. M. (1996) Virus Res. *41*, 43.

Huang, W., Nardelli, B. and Tam, J. P. (1994) Mol. Immunol. *31*, 1191.

Hudecz, F. and Price, M. R. (1992) J. Immunol. Meth. *147*, 201.

Hudecz, F. and Szekerke, M. (1980) Coll. Czech. Chem. Commun. *45*, 933.

Hudecz, F. and Szekerke, M. (1985) Coll. Czech. Chem. Commun. *50*, 103.

Hui, K. Y., Haber E. and Matsueda, G. E. (1986) Hybridoma *5*, 215.

Hunter, R., Stickland, F. and Kezdy, F. (1981) J. Immunol. *127*, 1244.

Hunter, R. L., Kidd, M. R., Olsen, M. R., Patterson, P. S. and Lal, A. A. (1995) J. Immunol. *154*, 1762.

Hurn, B. A. L. and Chantler, S. M. (1980) Meth. Enzymol. *70*, 104.

Hurrell, J. G. R., Smith, J. A. and Leach, S. J. (1978) Immunochemistry *15*, 297.

Hurrell, J. G. R., Smith, J. A., Todd, P. E. and Leach, S. J. (1977) Immunochemistry *14*, 283.

Huynh, T. V., Young, R. A. and Davis, R W. (1985) In: DNA Cloning Techniques: A Practical Approach, Vol. 1 (Glover, D. M., ed.). IRL Press, Oxford, p. 49.

Ibrahimi, I. M. Prager, E. M., White, T J. and Wilson, A. C. (1979) Biochemistry *13*, 2736.

Iinuma, H., Nerome, K., Yoshioka, Y. and Okinaga, K. (1995) Scand. J. Immunol. *41*, 1.

Imagawa, M., Yoshitake, S., Hamaguchi, Y., Ishikawa, E., Niitsu, Y., Urushizaki, I., Kanazawa, R., Tachibana, S., Nakazawa, N. and Ogawa, H. (1982) J. Appl. Biochem. *4*, 41.

Incefy, G. S., Ishimura, K., Wang, J. G. Unson, C. G. and Arickson, B. W. (1986) J. Immun. Meth. *89*, 9.

Itoh, Y., Itoh, K., Frank, M. B. and Reichlin, M. (1992) Autoimmunity *14*, 89.

Itoh, Y., Takai, E., Ohnuma, H., Kitajima, K., Tsuda, F., Machida, A., Mishiro, S., Nakamura, T., Miyakawa, Y. and Mayumi, M. (1986) Proc. Natl. Acad. Sci. USA *83*, 9174.

Ivanov, B. B., Meshcheryakova, E. A., Andronova, T. M. and Ivanov, V. T. (1994) Immunol. Invest. *23*, 201.

Ivanov, V. S., Suvorova, Z. K., Tchikin, L. D., Kozhich, A. T. and Ivanov, V. T. (1992) J. Immunol. Meth. *153*, 229.

Ivanyi, J. and Cerny, J. (1969) Curr. Top. Microbiol. Immunol. *49*, 114.

Jackson, D. C., Murray, J. M., White, D. O., Fagan, C. N. and Tregear, G. W. (1982) Virology *120*, 273.

Jackson, D. C., O'Brien-Simpson, N., Ede, N.J. and Brown, L. E. (1997) Vaccine *15*, 1697.

Jacob, C. O., Arnon, R. and Sela, M. (1985) Mol. Immunol. *22*, 1333.

Jacob, C. O., Arnon, R. and Sela, M. (1986/87) Immunol. Lett. *14*, 43.

Jacob, C. O., Pines, M. and Arnon, IR. (1 984) EMBO. J. *3*, 2889.

Jacob, C. O., Sela, M. and Arnon, R. (1983) Proc. Natl. Acad. Sci. USA *80*, 7611.

Jaegle, M., Briand, J. P., Burckard, J. and Van Regenmortel, M. H. V. (1988) Ann. Inst. Pasteur Virol. *139*, 39.

Jakoby, W. B. and Wilchek, M. (1974) Meth. Enzymol. *34*, 3.

James, J. A., Gross, T., Scofield, R. H. and Harley, J. B. (1995) J. Exp. Med. *181*, 453.

James, J. A. and Harley, J. B. (1992) J. Immunol. *148*, 2074.

James, J. A. and Harley, J. B. (1995) Clin. Exp. Rheum. *13*, 299.

James, J. A. and Harley, J. B. (1996) J. Immunol. *156*, 4018.

James, J. A., Mamula, M. J. and Harley, J. B. (1994a) Clin. Exp. Immunol. *98*, 419.

James, J. A., Scofield, R. H. and Harley, J. B. (1994b) Scand. J. Immunol. *39*, 557

Jameson, B. A., Bonin, J., Wimmer. E. and Kew, O. M. (1985) Virology *143*, 337.

Jameson, B. A. and Wolf, H. (1988) CABIOS *4*, 181.

Janin, J. (1979) Nature *171*, 935.

Janin, J. (1997) Structure *5*, 473.

Janin, J., Wodak, S., Levitt, M. and Maigret, B. (1978) J. Mol. Biol. *125*, 357.

Jeener, R., Lemoine, P. and Lavand'Homme, C. (1954) Biochem. Biophys. Acta *14*, 321.

Jemmerson, R. (1987) Proc. Natl. Acad. Sci. USA *84*, 9180.

Jemmerson, R. and Blankenfeld, R. (1989) Mol. Immunol. *26*, 301.

Jemmerson, R. and Hutchinson, R. M. (1990) Eur. J. Immunol. *20*, 579.

Jemmerson, R., Morrow, P. R., Klinman, N. R. and Paterson, Y. (1985) Proc. Natl. Acad. Sci. USA *82*, 1508.

Jemmerson, R. and Paterson, Y. (1986) BioTechniques *4*, 18.

Jerne, N. K. (1960) Ann. Rev. Microbiol. *14*, 341.

Jerry, D. J. (1993) Biotechniques *14*, 464.

Ji, T. H. and Ji, I. (1982) Anal. Biochem. *121*, 286.

Jin, L., Fendly, B. M. and Wells, J. A. (1992) J. Mol. Biol. *226*, 851.

Jin, L. and Wells, J. A. (1994) Prot. Science *3*, 2351.

Johnson, A. G. (1994) Clin. Microbiol. Rev. *7*, 277.

Johnson, D. A., Gautsch, J. W., Sportsman, J. R. and Elder, J. H. (1984) Gene Anal. Tech. *1*, 3.

Johnson, H. M., Langford, M. P., Lachchaura, B., Chan, T.-S. and Stanton, G. J. (1982) J. Immunol. *129*, 2357.

Johnson, L. M., Snyder, M., Chang, L. M. S., Dawis, R. W. and Campbell, J. L. (1985) Cell *43*, 369.

Johnson, T., Quibell, M. and Sheppard, R. C. (1995) J. Pept. Sci. *1*, 11.

Johnsson, B., Löfas, S. and Lindqvist, G. (1991) Anal. Biochem. *198*, 268.

Johnstone, A. P. and Turner, M. W. (1997) Immunochemistry 1—A Practical Approach, Oxford University Press, Oxford, p. 288.

Joisson, C., Dubs, M. C., Briand, J. P. and Van Regenmortel, M. H. V. (1992) Res. Virol. *143*, 167.

Joisson, C., Kuster, F., Plaué, S. and Van Regenmortel, M. H. V. (1993) Arch. Virol. *128*, 299.

Jönsson, U. and Malmqvist, M. (1992) In: Advances in Biosensors, Vol. 2 (Turner, A., ed.). JAI Press, San Diego, p. 291.

Joyce, S. and Nathenson, S.G. (1994) Curr. Opin. Immunol. *6*, 24.

Jung, G. and Bessler, W. G. (1995) In: Synthetic Peptides in Medicine and Biology. CRC Press, Boca Raton, p. 159.

Just, M., Berger, R., Drechsler, H., Brantschen, S. and Glück, R. (1992) Vaccine *10*, 737.

Kabeya, H., Ohashi, K., Ohishi, K., Sugimoto, C., Amanuma, H. and Onuma, M. (1996) Vaccine *14*, 1118.

Kabsch, W. and Sander, C. (1983) FEES Lett. *155*, 179.

Kam-Morgan, L. N. W., Smith-Gill, S. J., Taylor, M. G., Zhang, L., Wilson, A. C. and Kirsch, J. F. (1993) Proc. Natl. Acad. Sci. USA *90*, 3958.

Kanda, P., Kennedy, R. C. and Sparrow, J. T. (1986) In: Protides of the Biological Fluids, Vol. 34 (Peeters, H., ed.). Pergamon Press, Oxfordm p. 125.

Kanda, P., Kennedy, R. C. and Sparrow, J. T. (1991) Int. J. Peptide Prot. Res. *38*, 385.

Kang, C.-Y., Brunck, T., Kieber-Emmons, T., Blalock, J. and Kohler, H. (1988) Science *240*, 1034.

Kantrong, S., Saunal, H., Briand, J.-P. and Sako, N. (1995) Arch. Virol. *140*, 453.

Karjalainen, K (1994) Curr. Opin. Immunol. *6*, 9.

Karlsen, A., Lernmark, A., Kofod, H. and Dyrberg, T. (1990) J. Immunol. Meth. *128*, 151.

Karlsson, R., Fägerstam, L., Nilshans, H. and Persson, B. (1993) J. Immunol. Meth. *166*, 75.

Karlsson, R. and Fält, A. (1997) J. Immunol. Meth. *200*, 121.

Karlsson, R., Michaelsson, A. and Mattsson, L. (1991) J. Immunol. Meth. *145*, 229.

Karlsson, R. and Roos, H. (1997) In: Principles and Practice of Immunoassay (Price, C. P. and Newman, D. J., eds.). MacMillan, London, p. 99.

Karlsson, R., Roos, H., Fägerstam, L. and Persson, B. (1994) Methods *6*, 99.

Karplus, P. A. and Schulz, G. B. (1985) Naturwissenschaften *72*, S212.

Kato, T., Sasakawa, H., Suzuki, S., Shirako, M., Tashiro, F., Nishioka, K. and Yamamoto, K. (1995) Arthritis Rheum. *38*, 990.

Kaumaya, P. T. P., Kobs-Conrad, S., DiGeorge, A. M. and Stevens, V. C. (1994) In: Peptides: Design, Synthesis and Biological Activity (Basava, C. and Anantharamaiah, G. M., eds.). Birkhäuser, Boston, p. 133.

Kaumaya, P. T. P., Van Buskirk, A. M., Goldberg, E. and Pierce, S. K. (1992) J. Biol. Chem. 267, 6338.

Kawamura, H., Rosenberg, S. A. and Berzofsky, J. A. (1985) J. Exp. Med. 162, 381.

Kelley, R. F. (1996) In: Structure of Antigens, Vol. 3. (Van Regenmortel, M. H. V., ed.). CRC Press, Boca Raton, p. 1.

Kemeny, D. M. (1991) A Practical Guide to ELISA, Pergamon Press, Oxford, 115 pp.

Kemeny, D. M. and Challacombe, S. J. (1988) ELISA and other Solid-Phase Immunoassays, John Wiley, Chichester, 367 pp.

Kennedy, R. C., Dreesman, G. R., Chanh, T. C., Boswell, R. N., Allan, J. S., Lee, T.-H., Essex, M., Sparrow, J. T., Ho, D. D. and Kanda, P. (1987) J. Biol. Chem. 262, 5769.

Kennedy, R. C., Henkel, R. D., Pauletti., D., Allan, J. S., Lee, T. H., Essex, M. and Dreesman, G. R. (1986) Science 231, 1556.

Kennel, S. J. (1982) J. Immunol. Meth. 55, 1.

Kenney, J. S., Hughes, B. W., Masada, M. P. and Allison, A. C. (1989) J. Immunol. Meth. 121, 157.

Kent, S. and Clark-Lewis, I. (1985) In: Synthetic Peptides in Biology and Medicine (Alitalo, K., Partanen, P. and Vaheri, A., eds.). Elsevier Science, Amsterdam, p. 29.

Khudyakov, Y. E., Khudyakova, N. S., Jue, D. L., Lambert, S. B., Fang, S. and Fields, H. A. (1995) Virology 206, 666.

Kiefer, H. (1979) In: Immunological Methods, Vol. 1 (Lefkovits, H. and Pernis, B., eds.). Academic Press, New York, p. 137.

Kieffer, B., Koehl, P., Plaué, S. and Lefèvre, J. F. (1993) J. Biomol. NMR 3, 91.

King, T. P., Li, Y. and Kochoumian, L. (1978) Biochemistry 17, 1499.

Kitagawa, T. and Aikawa, T. (1976) J. Biochem. 79, 233.

Klaus, G. G. B. and Cross, A. M. (1974) Cell. Immunol. 14, 226.

Kleid, D. G., Yansura, D., Small, B., Dowbenko, D., Moore, D. M., Grubman, M. J., McKercher, P. D., Morgan, D. O., Robertson, B. H. and Bachrach, H. L. (1981) Science 214, 1125.

Klein Gunnewiek, J. M. T., van de Putte, L. B. A. and van Venrooij, W. J. (1997) Clin. Exp. Rheum. 15, 549.

Kobayashi, T., Fujio, H., Kondo, K., Dohi, Y., Hirayama, A., Takagaki, Y., Kosaki, G. and Amano, T. (1982) Mol. Immunol. 19, 619.

Kohn, J. and Wilchek, M. (1983) FEBS Lett. 154, 209.

Koolen, M. J., Borst, M. A., Horzinek, M. C. and Spaan, W. J. (1990) J. Virol. *64*, 6270.

Korn, A. H., Feairheller, S. H. and Filachione, E. M. (1972) J. Mol. Biol. *65*, 525.

Koshland, D. E., Nemethy, G. and Filmer, D. (1966) Biochemistry *5*, 365.

Krchnak, V., Mach, O. and Maly, A. (1989) Meth. Enzymol. *178*, 586.

Kricka, L. J. (1985) In: Ligand-binder Assays. Labels and Analytical Strategies (Schwartz, M. K., ed.). Marcel Dekker, New York, p. 53.

Kumar, A., Arora, R., Kaur, P., Chauhan, V. S. and Sharma, P. (1992) J. Immunol. *148*, 1499.

Kumar, V. (1994) In: Immunochemistry (Van Oss, C. J. and Van Regenmortel, M. H. V., eds.). Marcel Dekker, New York, p. 829.

Kutubuddin, M., Kolaskar, A. S., Galande, S., Gore, M. M., Guish, S. N. and Banerjee, K. (1991) Mol. Immunol. *28*, 149.

Kutubuddin, M., Simons, J. and Chow, M. (1992a) J. Virol. *55*, 3042.

Kutubuddin, M., Simons, J. and Chow, M. (1992b) J. Virol. *66*, 5967.

Kwong, P. D., Wyatt, R., Robinson, J., Sweet, R. W., Sodroski, J. and Hendrickson, W. A. (1998) Nature *393*, 648.

Kyte, J. and Doolittle, R. F. (1982) J. Mol. Biol. *157*, 105.

Laczko, I., Miklos, H., Elemer., V. and Gabor, K. T. (1998) Biochem. Biophys. Res. Comm. *249*, 213.

Ladbury, J. E. (1996) Chem. Biol. *3*, 973.

Laemmli, U. K. (1970) Nature *227*, 680.

Lagacé, J., Arsenault, S. and Cohen, E. A. (1994) J. Immunol. Meth. *175*, 131.

Lairmore, M. D., Lal, R. B. and Kaumaya, P. T. P. (1995) Biomed. Pept. Prot. Nucl. Acids *1*, 117.

Lake, D. F., Schluter, S. F., Wang, E., Bernstein, R. M., Edmundson, A. B. and Marchalonis, J. J. (1994) Proc. Natl. Acad. Sci. USA *91*, 10849.

Lam, K. S., Lake, D., Salmon, S. E., Smith, J., Chen, M.-L., Wade, S., Abdul-Latif, F., Leblova, Z., Ferguson, R. D., Krchnak, V., Sepetov, N. F. and Lebi, M. (1996) Methods *9*, 482.

Lancet, D., Horovitz, A. and Katchalski-Katzir, E. (1994) In: The Lock-and-Key Principle. The State of the Art – 100 Years on (Behr, J. P., ed.). John Wiley, Chichester, p. 25.

Lando, G. and Reichlin, M. (1982) J. Immunol. *129*, 212.

Lane, D. and Koprowski, H. (1982) Nature *296*, 200.

Langbeheim, H., Arnon, R. and Sela, M. (1976) Proc. Natl. Acad. Sci. USA *73*, 4636.

Langedijk, J. P., Middel, W. G., Schaaper, W. M., Meloen, R. H., Kramps, J. A., Brandenburg, A. H. and Van Oirschot, J. T. (1996) J. Immunol. Meth. *193*, 157.

Langeveld, J. P. M., Casal, J. I., Osterhaus, A. D. M. E., Cortés, E., De Swart, R., Vela, C., Dalsgaard, K., Puijk, W., Schaaper, W. M. M. and Meloen, R. H. (1994a) J. Virol. *68*, 4506.

Langeveld, J. P. M., Casal, J. I., Cortés, E., Van de Wetering, G., Boshuizen, R. S., Schaaper, W. M. M., Dalsgaard, K. and Meloen, R. H. (1994b) Vaccine *12*, 1473.

Langeveld, J. P. M., Casal, J. I. and Vela, C., Dalsgaard, K., Smale, S. H., Puijk, W. C. and Meloen, R. H. (1993) J. Virol. *67*, 765.

Langeveld, J. P. M., Kamstrup, S., Uttenthal, A., Strandbygnard, B., Vela, C., Dalsgaard, K., Beekman, N. J. C. M., Meloen, R. H. and Casal, J. I. (1995) Vaccine *13*, 1.

Laporte, J., Grosclaude, J., Wantyghem, J., Bernard, S. and Rouse, P. (1973) C.R. Acad. Sci. *276*, 3399.

LaRosa, G. J., Davide, J. P., Weinhold, K., Waterbury, J. A., Profy, A. T., Lewis, J. A., Langlois, A. J., Dreesman, G. R., Boswell, R. N., Shadduck, P., Holley, L. H., Karplus, M., Bolognesi, D. P., Matthews, T. J., Emini, E. A. and Putney, S. D. (1990) Science *249*, 932.

Lasic, D. and Martin, F. (1995) Stealth Liposomes, CRC Press, Boca Raton.

Laune, D., Molina, F., Ferrieres, G., Mani, J.-C., Cohen, P., Simon, D., Bernardi, T., Piechaczyk, M., Pau, B. and Granier, C. (1997) J. Biol. Chem. *272*, 30937.

Lauritzen, E., Flyge, H. and Holm, A. (1994) In: Antibody Techniques, Academic Press, p. 227.

Lauritzen, E., Masson, M., Rubin, I., Bjerrum, O. J. and Holm, A. (1993) Electrophoresis *14*, 852.

Lauritzen, E., Masson, M., Rubin, I. and Holm, A. (1990) J. Immunol. Meth. *131*, 257.

Laver, W. G., Air, G. M., Webster, R. G. and Smith-Gill, S. J. (1990) Cell *61*, 553.

Lavoie, T. B., Drohan, W. N. and Smith-Gill, S. J. (1992) J. Immunol. *148*, 503.

Le Guern, A., Wetterskog, D., Marche, P. N. and Kindt, T. J. (1987) Mol. Immunol. *24*, 455.

Lea, S., Abughazaleh, R., Blakemore, W., Curry, S., Fry, E., Jackson, T., King, A., Logan, D., Newman, J. and Stuart, D. (1995) Structure *3*, 571.

Leach, S. J. (1983) Biopolymers *22*, 425.

Leach, S. J. (1984) Ann. Sclavo *2*, 21.

Leclerc, C., Deriaud, E., Mimic, V. and Van der Werf, S. (1991) J. Virol. *65*, 711.

Leclerc, C., Przewlocki, G., Schutze, M. P. and Chedid, L. (1987) Eur. J. Immunol. *17*, 269.

Leclerc, C. and Ronco, J. (1998) Immunol. Today *19*, 300.

Lee, A. C. J., Powell, J. E., Tregear, G. W., Niall, H. D. and Stevens, V. C. (1980) Mol. Immunol. *17*, 749.

Lee, C. L. and Atassi, M. Z. (1976) Biochem. J. *159*, 89.

Lee, V. H. L. (1986) Pharm. Intern. *7*, 208.

Lefkovits, I. (1997) Immunology Methods Manual, Academic Press, London, p. 560.

Lehtonen, O. P. and Viljanen, M. K. (1980) J. Immunol. Meth. *34*, 61.

Leinikki, P., Lehtinen, M., Hyöty, H., Parkkonen, P., Kantanen, M. L. and Hakulinen, J. (1993) Adv. Vir. Res. *42*, 149.

Lenstra, J. A., Erkens, J. H. F., Langeveld, J. G. A., Posthumus, W. P. A., Meloen, R. H., Gebauer, F., Correa, I., Enjuanes, L. and Stanley, K. K. (1992) J. Immunol. Meth. *152*, 149.

Lenstra, J. A., Kusters, J. G. and Van der Zeijst, B. A. M. (1990) Arch. Virol. *110*, 1.

Lenstra, J. A. and Van Vliet, A. H. M. (1996) In: Epitope Mapping Protocols (Morris, G. E., ed.). Humana Press, Totowa, New Jersey, p. 287.

Leonetti, M., Cotton. J., Leroy, S., Mourier, G. and Ménez, A. (1995) J. Immunol. *155*, 210.

Lerner, R. A. (1982) Nature *299*, 592.

Lerner, R. A. (1984) Adv. Immunol. *36*, 1.

Lerner, R. A., Green, N., Alexander, H., Liu, F.-T., Sutcliffe, J. G. and Shinnick, T. M. (1981) Proc. Natl. Acad. Sci. USA *78*, 3403.

Lescar, J., Pellegrini M., Souchon, H., Tello, D., Poljak, R. J., Peterson, N., Greene, M. and Alzari, P. M. (1995) J. Biol. Chem. *270*, 18067.

Leserman, L. D., Barbet, J., Kourilsky, F. and Weinstein, J. N. (1980) Nature *288*, 602.

Lesk, A. M. and Tramontano, A. (1993) In: Structure of Antigens, Vol. 2 (Van Regenmortel, M. H. V., ed.). CRC Press, Boca Raton, p. 1.

Leslie, G. A. and Clem, L. W. (1969) J. Exp. Med. *130*, 1337.

Letvin, N. L. (1998) Science *280*, 18751888.

Levi, M., Sällberg, M., Ruden, U., Herlyn, D., Maruyama, H., Wigzell, H., Marks, J. and Wahren, B. (1993a) Proc. Natl. Acad. Sci. USA *90*, 4374.

Levi, M., Sällberg. M., Ruden, U., Herlyn, D., Maruyama, H., Wigzell, H., Marks, J. and Wahren, B. (1993b) Proc. Natl. Acad. Sci. USA *90*, 4374.

Levi, R., Aboud-Pirak, E., Leclerc, C., Lowell, G. H. and Arnon, R. (1995) Vaccine *13*, 1353.

Levitt, M. (1976a) Biochemistry *17*, 4277.

Levitt, M. (1976b) J. Mol. Biol. *104*, 59.

Lew, A. M., Anders, F., Edwards, S. J. and Langford, C. J. (1988) Immunology *65*, 311.

Liddell, E. and Weeks, I. (1995) In: Antibody Technology (Liddell, E. and Weeks, I., eds.). BIOS Scientific Publishers, Oxford, p. 85.

Likhite, V. and Sehon, A. (1967) In: Methods in Immunology and Immunochemistry, Vol. 1 (Williams, C. A. and Chase, M. W., eds.). Academic Press, New York, p. 150.

Lin, C., Mihal, K. A. and Krueger, R. J. (1990) Biochim. Biophys. Acta *1038*, 382.

Lipford, G. B., Bauer, S., Wagner, H. and Heeg, K. (1995) Immunology *84*, 298.

Lipford, G. B., Wagner, H. and Heeg, K. (1994) Vaccine *12*, 73.

Liu, F. T., Zinnecker, M., Hamaoka, T. and Katz, D. H. (1979) Biochemistry *18*, 690.

Lloyd Jones, G., Edmundson, H. M., Spencer, L., Gale, J. and Saul, A. (1989) J. Immunol. Meth. *123*, 211.

Lloyd Jones, G., Lord, R., Spencer, L. and Saul, A. (1991) Immunol. Lett. *27*, 209.

Lloyd Jones, G., Spencer, L., Lord, R., Mollard, R., Pye, D. and Saul, A. (1990) Immunol. Len. *24*, 253.

Lloyd-Williams, P., Albericio, F. and Giralt, E. (1997) Chemical Approaches to the Synthesis of Peptides and Proteins, CRC Press, New York.

Logan, D., Abu-Ghazaleh, R., Blakemore, W., Curry, S., Jakson, T., King, A., Lea, S., Lewis, R., Newman, J., Parry, N., Rowlands, D., Stuart, D. and Fry, E. (1993) Nature *362*, 566.

Loleit, M., Tröger W., Wiesmüller, K.-H., Jung, G., Stecker, M. and Bessler, W. G. (1990) Biol. Chem. Hoppe-Seyler *371*, 967.

Londono, L. P., Chatfield, S., Tindle, R. W., Herd, K., Gao, X. M., Frazer, I. and Dougan, G. (1996) Vaccine *14*, 545.

Loomans, E. E. M. G., Gribnau, T. C. J., Bloemers, H. P. J. and Schielen, W. J. G. (1998a) J. Immunol. Meth. *221*, 119.

Loomans, E. E. M. G., Gribnau, T. C. J., Bloemers, H. P. J. and Schielen, W. J. G. (1998b) J. Immunol.Meth. *221*, 131.

Loomans, E. E. M. G., Petersen-Van Ettekoven, A., Bloemers, H. P. J. and Schielen, W. J. G. (1997) Anal. Biochem. *248*, 117.

Lopez de Turiso, J. A., Cortes, E., Ranz, J., Garcia, J., Sanz, A., Vela, C. and Casal, J. I. (1991) J. Gen. Virol. *72*, 2445.

Lövgren, K., Kaberg, H. and Morein, B. (1990) Clin. Exp. Immunol. *82*, 435.

Lövgren, K., Lindmark, J., Pipkorn, R. and Morein, B. (1987) J. Immunol. Meth. *98*, 137.

Lövgren, K. and Morein, K. (1988) Biotechnol. Appl. Biochem. *10*, 161.

Lowell, G. H. (1990) In: New Generation Vaccines (Woodrow, G. C. and Levine, M. M., eds.). Marcel Dekker, New York, p. 141.

Lowell, G. H., Ballou, W. R., Smith, L. F., Wirtz, R. A., Zollinger, W. D. and Hockmeyer, W. D. (1988) Science *240*, 800.

Lu, S., Reyes, V. E., Bositis, C. M., Goldschmidt, T. G., Lam, V., Sorli, C. H., Torgerson, R. R., Lew, R. A. and Humphreys, R. E. (1992) In: Structure of

Antigens, Vol. 1 (Van Regenmortel, M. H. V., ed.). CRC Press, Boca Raton, p. 81.

Lu, Y.-A., Clavijo, P., Galantino, M., Shen, Z.-Y., Liu, W. and Tam, J. P. (1991) Mol. Immunol. 28, 623.

Lucey, D. R., Van Cott, T. C., Loomis, L. D., Bethke, F. R., Hendrix, C. W., Melcher, G. P., Redfield, R. R. and Birx, D. I. (1993) J. Acquir. Immune Defic. Syndr. 6, 994.

Luka, J., Sternas, L., Jornvall, H., Klein, G. and Lerner, R. (1983) Proc. Natl. Acad. Sci. USA 80, 1199.

Lyons, D. S., Lieberman, S. A., Hampl, J., Boniface, J. J., Chien, Y. H., Berg, L. J. and Davis, M. M. (1996) Immunity 5, 53.

Macquaire, F., Baleux, F., Giaccobi, E., Huynh-Dinh, T., Neumann, J.-M. and Sanson, A. (1992) Biochemistry 31, 2576.

Madden, D. R. (1995) Ann. Rev. Immunol. 13, 587.

Maeji, N. J., Bray, A. M., Valerio, R. M., Seldon, M. A., Wang, J. X. and Geysen, H. M. (1991) Pept. Res. 4, 142.

Maeji, N. J., Bray, A. M., Valerio, R. M. and Wang, W. (1995) Pept. Res. 8, 33.

Maeji, N. J., Valerio, R. M., Bray, A. M., Campbell, R. A. and Geysen, H. M. (1994) Reactive Polymers 22, 203.

Mäkelä, O. (1965) J. Immunol. 95, 378.

Mäkelä, O. and Seppälä, I. J. T. (1986) In: Handbook of Experimental Immunology and Immunochemistry, Vol. 1.3.1 (Weir, D. M., ed.).

Malby, R. L., Tulip, W. R., Harley, V. R., McKimm-Breschkin, J. L., Laver, W. G., Webster, R. G. and Colman, P. M. (1994) Structure 2, 733.

Malley, A., Saha, A. and Halliday, W. J. (1965) J. Immunol. 95, 141.

Malmqvist, M. (1996) Methods 9, 525.

Malvoisin, E. and Wild, F. (1990) J. Virol. 64, 5160.

Manavalan, P. and Ponnuswamy, P. K. (1978) Nature 275, 673.

Manganaro, M., Ogra, P. L. and Ernst, P. B. (1994) Int. Arch. Allergy Immunol. 103, 223.

Mani, J.-C., Marchi, V. and Cucurou, C. (1994) Mol. Immunol. 31, 439.

Marchalonis, J. J., Ampel, N. M., Schluter, S. F., Garza, A., Lake, D. F., Galgiani, J. N. and Landsperger, W. J. (1997) Clin. Immunol. Immunopathol. 82, 174.

Marchalonis, J. J., Lake, D. F., Schluter, S. F. K. D., Watson, R. R., Ampel, N. M. and Galgiani, J. N. (1995) Adv. Exp. Med. Biol. 383, 211.

Margalit, H., Spouge, J. L., Cornette, J. L., Cease, K. B., Delisi, C. and Berzofsky, J. A. (1987) J. Immunol. 138, 2213.

Margis, R., Hans, F. and Pinck, L. (1993) Arch. Virol. 131, 225.

Marguerite, M., Bossus, M., Mazingue, C., Wolowczuk, I., Gras-Masse, H., Tartar, A., Capron, A. and Auriault, C. (1992) Mol. Immunol. 29, 793.

Mariani, M., Bracci, L., Presentini, R., Nucci, D., Neri, P. and Antoni, G. (1987) Mol. Immun. *24*, 297.

Mariottini, P., Chomyn, A., Attardi, G., Trovato, D., Strong, D. D. and Doolittle, R. F. (1983) Cell *32*, 1269.

Mariuzza, R. A., Phillips, S. E. V. and Poljak, R. J. (1987) Ann. Rev. Biophys. Biophys. Chem. *16*, 139.

Mariuzza, R. A. and Poljak, R. J. (1993) Curr. Opin. Immunol. *5*, 50.

Maron, E. and Bonavida, B. (1971) Biochim. Biophys. Acta *229*, 273.

Marsden, H. S., Owsianka, A. M., Graham, S., McLean, G. W., Robertson, C. A. and Subak-Sharpe, J. H. (1992) J. Immunol. Meth. *147*, 65.

Martin, F. J. and Papahadjopoulos, D. (1982) J. Biol. Chem. *255*, 286.

Martinon, F., Gras-Masse, H., Boutillon, C., Chirat, F., Deprez, B., Guillet, J.-G., Gomard, E., Tartar, A. and Levy, J.-P. (1992). J. Immunol. *149*, 3416.

Maruyama, T., Thornton, G. B., Iino, S., Kurokawa, K. and Milich, D. R. (1992) J. Immunol. Methods *155*, 65.

Mateu, M. G. (1995) Vir. Res. *38*, 1.

Matrisian, L. M., Bowden, G. D, Krieg, P., Furstenberger, G., Briand, J. P., Leroy, P. and Breathnach, R. (1986) Proc. Natl. Acad. Sci. USA *83*, 9413.

Matsui, K., Boniface, J. J., Steffner, P., Reay, P. A. and Davis, M. M. (1994) Proc. Natl. Acad. Sci. USA *91*, 12862.

Matsumura, M., Fremont, D. H., Peterson, P. A. and Wilson, I. A. (1992) Science *257*, 927.

Mattioli, S., Imberti, L., Stellini., R. and Primi, D. (1995) J. Virol. *69*, 5294.

Maul, G. G., Jimenez, S. A., Riggs, E. and Ziemnicka-Kotula, D. (1989) Proc. Natl. Acad. Sci. USA *86*, 8492.

Maurice, J. (1995) Science *267*, 320.

Mayer, R. J. and Walker, J. H. (1978) In: Techniques in Protein and Enzyme Biochemistry (Kornberg, H. L., Metcalfe, J. C., Northcote, D. N., Pogson, C. I. and Tipton, K. F., eds.). Elsevier, Amsterdam, p. 1.

Mayer, R. J. and Walker, J. H. (1987) Immunochemical Methods in Cell and Molecular Biology, Academic Press, London, 325 pp.

McCahon, D., Crowther, J. R. and Belsham, G. J. (1989) J. Gen. Virol. *70*, 639.

McCauliffe, D. P., Yin, H., Wang, L.-X. and Lucas, L. (1994) J. Rheumatol. *21*, 1073.

McCoy, A. J., Epa, V. C. and Colman, P. M. (1997) J. Mol. Biol. *268*, 570.

McGhee, J. R., Mestecky, J., Dertzbaugh, M. T., Eldridge, J. H., Hirasawa, M. and Kiyono, H. (1992) Vaccine *10*, 75.

McLean, G. W., Gross, A. M., Munns, M. S. and Marsden, H. S. (1992) J. Immunol. Meth. *155*, 113.

McLean, G. W., Owsianka, A. M., Subak-Sharpe, J. H. and Marsden, H. S. (1991) J. Immunol. Meth. *137*, 149.

McMillan, S., Seiden, M., Houghten, R., Clevinger, B., Davie, J. M. and Lerner, R. A. (1983) Cell *35*, 859.

McNeilage, L. J., Macmillan, E. M. and Whittingham, S. F. (1990) J. Immunol. *145*, 3829.

McNeill, D. and Freiberger, P. (1993) Fuzzy Logic, Simon & Schuster, New York, 319 pp.

Means, G. E. and Feeney, R. E. (1971) Chemical Modification of Proteins, Holden-Day, San Francisco, 254 pp.

Means, G. E. and Feeney, R. E. (1995) Anal. Biochem. *224*, 1.

Mehra, V., Sweetser, D. and Young, R. A. (1986) Proc. Natl. Acad. Sci. USA *83*, 7013.

Meistrich, M. L., Trostle-Weige, P.1K., Lin, R., Bhatnagar, Y. M. and Allis, C. D. (1992) Mol. Reprod. Develop. *31*, 170.

Men, Y., Candert, B., Merkle, H. P. and Corradin, G. (1996) Vaccine *14*, 1442.

Menez, A., Pillet, L., Léonetti, M., Bontems, F. and Maillère, B. (1992) In: Structure of Antigens, Vol. 1 (M. H. V. Van Regenmortel, ed.). CRC Press, Boca-Raton, 293 pp.

Meola, A., Delmastro, P., Monaci, P., Luzzago, A., Nicosia, A., Felici, F., Cortese, R. and Galfré, G. (1995) J. Immunol. *154*, 3162.

Merrifield, R. B. (1963) J. Am. Chem. Soc. *85*, 2149.

Metrione, R. M. (1982) Anal. Biochem. *120*, 91.

Metzger, D. W., Chang, L. K., Miller, A. and Sercarz, E. E. (1984) Eur. J. Immunol. *14*, 87.

Mierendorf, R. C. and Dimond, R. L. (1983) Anal. Biochem. *135*, 221.

Migliorini, P., Betschart, B. and Corradin, G. (1993) Eur. J. Immunol. *23*, 582.

Milich, D. R. (1989) Adv. Immunol. *45*, 195.

Milich, D. R., Hughes, J. L., McLachlan, A., Thornton, G. B. and Moriarty, A. (1988) Proc. Natl. Acad. Sci. USA *85*, 1610.

Milich, D. R., Thornton, G. B., Neurath, A. R., Kent, S. B. H., Michel, M., Tiollais, P. and Chisari, F. V. (1985) Science *228*, 1195.

Milton, L. R. C., Milton, S. C. F., Von Wechmar, M. B. and Van Regenmortel, M. H. V. (1980) Mol. Immunol. *17*, 1205.

Milton, L. R. C. and Van Regenmortel, M. H. V. (1979) Mol. Immunol. *16*, 179.

Minor, P. D., Ferguson, M., Evans, D. M. A., Almond, J. W. and Icenogle, J. P. (1986) J. Gen. Virol. *67*, 1283.

Misaki, Y., Yamamoto, K., Yanagi, K., Miura, H., Ichijo, H., Kato, T., Mato, T., Welling-Wester, S., Nishioka, K. and Ito, K. (1993) Eur. J. Immunol. *23*, 1064.

Miyazaki, S., Shimura, J., Hirose, S., Sanokawa, R., Tsurui, H., Wakiya, M., Sugawara, H. and Shirai, T. (1997) Intern. Immunol. *9*, 771.

Modrow, S., Höflacher, B., Mertz, R. and Wolf, H. (1989) J. Immunol. Meth. *118*, 1.

Modrow, S. and Wolf, H. (1990) In: Immunochemistry of Viruses. The Basis for Serodiagnosis and Vaccines, Vol. II (Van Regenmortel, M. H. V. and Neurath, A. R., eds.). Elsevier, Amsterdam, p. 83.

Molina, F., Laune, D., Gougat, C., Pau, B. and Granier, C. (1996) Pept. Res. 9, 151.

Monsan, P., Puzo, G. and Mazarguil, H. (1975) Biochimie 57, 1281.

Morein, B. (1988) Nature 332, 287.

Morel-Montero, A. and Delaage, M. (1994) In: Immunochemistry (Van Oss, C. J. and Van Regenmortel, M. H. V., eds.). Marcel Dekker, New York, p. 357.

Moreno, A. and Patarroyo, E. (1995) Curr. Opin. Immunol. 7, 607.

Morgan, D. O. and Moore, D. M. (1990) Am. J. Vet. Res. 51, 40.

Mori, T., Sugawa, H., Piraphatdist., T., Inoue, D., Enomoto, T. and Imura, H. (1991) Biochem. Biophys. Res. Commun. 178, 165.

Morris, J. C., Gibson, J. L., Haas, E..J., Bergert, E. R., Dallas, J. S. and Prabhakar, B. S. (1994) Autoimmunity 17, 287.

Morrow, P. R., Rennick, D. M., Leung, C. Y. and Benjamini, E. (1984) Mol. Immunol. 21, 301.

Morton, T. A., Myszka, D. G. and Chaiken, I. M. (1995) Anal. Biochem. 227, 176.

Moser, O., Gagey, M. J., Godefroy-Colburn, T., Stussi-Garaud, C., Ellwartt-Tschurtz, M., Nitschko, H. and Mundry, K. W. (1988) J. Gen. Virol. 69, 1367.

Mowat, A. M. and Donachie, A. M. (1991) Immunol. Today 12, 383.

Müller, G. M., Shapira, M. and Arnon, R. (1982) Proc. Natl. Acad. Sci. USA 79, 569.

Muller, S., Barakat, S., Watts, R., Joubaud, P. and Isenberg, D. (1990a) Clin. Exp. Rheum. 8, 445.

Muller, S., Benkirane, N., Guichard, G., Van Regenmortel, M. H. V. and Brown, F. (1998) Exp. Opin. Invest. Drugs 7, 1429.

Muller, S., Benkirane, N., Hovanessian, A. and Briand, J. P. (1999) Unpublished data.

Muller, S., Bonnier, D., Thiry, M. and Van Regenmortel, M. H. V. (1989) Int. Arch. Allergy Appl. Immunol. 89, 288.

Muller, S., Briand, J. P., Barakat, S., Lagueux, J., Poirier, G. G., De Murcia, G. and Isenberg, D. A. (1994) Clin. Immunol. Immunopathol. 73, 187.

Muller, S., Briand, J. P. and Van Regenmortel, M. H. V. (1988) Proc. Natl. Acad. Sci. USA 85, 8176.

Muller, S., Guichard, G., Benkirane, N., Brown, F., Van Regenmortel, M. H. V. and Briand, J. P. (1995) Pept. Res. 8, 138.

Muller, S., Himmelspach, K. and Van Regenmortel, M. H. V. (1982) EMBO J. 1, 421.

Muller, S., Plaué, S., Couppez, M. and Van Regenmortel, M. H. V. (1986) Mol. Immunol. 23, 593.

Muller, S., Plaué, S., Samama, J. P., Valette, M., Briand, J. P. and Van Regenmortel, M. H. V. (1990b) Vaccine 8, 308.

Muller, S. and Van Regenmortel, M. H. V. (1993) In: Structure of Antigens, Vol. 2 (Van Regenmortel, M. H. V., ed.). CRC Press, Boca Raton, p. 149.

Munesinghe, D. Y., Clavijo, P., Calle, M. C., Nussenzweig, R. S. and Nardin, E. (1991) Eur. J. Immunol. 21, 3015.

Murdin, A. D. and Doel, T. R. (1987a) J. Biol. Stand. 15, 39.

Murdin, A. D. and Doel, T. R. (1987b).J. Biol. Stand. 15, 58.

Muro, Y., Tsai, W.-M., Houghten, R. and Tan, E. M. (1994) J. Biol. Chem. 269, 18529.

Mutter, M. and Tuchscherer, G. (1988) Macromol. Chem. Rapid Commun. 9, 437.

Myszka, D. G. (1997) Curr. Opin. Biotechnol. 8, 50.

Naim, J. O., Hinshaw, J. R. and Van Oss, C. J. (1989) Immunol. Invest. 18, 817.

Nardelli, B., Lu, Y.-A., Shiu, D. R., Delpierre-Defoort, C., Profy, A. T. and Tam, J. P. (1992) J. Immunol. 148, 914.

Nardin, E. H., Oliveira, G. A., Calvo-Calle, J. M. and Nussenzweig, R. S. (1995) Adv. Immunol. 60, 105.

Naruse, H., Ogasawara, K., Kaneda, R., Hatakeyama, S., Itoh, T., Kida, H., Miyazaki, T., Good, R. A. and Onoé, K. (1994) Proc. Natl. Acad. Sci. USA 91, 9588.

Neidhart, D. J., Kenyon, G. L., Gerlt, J. A. and Petsko, G. A. (1990) Nature 347, 692.

Neurath, A. R. (1993) In: Immunochemistry of AIDS (Norrby, E., ed.). Karger, Basel, p. 34.

Neurath, A. R. and Kent, S. B. H. (1985) In: Immunochemistry of viruses. The Basis for Serodiagnosis and Vaccines (Van Regenmortel, M. H. V. and Neurath, A. R., eds.). Elsevier, Amsterdam, p. 325.

Neurath, A. R. and Kent, S. B. H. (1988) Adv. Vir. Res. 34, 65.

Neurath, A. R., Kent, S. B. H. and Strick, N. (l984a) J. Gen. Virol. 65, 1009.

Neurath, A. R., Kent, S. B. H. and Strick, N. (1984b) Science 224, 392.

Neurath, A. R., Kent, S. B. H., Strick, N. and Parker, K. (1986a) In: Protides of the Biological Fluids, Vol. 34 (Peeters, H., ed.). Pergamon Press, Oxford, p. 141.

Neurath, A. R., Kent, S. B. H., Strick, N., Offensperger, W., Wahl, S., Christman, J. K. and Acs, G. (1986b) In: Protides of the Biological Fluids, Vol. 34 (Peeters, H., ed.). Pergamon Press, Oxford, p. 129.

Neurath, A. R., Kent, S. B. H., Strick, N., Taylor, P. and Stevens, C. E. (1985a) Nature 315, 154.

Neurath, A. R. and Rubin, B. A. (1971) Viral Structural Components as Immunogens of Prophylactic Value, Karger, Basel, pp. 87.

Neurath, A. R., Strick, N., Kent, S. B. H., Offensperger, W., Wahl, S., Christman, J. K. and Acs, G. (1985b) J. Virol. Meth. *12*, 185.

Neurath, A. R.. and Thanavala, Y. (1990) In: Immunochemistry of Viruses II. The Basis for Serodiagnosis and Vaccines (Van Regenmortel, M. H. V. and Neurath, A. R., eds.). Elsevier, Amsterdam, p. 403.

New, R. R. C. (1995) In: Liposomes as Tools in Basic Research and Industry (Philippot, J. R. and Schuber, F., eds.). CRC Press, Boca Raton, p. 3.

Newman, K. D., Samuel, J. and Kwon, G. (1998) J. Control. Release *54*, 49.

Nezlin, R. (1994) In: Immunochemistry (Van Oss, C. J. and Van Regenmortel, M. H. V., eds.). Marcel Dekker, New York, p. 3.

Ngai, P. K. M., Ackermann, F., Wendt, H., Savoca, R. and Bosshard, H. R. (1993) J. Immunol. Meth. *158*, 267.

Nicholson, B. H. (1994a) In: Synthetic Vaccines (Nicholson, B. H., ed.). Blackwell Scientific, Oxford, p. 169.

Nicholson, B. H. (1994b) Synthetic Vaccines, Blackwell Scientific Publ., Oxford, p. 542.

Nicosia, A., Bartoloni, A., Perugini, M. and Rappuoli, R. (1987) Infect. Immun. *55*, 963.

Niman, H. L. (1984) Nature *307*, 180.

Niman, H. L., Houghten, R. A., Walker, L. A., Reisfeld, R. A., Wilson, I. A., Hogle, J. M. and Lerner, R. A. (1983) Proc. Natl. Acad. Sci. USA *80*, 4949.

Nisbet, A. D., Saundry, R. H., Moir, A. J. G., Fothergill, L. A. and Fothergill, J. E. (1981) Eur. J. Biochem. *115*, 335.

Niveleau, A., Bruno, C., Drouet, E., Brebant, R., Sergeant, A. and Troalen, F. (1995) J. Immunol. Meth. *182*, 227.

Norrby, E., ed. (1993) Immunochemistry of AIDS, Karger, Stockholm, 168 pp.

Norrby, E., Mufson, M. A., Alexander, H., Houghten, R. A. and Lerner, R. A. (1987) Proc. Natl. Acad. Sci. USA *84*, 6572.

Novotny, J., Handschumacher, M. and Bruccoleri, R. E. (1987) Immunol. Today *8*, 26.

Novotny, J., Handschumacher, M., Haber, E., Bruccoleri, R. E., Carlson, W. B., Fanning, D. W., Smith, J. A. and Rose, G. D. (1986) Proc. Natl, Acad. Sci. USA *83*, 226.

Nunez, A. M., Jakowlev, S., Briand, J. P., Gaire, M., Krust, A., Rio, M. C. and Chambon, P. (1987) Endocrinology *121*, 1759.

Nussberger, J., Matsueda, G., Re, R. N. and Haber, E. (1985) Mol. Immunol. *22*, 619.

O'Brien, W. E., McInnes, R., Kalumuck, K. and Adcock, M. (1986) Proc. Natl. Acad. Sci. USA *83*, 7211.

O'Reilly, D. R., Miller, L. K. and Luckow, V. A. (1992) Baculovirus Expression Vectors: A Laboratory Manual, W. H. Freeman & Company, New York.

O'Shannessy, D. J., Brigham-Burke, M. and Peck, K. (1992) Anal. Biochem. *205*, 132.

O'Shannessy, D. J., Brigham-Burke, M., Soneson, K. K., Hensley, P. and Brooks, I. (1993) Anal. Biochem. *212*, 457.

Oakley, R. H., Webster, J. C., Sar, M., Parker, C. R. J. and Cidlowski, J. A. (1997) Endocrinology *138*, 5028.

Obeid, O. E., Partidos, C. D., Howard, C. R. and Steward, M. W. (1995) J. Virol. *69*, 1420.

Obeid, O. E., Stanley, C. M. and Steward, M. W. (1996) Virus. Res. *42*, 173.

Obeid, O. E. and Steward, M. W. (1994) Immunology *82*, 16.

Oertle, M., Immergluck, K., Paterson, Y. and Bosshard, H. R. (1989) Eur. J. Biochem. *182*, 699.

Ogasawara, K., Naruse, H., Itoh, Y., Gotohda, T., Arikawa, J., Kida, H., Good, R. A. and Onoé, K. (1992) Proc. Natl. Acad. Sci. USA *89*, 8995.

Ogawa, T. (1994) J. Med. Microbiol. *41*, 349.

Ohguro, H., Chiba, S., Igarashi, Y., Matsumoto, H., Akino, T. and Palczewski, K. (1993) Proc. Natl. Acad. Sci. USA *90*, 3241.

Ohishi, K., Kabeya, H., Amanuma, H. and Onuma, M. (1996) Vaccine *14*, 1143.

Okawa, Y., Howard, C. R. and Steward, M. W. (1992) J. Immunol. Meth. *149*, 127.

Ota, A., Seki, J., Liu, X. L., Zhao, Y., Wang, X. H., Kondo, K., Sakato, N., Kinoshita, T. and Fujio, H. (1993) J. Biochem.Tokyo *113*, 314.

Ou, Y., Sun, D., Sharp, G. C. and Hoch, S. O. (1997) Clin. Immunol. Immunopathol. *83*, 310.

Padlan, E. A. (1994) Mol. Immunol. *31*, 169.

Padlan, E. A. (1996) Adv. Prot. Chem. *49*, 57.

Padlan, E. A., Silverton, E. W., Sheriff, S., Cohen, G. H., Smith-Gill, S. J. and Davies, D. R. (1989) Proc. Nat. Acad. Sci. USA *86*, 5938.

Palfreyman, J. W., Aitcheson, T. C. and Taylor, P. (1984) J. Immunol. Meth. *75*, 383.

Pancré, V., Gras-Masse, H., Delanoye, A., Herno, J., Capron, A. and Auriault, C. (1996) Scand. J. Immunol. *44*,.485.

Pandey, R. N., Davis, L. E., Anderson, B. A. and Hollenberg, P. F. (1986) J. Immunol. Meth. *94*, 237.

Panina-Bordignon, P., Tan, A., Termijtelen, A., Demotz, S., Corradin, G. and Lanzavecchia, A. (1989) Eur. J. Immunol. *19*, 2237.

Papahadjopoulos, D. and Gabizon, A. A. (1995) In: Liposomes as Tools in Basic Research and Industry (Philippot, J. R. and Schuber, F., eds.). CRC Press, Boca Raton, p. 177.

Papahadjopoulos, D. and Watkins, J. C. (1967) Biochem. Biophys. Acta *135*, 639.

Papkoff, J., Lai, M.-H. T., Hunter, T. and Verma, I. M. (1981) Cell *27*, 109.

Parker, J. M. R., Guo, D. and Hodges, R. S. (1986) Biochemistry *25*, 5425.

Parker, J. M. R. and Hodges, R. S. (1985) J. Protein Chem. *3*, 465.

Parratt, D., McKenzie, H., Nielsen, K. H. and Cobb, S. J., eds. (1982) Radioim-munoassay of Antibody and its Clinical Applications. Wiley, Chichester.

Parrish, C. R. (1994) Sem. Virol. *5*, 121.

Parrish, C. R., Aquadro, C. F. and Carmichael, L. E. (1988) Virology *166*, 293.

Parry, N. R., Barnett, P. V., Ouldridge, E. J., Rowlands, D. J. and Brown, F. (1989) J. Gen. Virol. *70*, 1493.

Parry, N. R., Syred, A., Rowlands, D. J. and Brown, F. (1988) Immunology *64*, 567.

Partidos, C. D., Delmas, A. and Steward, M. W. (1996) Molec. Immunol. *33*, 1223.

Partidos, C. D., Stanley, C. and Steward, M. (1992a) Mol. Immunol. *29*, 651.

Partidos, C. D., Obeid, O. E. and Steward, M. W. (1992b) Immunology *77*, 262.

Partidos, C. D., Shaw, D. M., Gander, G., Merkle, H. P., Howard, C. R. and Steward, M. W. (1994) Vacc. Res. *3*, 203.

Partidos, C. D., Stanley, C. M. and Steward, M. W. (1991) J. Gen. Virol. *72*, 1293.

Partidos, C. D. and Steward, M. W. (1992) J. Gen. Virol. *73*, 1987.

Partidos, C. D., Vohra, P., Anagnostopoulou, C., Jones, D. H., Farrar, G. H. and Steward, M. W. (1996) Mol. Immunol. *33*, 485.

Partidos, C. D., Vohra, P., Jones, D., Farrar, G. and Steward, M. W. (1997) J. Immunol. Meth. *206*, 143.

Patarroyo, G., Franco, L., Amador, R., Murillo, L. A., Rocha, C. L., Rojas, M. and Patarroyo, M. E. (1992) Vaccine *10*, 175.

Patel, V., Ferguson, M. and Minor, P. D. (1993) Virology *192*, 361.

Paterson, Y. (1985) Biochemistry *24*, 1048.

Paterson, Y. (1992) Nature *356*, 456.

Paterson, Y., Englander, S. W. and Roder, H. (1990) Science *249*, 755.

Patschinsky, T., Walter, G. and Bister, K. (1984) Virology *136*, 348.

Paucha, E., Harvey, R. and Smith, A. E. (1984) J. Virol. *51*, 670.

Peeters, J. M., Hazendonk, T. G., Beuvery, E. C. and Tesser, G. I. (1989) J. Immunol. Meth. *120*, 133.

Pellequer, J. L. and Westhof, E. (1993) J. Mol. Graphics *11*, 204.

Pellequer, J. L., Westhof, E. and Van Regenmortel, M. H. V. (1991) Meth. Enzymol. *203*, 176.

Pellequer, J. L., Westhof, E. and Van Regenmortel, M. H. V. (1994) In: Peptide Antigens: A Practical Approach (Wisdom, G. B., ed.). IRL Press, Oxford, p. 7.

Peng, S. L. and Craft, J. E. (1996) In: Autoantibodies (Peter, J. B. and Shoenfeld, Y., eds.). Elsevier Science, Amsterdam, p. 774.

Pennington, M.. W. and Dunn, B. M. (1994) In: Meth. Mol. Biol., Vol. 35 (Pennington, M. W. and Dunn, B. M., eds.). Humana Press, New Jersey.

Perdew, G. H. (1994) Anal. Biochem. *220*, 214.

Pereboeva, L. A., Pereboev, A. V. and Morris, G. E. (1998) J. Med. Virol. *56*, 105.

Persson, H., Hennighausen, L., Taub, R., Degrado, W. and Leder, P. (1984) Science *225*, 687.

Peter, J. B. and Shoenfeld, Y. (1996) Autoantibodies, Elsevier, New York, p. 880.

Peters, K. and Richards, F. M. (1977) Ann. Rev. Biochem. *46*, 523.

Petrovas, C. J., Vlachoyiannopoulos. P. G., Tzioufas, A. G., Alexopoulos, C., Tsikaris, V., Sakarellos-Daitsiotis, M., Sakarellos, C. and Moutsopoulos, H. M. (1998) J. Immunol. Meth. *220*, 59.

Pettersson, I. (1992) Mol. Biol. Rep. *16*, 149.

Pfaff, E., Mussgay, M., Bohm, H. O., Schulz, G. E. and Schaller, H. (1982) EMBO J. *1*, 869.

Philippot, J. R. and Schuber, F. (1995) Liposomes as Tools in Basic Research and Industry, CRC Press, Boca Raton, p. 1.

Phillips, N. C. (1992) Bull. Inst. Pasteur *90*, 205.

Phillips, N. C., Gagné, L., Ivanoff, N. and Riveau, G. (1996) Vaccine *14*, 898.

Phizicky, E. M. and Fields, S. (1995) Microbiol. Rev. *59*, 94.

Pique, L., Cesselin, F., Strauch, G., Valcke, J. C. and Bricaire, H. (1978) Immunochemistry *15*, 55.

Plaue, S. (1990) Int. J. Peptide Protein Res. *35*, 510.

Plaué, S., Muller, S., Briand, J. P. and Van Regenmortel, M. H. V. (1990) Biologicals *18*, 147.

Plaué, S., Muller, S. and Van Regenmortel, M. H. V. (1989) J. Exp. Med. *169*, 1607.

Playfair, J. H. L. and DeSouza, J. B. (1987) Clin. Exp. Immunol. *67*, 5.

Pogue, R. R., Eron, J., Frelinger, J. A. and Matsui, M. (1995) Proc. Natl. Acad. Sci. USA *92*, 8166.

Poisson, F., Baillou, A., Dubois, F., Janvier, B., Roingeard, P. and Goudeau, A. (1993) J. Clin. Microbiol. *31*, 2343.

Pollard, K. M. and Cohen, M. G. (1990) Autoimmunity *5*, 265.

Polson, A., Van Heerden, D. and Van der Merwe, K. J. (1985) Immunol. Invest. *14*, 223.

Polson, A., Von Wechmar, M. B. and Van Regenmortel, M. H. V. (1980) Immunol. Commun. *9*, 475.

Porges, A. J., Ng, T. S. Z. and Reeves, W. H. (1990) J. Immunol. *145*, 4222.

Posnett, D. N., McGrath, H. and Tam, J. P. (1988) J. Biol. Chem. *263*, 1719.

Prager, E. M., Wilson, A. C., Perin, J. P. and Jolles, P. (1978) Immunochemistry *15*, 577.

Prasad, L., Sharma, S., Vandonselaar, M., Quail, J. W., Lee, J. S., Waygood, E. B., Wilson, K. S., Dauter, Z. and Delbaere, L. T. J. (1993) J. Biol. Chem. *268*, 10705.

Presentini, R., Lozzi, M., Perin, F., Mariani, M., Casagli, M. C., Neri, P. and Antoni, G. (1986) In: Protides of the Biological Fluids, 34th Colloquium (Peeters, H., ed.). Pergamon, Oxford, p. 31.

Price, J. O., Whitaker, J. N., Vasu, R. I. and Metzger, D. W. (1986) J. Immunol. *136*, 2426.

Price, P. and Newman, D. J. (1997) Principles and Practice of Immunoassay, 2nd, MacMillan, London, 667 pp.

Pruijn, G. J. M. Schoute, F., Thijssen, J. P. H., Smeenk, R. J. T. and van Venrooij, W. J. (1997a) J. Autoimmun. *10*, 127.

Pruijn, G. J. M., Simons, F. H. M. and van Venrooij, W. J. (1997b) Eur. J. Cell Biol. *74*, 123.

Przewlocki, G., Audibert, F., Jolivet, M., Chedid, L., Kent, S. B. H. and Neurath, A. R. (1986) Biochim. Biophys. Res. Commun. *140*, 557.

Query, C. C. and Keene, J. D. (1987) Cell *51*, 211.

Quesniaux, V., Tees, R., Schreier, M. R., Maurer, G. and Van Regenmortel, M. H. V. (1987a) Clin. Chem. *33*, 32.

Quesniaux, V., Tees, R., Schreier, M. H.. Wenger, R. and Van Regenmortel, M. H. V. (1987b) Molec. Immunol. *24*, 1159.

Quesniaux, V., Tees, R., Schreier, M. H., Wenger, R. M., Donatsch, P. and Van Regenmortel, M. H. V. (1986) In: Ciclosporin. Progress in Allergy, Vol. 38, Karger, Basel, p. 108.

Quesniaux, V. F. J., Schmitter, D., Schreier, M. H. and Van Regenmortel, M. H. V. (1990) Molec. Immunol. *27*, 227.

Ragone, R., Facchiano, F., Facchiano, A., Facchiano, A. M. and Colonna, G. (1989) Protein Eng. *2*, 497.

Rajnavölgyi, E., Lanyi, A., Hudecz, F., Kurucz, I., Kiss, K., Laszlo, G., Szekerke, M. and Gergely, J. (1989) Molec. Immunol. *26*, 949.

Rauffer, N., Zeder-Lutz, G., Wenger, R. M., Van Regenmortel, M. H. V. and Alschuh, D. (1994) Mol. Immunol. *31*, 913.

Rauffer-Bruyère, N., Chatellier, J., Weiss, E., Van Regenmortel, M. H. V. and Altschuh, D. (1997) Mol. Immunol. *34*, 165.

Reay, P. A., Kantor, R. M. and Davis, M. M. (1994) J. Immunol. *152*, 3946.

Reichlin, M. (1980) Meth. Enzymol. *70*, 159.

Reichlin, M., Rader, M. and Harley, J. B. (1989) Clin. Exp. Immunol. *76*, 373.

Reynolds, S. R., Dahl, C. E. and Harn, D. A. (1994) J. Immunol. *152*, 193.

Reynolds, S. R., Schoemakcr, C. B. and Harn, D. A. (1992) J. Immunol. *149*, 3995.

Ribi, E., Cantrell, J., Feldner, T., Meyers., K. and Peterson, J. (1986) In: Microbiology – 1986 (Levie, L., ed.). American Society for Microbiology, Washington, DC, p. 9.

Ribi, E., Cantrell, J. L., Takayama, K., Qureshi, N., Peterson, J. and Ribi, H. O. (1984) Rev. Infect. Dis. *6*, 567.

Ricchiuti, V., Briand, J. P., Meyer, O., Isenberg, D. A., Pruijn, G. and Muller, S. (1994a) Clin. Exp. Immunol. *95*, 397.

Ricchiuti, V., Isenberg, D. A. and Muller, S. (1994b) J. Autoimmun. *7*, 611.

Ricchiuti, V. and Muller, S. (1994) In: Autoimmune Diseases (Isenberg, D. A. and Horsfall, A. C., eds.). Bios Scientific, Oxford, p. 101.

Ricchiuti, V., Pruijn, G. J. M., Thijssen, J. P. H., van Venrooij, W. J. and Muller, S. (1997) J. Autoimmunity *10*, 181.

Richalet-Sécordel, P., Rauffer-Bruyère, N., Christensen, L. L. H., Ofenloch-Haehnle, B., Seidel, C. and Van Regenmortel, M. H. V. (1997) Anal. Biochem. *249*, 165.

Richalet-Sécordel, P. and Van Regenmortel, M. H. V. (1991) FEMS Microbiol. Immunol. *89*, 57.

Richalet-Sécordel, P. M., Deslandres, A., Plaué, S., You, B., Barré-Sanoussi, F. and Van Regenmortel, M. H. V. (1994a) FEMS Immunol. Med. Microbiol. *9*, 77.

Richalet-Sécordel, P. M., Poisson, F. and Van Regenmortel, M. H. V. (1996) Clin. Diag. Virol. *5*, 111.

Richalet-Sécordel, P. M., Zeder-Lutz, G., Plaué, S., Sommermeyer-Leroux, G. and Van Regenmortel, M. H. V. (1994b) J. Immunol. Meth. *176*, 221.

Richards, F. F. and Konigsberg, W. H. (1973) Immunochemistry *10*, 545.

Richardson, J. S. (1981) Adv. Prot. Chem. *34*, 167.

Rico, M. J., Korman, N. J., Stanley, J. R., Tanaka, T. and Hall, R. P. (1990) J. Immunol. *145*, 3728.

Riemekasten, G., Marell, J., Trebeljahr, G., Klein, R., Hausdorf, G., Häupl, T., Schneider-Mergener, J., Burmester, G. R. and Hiepe, F. (1998) J. Clin. Invest. *102*, 754.

Rigby, M. A., Mackay, N., Reid, G., Osborne, R., Neil, J. C. and Jarrett, O. (1996) Vaccine *14*, 1095.

Riley, E. (1995) Curr. Opin. Immunol. *7*, 612.

Rimmelzwaan, G. F., Carlson, J., Uytdehaag, F. G. C. M. and Osterhaus, A. D. M. E. (1990) J. Gen. Virol. *71*, 2741.

Rini, J. M., Schulze-Gahmen, U. and Wilson, I. A. (1992) Science *255*, 959.

Rini, J. M., Stanfield, R. N., Stura, B. A., Salina, P. A., Profy, A. T. and Wilson, I. A. (1993) Proc. Natl. Acad. Sci. USA *90*, 6325.

Ritchie, R. F. (1986) In: Manual of Clinical Laboratory Immunology (Rose, N. R., Friedman, H. and Fahey, J. L., eds.). American Society for Microbiology, Washington, DC, p. 4.

Rivier, J., Miller, C., Spicer, M., Andrews, J., Porter, J., Tuchscherer, G. and Mutter, M. (1990) In: Solid-Phase Synthesis (Epton, R., ed.). SPCC, Birmingham, p. 39.

Robbins, K. C., Antoniades, H. N., Sushikumar, G. D., Hunkapiller, M. W. and Aaronson, S. A. (1983) Nature *305*, 605.

Roberts, V. A., Getzoff, E. D. and Tainer, J. A. (1993) In: Structure of Antigens, Vol. 2 (Van Regenmortel, M. H. V., ed.). CRC Press, Boca Raton, p. 31.

Robinson, P. J., Dunnill, P. and Lilly, M. D. (1971) Biochim. Biophys. Acta *242*, 659.

Robuccio, J. A., Griffith, J. W., Chroscinski, E. A., Cross, P. J., Light, T. E. and Lang, C. M. (1995) Lab. Anim. Sci. *45*, 420.

Rodda, S. J., Geysen, H. M., Mason, T. J. and Schoofs, P. G. (1986) Mol. Immunol. *23*, 603.

Rodda, S. J., Maeji, N. J. and Tribbick, G. (1996) In: Epitope Mapping Protocols (Morris, G. E., ed.). Humana Press, Totowa, New Jersey, p. 137.

Rodda, S. J. and Tribbick, G. (1996) Methods *9*, 473.

Rodriguez, A., Saiz, J. C., Novella, I. S., Andreu, D. and Sobrino, F. (1994) Virology *205*, 24.

Roivainen, M., Narvanen, A., Korkolainen, M., Huhtala, M. L. and Hovi, T. (1991) Virology *180*, 99.

Rojo, S., Lopez de Castro, J. A., Aparicio, P., Van Seventer, G. and Bragado, R. (1986) J. Immunol. *137*, 904.

Rokeach, L. A. and Hoch, S. O. (1992) Mol. Biol. Rep. *16*, 165.

Rokeach, L. A., Janatipour, M. and Hoch, S. O (1990) J. Immunol. *144*, 1015.

Rokeach, L. A., Jannatipour, M., Haselby, J. A. and Hoch, S. O. (1992) Clin. Immunol. Immunopathol. *65*, 315.

Rombaut, B., Boeyé, A., Ferguson, M., Minor, P. D., Mosser, A. and Rueckert, R. (1990) Virology *174*, 305.

Rongen, H. A. H., Bult, A. and Van Bennekom, W. P. (1997) J. Immun. Meth. *204*, 105.

Rooman, M. J. and Wodak, S. (1988) Nature *335*, 45.

Rosa, C., Osborne, S., Garetto, F., Griva, S., Rivella, A., Calabresi, G., Guaschino, R. and Bonelli, F. (1995) J. Virol. Meth. *55*, 219.

Rose, D. R., Przybylska, M., To, R. J., Kayden, C. S., Oomen, R. P., Vorberg, E., Young, N. M. and Bundle, D. R. (1993) Prot. Sci. *2*, 1106.

Rose, G. D., Geselowitz, A. R., Lesser, G. J. Lee, R. H. and Zehfus, M. H. (1985a) Science *229*, 834.

Rose, G. D., Gierasch, L. M. and Smith, J. A. (1985b) Adv. Prot. Chem. *37*, 1.

Rose, K., Vilaseca, L. A., Werlen, R., Meunier, A., Fisch, I., Jones, R. M. L. and Offord, R. E. (1991) Bioconjugate Chem. *2*, 154.

Rose, K., Zeng, W., Brown, L. E. and Jackson, D. C. (1995) Mol. Immunol. *32*, 1031.

Rothbard, J. B. and Taylor, W. R. (1988) EMBO J. *7*, 93.

Rouser, G., Fleischer, S. and Yamamoto., A. (1970) Lipids *5*, 494.

Routsias, J. G., Sakarellos-Daitsiotis, M., Detsikas, E., Tzioufas, A. G., Sakarellos, C. and Moutsopoulos, H. M. (1994) Clin. Exp. Immunol. 98, 414.

Routsias, J. G., Sakarellos-Daitsiotis, M., Tsikaris, V., Sakarellos, C., Moutsopoulos, H. M. and Tzioufas, A. G. (1998) Scand. J. Immunol. 47, 280.

Routsias, J. G., Tzioufas, A. G., Sakarellos-Daitsiotis, M., Sakarellos, C. and Moutsopoulos, H. M. (1996) Eur. J. Clin. Invest. 26, 514.

Rowland-Jones, S., Tan, R. and McMichael, A. (1997) Adv. Immunol. 65, 448.

Rowlands, D. J., Clarke, B. E., Carroll, A. R., Brown, F., Nicholson, B. H., Bittle, J. L., Houghten, R. A. and Lerner, R. A. (1983) Nature 306, 694.

Rueckert, R. (1990) In: Virology (Fields, B. N. and Knipe, D. M., eds.). Raven Press, New York, p. 507.

Rüegg, U. T. and Rudinger, J. (1977) Meth. Enzymol. 47, 111.

Ruppert, A., Arnold, N. and Hobom, G. (1994) Vaccine 12, 492.

Russell, J. K., Hayes, M. P., Carter, J. M., Torres, B. A., Dunn, B. M., Russell, S. W. and Johnson, H. M. (1986) J. Immunol. 136, 3324.

Sabbatini, A., Bombardieri, S. and Migliorini, P. (1993a) Eur. J. Immunol. 23, 1146.

Sabbatini, A., Dolcher, M. P., Marchini, B., Bombardieri, S. and Migliorini, P. (1993b) J. Rheumatol. 20, 1679.

Saito, N. G. and Paterson, Y. (1996) Methods 9, 516.

Saitta, M. R., Arnett, F. C. and Keene J. D. (1994) J. Immunol. 152, 4192.

Sallberg, M., Sherefa, K. and Zhang, Z. X. (1994) Biochem. Biophys. Res. Commun. 205, 1386.

Sambrook, J., Fritsch, E. F. and Maniatis, T. (1989) In: Molecular Cloning: A Laboratory Manual, 2nd edition, Cold Spring Harbor Laboratory Press, New York, 8.2.

Samokhin, G. P. and Filimonov, I. N. (1985) Anal. Biochem. 145, 311.

Sansonno, D. F., DeTomaso, P., Papanice, M. A. and Manghisi, O. G. (1996) J. Immunol. Meth. 90, 131.

Saper, M. A., Bjorkman, P. J. and Wiley, D. C. (1991) J. Mol. Biol. 219, 277.

Sarnesto, A., Ranta, S., Seppälä, I. J. T. and Mäkelä, O. (1983) Scand. J. Immunol. 17, 507.

Sarobe, P., Lasarte, J. J., Golvano, J., Guillon, A., Civeira, M. P., Prieto, J. and Borras-Cuesta, F. (1991) Eur. J. Immunol. 21, 1555.

Sarobe, P., Pendleton, C. D., Akatsuka, T., Lau, D., Engelhard, V. H., Feinstone, S. M. and Berzofsky, J. A. (1998) J. Clin. Invest. 102, 1239.

Satoh, M., Ajmani, A. K., Ogasawara, T., Langdon, J. J., Hirakata, M., Wang, J. and Reeves, W. H. (1994) J. Clin. Invest. 94, 1981.

Satterthwait, A. C., Arrhenius, T., Hagopian, R. A., Zavala, F., Nussenzweig, V. and Lerner, R. A. (1989) Phil. Trans. R. Soc. Lond. B 323, 565.

Saunal, H., Karlsson, R. and Van Regenmortel, M. H. V. (1997) In: Immunochemistry 2: A Practical Approach (Johnstone, A. P. and Turner, M. W., eds.). IRL Press, Oxford, p. 1.

Saunal, H. and Van Regenmortel, M. H. V. (1995a) Virology *213*, 462.

Saunal, H. and Van Regenmortel, M. H. V. (1995b) J. Immunol. Meth. *183*, 33.

Saunal, H., Witz, J. and Van Regenmortel, M. H. V. (1993) J. Gen. Virol. *74*, 897.

Sauzet, J. P., Déprez, B., Martinon, F., Guillet, J.-G., Gras-Masse, H. and Gomard, E. (1995) Vaccine *13*, 1339.

Savoca, R., Schwab, C. and Bosshard, H. R. (1991) J. Immun. Meth. *141*, 245.

Schaaper, M. M., Lankhof, H., Puijk, W. C. and Meloen, R. H. (1989) Mol. Immunol. *26*, 81.

Schaaper, W. M. M., Lu, Y.-A., Tam, J. P. and Meloen, R. H. (1990) In: Proceedings of the Eleventh American Peptide Symposium (Rivier, J. E. and Marshall, G. R., eds.). Escom Press, p. 765.

Scheefers-Borchel, U., Müller-Berghaus, G., Fumge, P., Eberle, R. and Heimburger, N. (1985) Proc. Natl. Acad. Sci. USA *82*, 7091.

Schellekens, G. A., de Jong, B. A. W., van den Hoogen, F. H. J., van de Putte, L. B. A. and van Venrooij, W. J. (1998) J. Clin. Invest. *101*, 273.

Schellekens, G. A., Lasonder, F., Feijlbrief, M., Koedijk, D. G. A. M., Drijfhout, J. W., Scheffer, A. J., Welling-Wester, S. and Welling, G. W. (1994) Eur. J. Immunol. *24*, 3188.

Schild, H., Deres, K., Wiesmüller, K.-Fl., Jung, G. and Rammensee, H. G. (1991) Eur. J. Immunol, *21*, 2649.

Schlomai, J. and Zadok, A. (1984) Nucl. Acids Res. *12*, 8017.

Schmitz, H. E., Atassi, H. and Atassi, M. Z. (1983a) Mol. Immunol. *20*, 719.

Schmitz, H. E., Atassi, H. and Atassi, Z. (1983b) Immunol. Commun. *12*, 161.

Schroer, J. A., Bender, T., Feklmann, R. J. and Kim, K. J. (1983) Eur. J. Immunol. *13*, 693.

Schuber, F. (1995) In: Liposomes as Tools in Basic Research and Industry (Philippot, J. R. and Schuber, F., eds.). CRC Press, Boca Raton, USA, 21.

Schulze-Gahmen, U., Klenk, H. D. and Beyreuther, K. (1986) Eur. J. Biochem. *159*, 283.

Schulze-Gahmen, U., Prinz, H., Glatter, U. and Beyreuther, K. (1985) EMBO J. *4*, 1731.

Schulze-Gahmen, U., Rini, J. M., Arevalo, J., Stura, E. A., Kenten, J. H. and Wilson, I. A. (1988) J. Biol. Chem. *263*, 17100.

Schulze-Gahmen, U., Rini, J. M. and Wilson, I. A. (1993) J. Mol. Biol. *234*, 1098.

Schutze, M. P., Derlaud, E., Przewlocki, G. and Leclerc, C. (1989) J. Immunol. *142*, 2635.

Schutze, M. P., Leclerc, C., Jolivet, M., Audibert, F. and Chedid, L. (1985) J. Immunol. *135*, 2319..

Schwartz, F. P., Tello, D., Goldbaum, F. A., Mariuzza, R. A. and Poljak, R. J. (1995) Eur. J. Biochem. *228*, 388.

Schwartz, R. H. (1985) Ann. Rev. Immunol *3*, 237.

Scibienski, R. J. (1973) J. Immunol. *111*, 114.

Scofield, R. H. and Harley, J. B. (1991) Proc. Natl. Acad. Sci. USA *88*, 3343.

Scott, J. K. (1992) Trends Biechem. Sci. *17*, 241.

Scott, J. K. and Smith, G. P. (1990) Science *249*, 386.

Seagar, M. J., Labbé-Jullié, C., Granier, C., Goll, A., Glossmann, H., Van Rietschoten, J. and Couraud, F. (1986) Biochemistry *25*, 4051.

Seki, J., Wang, X. H., Ota, A., Suzuki, Y., Sakato, N. and Fujio, H. (1992) J. Biochem. Tokyo *111*, 259.

Sela, M. (1969) Science *166*, 1365.

Sela, M. and Zisman, F. (1997) FASEB J. *11*, 449.

Semler, B., Anderson, C., Hanecak, L., Dorner, L. and Wimmer, F. (1982) Cell *28*, 405.

Sercarz, F. F. (1998) Immunol. Rev. *164*, 5.

Sercarz, F. F. and Berzofsky, J. A. (1987) Immunogenicity of Protein Antigens: Repertoire and Regulation, CRC Press Inc., Boca Raton, Florida.

Sette, A., Alexander, J., Ruppert, J., Snoke, K., Franco, A., Ishioka, G. and Grey, H. M. (1994) Annu. Rev. Immunol. *12*, 413.

Shapira, M., Jibson, M., Müller, G. and Arnon, R. (1984) Proc. Natl. Acad. Sci. USA *81*, 2461.

Sharma, B. K., Ray, A. and Murthy, N. S. (1996) Eur. J. Cancer *32A*, 872.

Shaw, D. M., Stanley, C. M., Partidos, C. D. and Steward, M. W. (1993) Mol. Immunol. *30*, 961.

Sheriff, S., Silverton, F. W., Padlan, E. A., Cohen, G. H., Smith-Gill, S., Finzel, B. C. and Davies, D. R. (1987) Proc. Natl. Acad. Sci. USA *84*, 8075.

Sheth, H. B., Glasier, L. M. G., Ellert.. N. W., Cachia, P., Kohn, W., Lee, K. K., Paranchych, W., Hodges, R. S. and Irvin, R. T. (1995) Biomed. Pept. Prot. Nud. Acids *1*, 141.

Shi, P. T., Riehm, J. P., Todd, P. E. E. and Leach, S. J. (1984) Mol. Immunol. *21*, 489.

Shirai, M., Pendleton, C. D., Ahlers, J., Takeshita, T., Newman, M. and Berzofsky, J. A. (1994) J. Immunol. *152*, 549.

Shoham, M. (1993) J. Mol. Biol. *232*, 1169.

Shuler, K. R., Dunham, R. G. and Kanda, P. (1992) J. Immunol. Meth. *156*, 137.

Siddiqui, W. A., Taylor, D. W., Kan, S.-C., Kramer, K., Richmond-Crum, S. M., Kotani, S., Shiba, T. and Kusumoto, S. (1978) Science *201*, 1237.

Sigel, M. B., Sinha, Y. N. and VanderLaan, W. P. (1983) Meth. Enzymol. *93*, 3.

Silver, M. L., Guo, H. C., Strominger, J. L. and Wiley, D. C. (1992) Nature *360*, 367.

Simard, C., Nadon, F., Seguin, C., Thien, N. N., Binz, H., Basso, J., Laliberte, J. F. and Trudel, M. (1997) Vaccine *15*, 423.

Singh, M., Carlson, J. R., Briones, M., Ugozzoli, M., Kazzaz, J., Barackman, J., Ott, G. and O'Hagan, D. (1998) Vaccine *16*, 1822.

Sinigaglia, F., Guttinger, M., Kilgus, J., Doran, D. M., Matile, H., Etlingerr, H., Trzeciak, A., Gillessen, D. and Pink, J. R. L. (1988) Nature *336*, 778.

Sioud, M., Førre, Ø. and Dybwad, A. (1996) Clin. Immunol. Immunopathol. *79*, 105.

Sloostra, J. W., Puijk, W. C., Ligtvoet, G. J., Langeveld, J. P. M. and Meloen, R. H. (1995) Mol. Diversity *1*, 87.

Smith, A. M. and Benjamin, D. C. (1991) J. Immunol. *146*, 1259.

Smith, A. M., Woodward, M. P., Hershey, C. W., Hershey, E. D. and Benjamin, D. C. (1991) J. Immunol *146*, 1254.

Smith, J. A., Hurrel, J. G. R. and Leach, S. J. (1977) Immunochemistry *14*, 565.

Smith, R. C., Neff, A. W. and Malacinski, G. M. (1986) J. Embryol. Exp. Morphol. *97*, 45.

Smith-Gill, S. J., Wilson, A. C., Potter, M., Prager, F. M., Feldmann, R. J. and Mainhart, C. R. (1982) J. Immunol. *128*, 314.

Smyth, M. S., Hoey, F. M., Trudgett, A., Martin, S. J. and Brown, F. (1990) J. Gen. Virol. *71*, 231.

Snyder, M., Elledge S., Sweetser, D., Young, R. A. and Davis, R. W. (1987) Meth. Enzymol. *154*, 107.

Snyder, S. L. and Vannier, W. E. (1984) Biochim. Biophys. Acta *772*, 288.

Soderquist, M. F. and Walton, A. G. (1980) J. Colloid Interface Sci. *75*, 386.

Søndergard-Andersen, J., Lauritzen, F., Lind, K. and Holm, A. (1990) J. Immunol. Meth. *131*, 99.

Soutar, A. J. and Palfreyman, J. W. (1986) In: Protides of the Biological Fluids, Vol. 34 (Peeters, H., ed.). Pergamon Press, New York, p. 99.

Spangler, B. D. (1991) J. Immunol. *146*, 1591.

Spirer, Z., Zakuth, V., Bogair, H. and Fridkin, M. (1977) Eur. J. Immunol. *7*, 69.

St. Clair, F. W., Kenan, D., Burch, J. A. J., Keene, J. D. and Pisetsky, D. S. (1990) J. Immunol. *144*, 3868.

Stanfield, R. L., Fieser, T. M., Lerner, R. A. and Wilson, I. A. (1990) Science *248*, 712.

Stanfield, R. L., Takimotokamimura, M., Rini, J. M., Profy, A. T. and Wilson, I. A. (1993) Structure *1*, 83.

Stanfield, R. L. and Wilson, I. A. (1994) Trends Biotech *12*, 275.

Staros, J. V., Wright, R. W. and Swingle, D. M. (1986) Anal. Biochem. *156*, 220.

Stemmer, C., Briand, J. P. and Muller, S. (1994) Mol. Immunol. *31*, 1037.

Stemmer, C., Briand, J. P. and Muller, S. (1997) J. Mol. Biol. *273*, 52.

Stemmer, C. and Muller, S. (1996) In: Autoantibodies (Peter, J. B. and Shoenfeld, Y., eds.). Elsevier Science, p. 373.

Stemmer, C., Richalet-Secordel, P., van Bruggen, M., Kramers, K., Berden, J. and Muller, S. (1996) J. Biol. Chem. 271, 21257.

Stephen, C. W. and Lane, D. P. (1992) J. Mol. Biol. 225, 577.

Stern, L. J., Brown, J. H., Jardetzky, T. S., Gorga, J. C., Uraban, R. G., Strominger, J. L. and Wiley, D. C. (1994) Nature 368, 215.

Stetler, D. A. and Jacob, S. T. (1984) J. Biol. Chem. 259, 13629.

Stevanovic, S. and Rammensee, H.-G. (1996) In: Structure of Antigens, Vol. 3 (Van Regenmortel, M. H. V., ed.). CRC Press, Boca Raton, p. 61.

Stevens, V. C., Chou, W. S., Powell, J. F., Lee, A. C. and Smoot, J. (1986) Immunol. Lett. 12, 11.

Steward, M. W. and Chargelegue, D. (1997) In: Weir's Handbook, 5th Edition, Vol. I. Blackwell Science, Cambridge, MA, 38.1.

Steward, M. W. and Howard, C. R. (1987) Immunol. Today 8, 51.

Steward, M. W., Stanley, C. M. and Obeid, O. F. (1995) J. Virol. 69, 7668.

Stewart-Tull, D. F. S. (1996) In: Methods in Molecular Medicine: Vaccine Protocols (Robinson, A., Farrar, G. and Wiblin, C., eds.). Humana Press, Totowa, New Jersey, p. 147.

Sülle, C. J., Thomas, L. J., Reyes, V. F. and Humphreys, R. F. (1987) Mol. Immunol. 24, 1021.

Stott, D. I. (1989) J. Immunol. Methods 119, 153.

Stott, D. I. (1994) In: Immunochemistry (Van Oss, C. J. and Van Regenmortel, M. H. V., eds.). Marcel Dekker, New York, p. 925.

Strassheim, L. M., Gruenberg, A., Veijalainen, P., Sgro, J.-Y. and Parrish, C. R. (1994) Virology 198, 175.

Strohmaier, K., Franze, R. and Adam, K. H. (1982) J. Gen. Virol. 59, 295.

Sturtevant, J. M. (1994) Curr. Opinion Struct. Biol. 4, 69.

Stussi-Garaud, C., Garaud, J. C., Berna, A. and Godefroy-Colburn, T. (1987) J. Gen. Virol. 68, 1779.

Su, H. and Caldwell, H. D. (1992) J. Exp. Med. 175, 227.

Süsal, C., Daniel, V., Kropelin, M., Uhle, C., Zimmermann, R. and Opelz, G. (1996) Eur. J. Clin. Chem. Biochem. 34, 14.

Sutcliffe, J. G., Shinnick, T. M., Green, N. and Lerner, R. A. (1983) Science 219, 660.

Sutcliffe, J. G., Shinnick, T. M., Green, N., Liu, F.-T., Niman, H. L. and Lerner, R. A. (1980) Nature 287, 801.

Suter, M. (1982) J. Immunol. Meth. 53, 103.

Suter, M. and Butler, J. F. (1986) Immunol. Lett. 13, 313.

Sutton (1993) Meth. Immunol. Anal. 1, 66.

Sweet, R. M. and Eisenberg, D. J. (1983) Mol. Biol. 171, 479.

Syu, W., Jr. and Kahan, L. (1989) J. Immunol. Meth. *118*, 153.

Szoka, F. and Papahadjopoulos, D. (1978) Proc. Natl. Acad. Sci. USA *75*, 4194.

Szoka, F. and Papahadjopoulos, D. (1980) Annu. Rev. Biophys. Bioeng. *9*, 467.

Tabara, H., Hill, R. J., Mello, C. C., Priess, J. R. and Kohara, Y. (1999) Development *126*, 1.

Tainer, J. A., Getzoff, F. D.. Alexander, H., Houghten, R. A., Olson, A. J., Lerner, R. A. and Hendrickson, W. A. (1984) Nature *312*, 127.

Tainer, J. A., Getzoff, F. D., Paterson, Y., Olson, A. J. and Lerner, R. A. (1985) Annu. Rev. Immunol. *3*, 501.

Takagaki, Y., Hirayama, A., Fujio, H. and Amano, T. (1980) Biochemistry *19*, 2498.

Takahashi, W. N. and Ishii, M. (1952) Phytopathology *42*, 690.

Takahashi, I., Okahashi, N., Matsushita, K., Tokuda, M., Kanamoto, T., Munekata, F., Russell, M. W. and Koga, T. (1991) J. Immunol. *146*, 332.

Talamo, R. C., Haber, F. and Austen, K. F. (1968) J. Immunol. *101*, 333.

Talmage, D. W. (1959) Science *129*, 1643.

Tam, J. P. (1988) Proc. Natl. Acad. Sci. USA *85*, 5409.

Tam, J. P. (1994) In: Peptide Antigens. A Practical Approach (Wisdom, G. B., ed.). IRL Press, Oxford, p. 83.

Tam, J. P., Clavijo, P., Lu, Y.-A., Nussenzweig, V., Nussenzweig, R. and Zavala, F. (1990) J. Exp. Med. *171*, 299.

Tam, J. P. and Lu Y. A. (1989) Proc. Natl. Acad. Sci. USA *86*, 9084.

Tam, J. P. and Spetzler, J. C. (1995) Biomed. Pept. Prot. Nucl. Acids *1*, 123.

Tam, J. P. and Zavala, F. (1989) J. Immunol. Meth. *124*, 53.

Tamura, T. and Bauer, H. (1982) EMBO J. *1*, 1479.

Tamura, T., Bauer, H., Birr, C. and Pipkorn, R. (1983) Cell *34*, 587.

Tanaka, T., Slamon, D. J. and Cline, M. J. (1985) Proc. Natl. Acad. Sci. USA *82*, 3400.

Tao, L., Shen, D., Pandey, S., Hao, W., Rich, K. A. and Fong, H. K. (1998) Mol. Vis. *4*, 25.

Tarrab-Hazdai, R., Schechtman, D. and Arnon, R. (1998) Infect. Immun. *66*, 4526.

Taussig, M. J. (1971) Immunology *21*, 51.

Telzak, F., Wolff, S. M., Dinarello, C. A., Conlon, T., El Khaly, A., Bahr, G.M., Choay, J. P., Morin, A. and Chedid, L. (1986) J. Infect. Dis. *153*, 628.

Thèze, J. and Sommé, G. (1979) Eur. J. Immunol. *9*, 294.

Thorell, J. I. and Larson, S. M. (1978) Radioimmunoassay and Related Techniques: Methodology and Clinical Applications, Mosby, C.V., St Louis, Missouri, 298.

Thornton, J. M., Edwards, M. S., Taylor, W. R. and Barlow, D. J. (1986) EMBO J. *5*, 409.

Thornton, J. M. and Sibanda, B. L. (1983) J. Mol. Biol. *167*, 443.

Tijssen, P. (1985) Practice and Theory of Enzyme Immunoassays, Elsevier, Amsterdam, 1.

Todd, P. F. F., East, I. J. and Leach, S. J. (1982) Trends Biochem. Sci. *7*, 212.

Tolou, H., Martelloni, M. and Durant, J. P. (1994) Pept. Res. *7*, 290.

Torchilin, V. P., Khaw, B. A., Smirnov, V. N. and Haber, F. (1979) Biochem. Biophys. Res. Commun. *89*, 1114.

Tormo, J., Blaas, D., Parry, N. R., Rowlands, D., Stuart, D. and Fita, I. (1994) EMBO J. *13*, 2247.

Towbin, H., Staehelin, T. and Gordon, J. (1979) Proc. Natl. Acad. Sci. USA *76*, 4350.

Traut, R. R., Bollen, A., Sun, T. T., Hershey, J. W. B., Sundberg, J. and Pierce, L. R. (1973) Biochemistry *12*, 3266.

Tribbick, G., Triantafyllou, B., Lauricella, R., Rodda, S. J., Mason, T. J. and Geysen, H. M. (1991) J. Immunol. Meth. *139*, 155.

Trifilieff, F., Dubs, M. C. and Van Regenmortel, M. H. V. (1991) Mol. Immunol. *28*, 889.

Troalen, F., Razafindratsita, A., Puisieux, A., Voeltzel, T., Bohuon, C., Bellet, D. and Bidart, J.-M. (1990) Mol. Immunol. *27*, 363.

Trudel, M., Nadon, F., Seguin. C. and Binz, H. (1991) Virology *185*, 749.

Trudelle, Y., Brack, A., Delmas, A., Pedoussaut, S. and Rivaille, P. (1987) Int. J. Pept. Prot. Res. *30*, 54.

Tsao, J., Chapman, J. M. S., Agbandje, M., Keller, W., Smith, K., Wu, H., Luo, M., Smith, T. J., Rossmann, M. G., Compans, R. W. and Parrish, C. R. (1991) Science *251*, 1456.

Tuaillon, N., André, C., Briand, J. P., Penner, F. and Muller, S. (1992) J. Immunol. *148*, 445.

Tuaillon, N., Muller, S., Pasquali, J. L., Bordigoni, P., Youinou, P. and Van Regenmortel, M. H. V. (1990) Int. Arch. Allergy Appi. Immunol. *91*, 297.

Tuchscherer, G. and Mutter, M. (1995) J. Pept. Sci. *1*, 3.

Tuchscherer, G., Servis, C., Corradin, G. Blum, U., Rivier, J. and Mutter, M. (1992) Prot. Science *1*, 1377.

Tulip, W. R., Varghese, J. N., Webster, R. G., Air, G. M., Laver, W. G. and Colman, P. M. (1989) Cold Spring Harbor Symp. Quant. Biol. *54*, 257.

Tulip, W. R., Varghese, J. N., Laver, W. G., Webster, R. G. and Colman, P. M. (1992a) J. Mol. Biol. *227*, 122.

Tulip, W. R., Varghese, J. N., Webster, R. G., Laver, W. G. and Colman, P. M. (1992b) J. Mol. Biol. *227*, 149.

Tung, A. S. (1983) Meth. Enzymol. *93*, 12.

Tung, A. S., Ju, S.-T., Sato, S and Nisonoff, A. (1976) J. Immunol. *116*, 676.

Turk, J. L. and Parker, D. (1977a) In: Immunochemistry: An Advanced Textbook (Glynn, L. F. and Steward, M. W., eds.). Wiley and Sons, Chichester, p. 445.

Turk, J. L. and Parker, D. (1977b) J. Invest. Dermatol. *68*, 336.

Tzioufas, A. G., Yiannaki, F., Sakarellos-Daitsiotis, M., Routsias, J. G., Sakarellos, C. and Moutsopoulos, H. M. (1997) Clin. Exp. Immunol. *108*, 191.

Underwood, P. A. (1985) J. Immunol. Meth. *85*, 295.

Uster, P. S., Allen T. M., Daniel, B. E., Mendez, C. J., Newman, M. S. and Zhu, G. Z. (1996) FEBS Lett. *386*, 243.

Vaidya, H. C., Dietzler, D. N. and Ladenson, J. H. (1985) Hybridoma *4*, 271.

Vaitukaitis, J., Robbins, J. B., Nieschlag, E. and Ross, G. T. (1971) J. Clin. Endocrinol. *33*, 988.

Vaitukaitis, J. L. (1981) Meth. Enzymol. *73*, 46.

Valerio, R. M., Benstead, M., Bray, A. M., Campbell, R. A. and Maeji, N. J. (1991) Anal. Biochem. *197*, 168.

Valero, M.-L., Camarero, J. A., Adeva, A., Verdaguer, N., Fita, I., Mateu, M. G., Domingo, E., Giralt, E. and Andreu, D. (1995) Biomed. Pept. Prot. Nucl. Acids *1*, 133.

Valmori, D., Pessi, A., Bianchi, F. and Corradin, G. (1992) J. Immunol. 149, 717.

Valmori, D., Sabbatini, A., Lanzavecchia, A., Corradin, G. and Matricardi, P. M. (1994) J. Immunol. *152*, 2921.

Van Binnendijk, R. S., Poelen, M. M. C. M., De Vries, P., Voorma, H. O., Osterhaus, A. D. M. F. and Uytdehaag, F. G. C. M. (1989) J. Immunol. *142*, 2847.

Van Cott, T., Loomis, L. D., Redfield, R. R. and Birx, D. L. (1992) J. Immunol. Meth. *146*, 163.

Van Cott, T. C., Bethke, F. R., Polonis, V. R., Gorny, M. K., Zolla-Pazner, S., Redfield, R. R. and Birx, D. L. (1994) J. Immunol. *153*, 449.

van Denderen, J., Hermans, A., Meeuwsen, T., Troelstra, C., Zegers, N., Boersma, W., Grosveld, G. and van Ewijk, W. (1989) J. Exp. Med. *169*, 87.

Van der Ploeg, J. R., Drijfhout, J. W., Feijlbrief, M., Bloemhoff, W., Welling, G. W. and Welling-Wester, S. (1989) J. Immunol. Methods *124*, 211.

Van der Werf, S. (1994) In: Synthetic Vaccines (Nicholson, B. H., ed.). Blackwell Scientific, p. 494.

Van der Werf, S., Briand, J. P., Plaué, S., Burckard, J., Girard, M. and Van Regenmortel, M. H. V. (1994) Res. Virol. *145*, 349.

Van der Werf, S., Charbit, A., Leclerc, C., Mimic, V., Ronco, J., Girard, M. and Hofnung, M. (1990) Vaccine 8, 269.

Van Eldick, L. J., Fok, K.-F., Erickson, B. W. and Watterson, D. M. (1983) Proc. Natl. Acad. Sci. USA *80*, 6775.

Van Eldick, L. J. and Lukas, T. J. (1986) Meth. Enzymol. *139*, 393.

Van Lierop, M. J., Nilsson, P. R., Wagenaar, J. P., Van Noort, J. M., Campbell, J. D., Glass, E. J., Joosten, I. and Hensen, E. J. (1995) Immunology *84*, 79.

Van Oss, C. J. (1994) In: Immunochemistry (Van Oss, C. J. and Van Regenmortel, M. H. V., eds.). Marcel Dekker, New York, p. 581.

Van Oss, C. J. (1995) Mol. Immunol. *32*, 199.

Van Oss, C. J. and Van Regenmortel, M. H. V. (1994) Immunochemistry, Marcel Dekker, New York, 1069 pp.

Van Regenmortel. M. H. V. (1966) Adv. Virus Res. *12*, 207.

Van Regenmortel, M. H. V. (1982) Serology and Immunochemistry of Plant Viruses, Academic Press, New York 302 pp.

Van Regenmortel, M. H. V. (1984) In: Hybridoma Technology in Agricultural and Veterinary Research (Stern, N. J. and Gamble, H. R., eds.). Rowman and Allanheld, Totowa, New Jersey, p. 43.

Van Regenmortel, M. H. V. (1986) In: The Plant Viruses, The Rod-Shaped Plant Viruses, Vol. 2 (Van Regenmortel, M.H.V. and Fraenkel-Conrat, H., eds.). Plenum Press, New York, p. 79.

Van Regenmortel, M. H. V. (1988) In: Laboratory Diagnosis of Infectious Diseases: Principles and Practice, Vol. 2 (Lennette, E. H., Halonen, P. and Murphy, F. A., eds.). Springer-Verlag, New York, p. 102.

Van Regenmortel, M. H. V. (1989) Immunol. Today *10*, 266.

Van Regenmortel, M. H. V. (1992a) FEMS Microbiol. Lett. *100*, 483.

Van Regenmortel, M. H. V. (1992b) In: Structure of Antigens, Vol. 1 (Van Regenmortel, M. H. V., ed.). CRC Press, Boca Raton, p. 1.

Van Regenmortel, M. H. V. (1992c) Mol. Biol. Reports *16*, 133.

Van Regenmortel, M. H. V. (1995) Biomed. Pept. Prot. & Nucl. Acids *1*, 109.

Van Regenmortel, M. H. V. (1996) Methods *9*, 465.

Van Regenmortel, M. H. V. (1997) In: Vaccines 97, Cold Spring Harbor Laboratory Press, p. 9.

Van Regenmortel, M. H. V. (1998a) J. Immunol. Meth. *216*, 37.

Van Regenmortel, M. H. V. (1998b) J. Dispersion Science and Technol. *19*, 1199.

Van Regenmortel, M. H. V. (1999a) Phil. Trans. Royal Soc. London, series B, *354*, 559.

Van Regenmortel, M. H. V. (1999b) Vaccine *18*, 216.

Van Regenmortel, M. H. V., Altschuh, D. and Klug, A. (1986) In: Synthetic Peptides as Antigens. Ciba Foundation Symposium 119, Wiley, Chichester, p. 76.

Van Regenmortel, M. H. V. and Azimzadeh, A. (1994) In: Immunochemistry (Van Oss, C. J. and Van Regenmortel, M. H. V., eds.). Marcel Dekker, New York, p. 805.

Van Regenmortel, M. H. V., Briand, J.-P., Muller, S. and Plaué, S. (1988) Synthetic Polypeptides as Antigens, Elsevier, New York, 227 pp.

Van Regenmortel. M. H. V. and Burckard, J. (1980) Virology *106*, 327.

Van Regenmortel, M. H. V. and Daney de Marcillac, G. (1988) Immunol. Lett. *17*, 95.

Van Regenmortel, M. H. V. and Muller, S. (1998) Curr. Opin. Biotech. *9*, 377.

Van Regenmortel, M. H. V. and Neurath, A. R. (1985) In: Immunochemistry of Viruses. The Basis for Serodiagnosis and Vaccines. (Van Regenmortel, M. H. V. and Neurath, A. R., eds.). Elsevier, Amsterdam.

Van Regenmortel, M. H. V. and Neurath, A. R. (1990) Immunochemistry of Viruses II. The Basis for Serodiagnosis and Vaccines, Elsevier, Amsterdam, 544 pp.

Van Regenmortel, M. H. V. and Pellequer, J. L. (1994) Peptide Res. *7*, 224.

van Rooijen, N. (1990) In: Bacterial Vaccines, Alan R. Liss Inc., 255 pp.

van Venrooij, W. J. and Maini, R. N. (1993) Manual of Biological Markers of Disease, Kluwer Acad. Publ., Dordrecht, The Netherlands.

van Venrooij, W. J. and Maini, R. N. (1994) Manual of Biological Markers of Disease, Kluwer Acad. Publ., Dordrecht, The Netherlands.

van Venrooij, W. J. and Van Gelder, C. W. G. (1994) Arthritis Rheum. *37*, 608.

Vermuri, S. and Rhodes, C. T. (1995) Pharm. Acta Helvetiae *70*, 95.

Viamontes, G. I., Audhya, T. and Goldstein, G. (1986) J. Immunol. Meth. *94*, 13.

Vidard, L. (1998) In: Immunological Techniques Made Easy (Cochet, O., Teillaud, J. L. and Sautès, C., eds.). John Wiley, Chichester, p. 184.

Vihinen-Ranta, M., Lindfors, E., Heiska, L., Veijalainen, P. and Vuento, M. (1996) Arch. Virol. *141*, 1741.

Vilaseca, L. A., Rose, K., Werlen, R., Meunier, A., Offord, R. F., Nichols, C. L. and Scott, W. L. (1993) Bioconjugate Chem. *4*, 515.

Vix, O., Rees, B., Thierry, J. C. and Altschuh, D. (1993) Proteins *15*, 339.

Volmer-Engert, R., Ehrard, B., Höhne, W., Hellwig, J. and Schneider-Mergener, J. (1994) Lett. Pept. Sci. *1*, 243.

Volpina, O. M., Yarov, A. V., Zhmak, M. N., Kuprianova, M. A., Chepurkin, A. V., Toloknov, A. S. and Ivanov, V. T. (1996) Vaccine *14*, 1375.

Von Heijne, G. (1981) Eur. J. Biochem. *116*, 419.

Vuilleumier, S. and Mutter, M. (1992) In: Structure of Antigens, Vol. 1 (Van Regenmortel, M. H. V., ed.). CRC Press, Boca Raton, p. 43.

Waga, S., Tan, E. M. and Rubin, R. L. (1987) Biochem. J. *244*, 675.

Wahren, M., Ringertz, N. R. and Pettersson, I. (1994) Scand. J. Immunol. *39*, 179.

Wahren, M., Rudén, U., Andersson, B., Ringertz, N. R. and Pettersson, I. (1992) J. Autoimmun. *5*, 319.

Wahren, M., Solomin, L., Pettersson, I. and Isenberg, D. (1996) J. Autoimmun. *9*, 537.

Wahren-Herlenius, M., Muller, S. and Isenberg, D. A. (1999) Immunol. Today, *20*, 234.

Wallukat, G., Wollenberger, A., Morwinski, R. and Pitschner, H. F. (1995) J. Mol. Cell. Cardiol. *27*, 397.

Walter, G. (1986) J. Immunol. Methods *88*, 149.

Walter, G., Hutchinson, M. A., Hunter, T. and Eckhart, W. (1982) Proc. Natl. Acad. Sci. USA *79*, 4025.

Walter, G., Scheidtmann, K. H., Carbone, A., Laudano, A. and Doolittle, R. F. (1980) Proc. Natl. Acad. Sci. USA *77*, 5197.

Wang, R. B., Charoenvit, Y., Corradin, G., Porrozzi, R., Hunter, R. L., Glenn, G., Alving, C. R., Church, P. and Hoffman, S. L. (1995) J. Immunol. *154*, 2784.

Watari, F., Dietzschold, B., Szokan, G. and Heber-Katz, F. (1987) J. Exp. Med. *165*, 459.

Weetall, H. H. and Filbert, A. M. (1974) Meth. Enzymol. *34*, 59.

Weijer, W. J., Welling, G. W. and Welling-Wester, S. (1986) Vaccines *86*, Cold Spring Harbor Laboratory, New York, p. 71.

Welling, G., Van Gorkum, J., Damhof, R. and Drijfhout, J. (1991) J. Chromatogr. *548*, 235.

Welling, G. W. and Fries, H. (1985) FEBS Lett. *182*, 81.

Welling, G. W., Weijer, W. J., Van der Zee, R. and Welling-Wester, S. (1985) FEBS Lett. *188*, 215.

Wellink, J., Jaegle, M. and Goldbach, R. (1987) J. Gen. Virol. *61*, 236.

Wells, J. A. (1991) Meth. Enzymol. *202*, 390.

Westhof, F., Altschuh, D., Moras, D., Bloomer, A. C., Mondragon, A., Klug, A. and Van Regenmortel, M. H. V. (1984) Nature *311*, 123.

Wheat, T. F., Shelton, J. A., Gonzales-Prevatt, V. and Goldberg, F. (1985) Mol. Immunol. *22*, 1195.

White, F. H. (1972) Meth. Enzymol. *25*, 541.

White, T. J., Ibrahimi, I. M. and Wilson, A. C. (1978) Nature *274*, 92.

White, W. I., Cassatt, D. R., Madsen, J., Burke, S. J., Woods, R. M., Wassef, N.M., Alving, C. R. and Koenig, S. (1995) Vaccine *13*, 1111.

Widder, K. J. and Green, R. (1985) Meth. Enzymol. *112*, 207.

Widmann, C., Romero, P., Maryanski, J. L., Corradin, G. and Valmori, D. (1992) J. Immunol. Meth. *155*, 95.

Wien, M. W., Filman, D. J., Stura, F. A., Guillot, S., Delpeyroux, F., Crainic, R. and Hogle, J. M. (1995) Nat. Struct. Biol. *2*, 232.

Wiesmüller, K.-H., Bessler, W. G. and Jung, G. (1992) Int. J. Pept. Prot. Res. *40*, 255.

Wiesmüller, K. H., Jung, G. and Hess, G. (1989) Vaccine *7*, 29.

Wikoff, W. R., Wang, C., Parrish, C. R., Chang, R. H., Strassheim, M. L., Baker, T. S. and Rossmann, M. G. (1994) Structure *2*, 595.

Wiley, D. C., Wilson, I. A. and Skehel, J. J. (1981) Nature *289*, 373.

Wiley, J. A., Richalet-Sécordel, P. and Van Regenmortel, M. H. V. (1984) In: Immunochemistry (Van Oss, C.J. and Van Regenmortel, M. H. V., eds.). Marcel Dekker, New York, p. 455.

Williams, D.C., Sharpe, N. G., Wallace, G. and Latchman, D. S. (1990) J. Autoimmunity 3, 715.

Williams, R. C., Jr., Staud, R., Malone, C. C., Payabyab, J., Byres, L. and Underwood, D. (1994) J. Immunol. 152, 4722.

Williams, W. V., Kieber-Emmons, T., Vonfeldt, J., Greene, M. I. and Weiner, D. B. (1991) J. Biol. Chem. 266, 5182.

Wilson, I. A., Halt, D. H., Tainer, J. A., Getzoff, F. D., Lerner, R. A. and Brenner, S. (1985) Proc. Natl. Acad. Sci. USA 82, 5255.

Wilson, I. A., Niman, H. L., Houghten, R. A., Cherenson, A. R., Connolly, M. L. and Lerner, R. A. (1984) Cell 37, 767.

Wilson, I. A., Skehel, J. J. and Wiley, D. C. (1981) Nature 289, 366.

Wilson, I. A. and Stanfield, R. L. (1993) Curr. Opin. Struct. Biol. 3, 113.

Wilson, I. A. and Stanfield, R. L. (1994) Curr. Opin. Struct. Biol. 4, 857.

Wilson, I. A., Stanfield, R. L., Jewell, D. A., Ghiara, J. B., Fremont, D. H. and Stura, F. A. (1994) Infect. Agent Dis. 3, 155.

Wilson, I. A., Stanfield, R. L., Rini, J. M., Arevalo, J. H., Schulze-Gahmen, U., Fremont, D. H. and Stura, E. A. (1991) In: Catalytic Antibodies (Ciba Foundation Symposium 159), John Wiley, Chichester, p. 13.

Winther, M. D., Allen, G., Bomford, M. H. and Brown, F. (1986) J. Immunol. 136, 1835.

Wold, F. (1972) Meth. Enzymol. 25, Part B, 623.

Wong, G., Arnheim, N., Clark, R., McCabe, P., Innis, M., Aldwin, L., Nitecki, D. and McCormick, F. (1986) Cancer Res. 46, 6029.

Worobec, E. A., Taneja, A. K., Hodges, R. S. and Paranchych, W. (1983) J. Bacteriol. 153, 955.

Wyatt, R., Kwong, P. D., Desjardins, E., Sweet, R. W., Robinson, J., Hendrickson, W. A. and Sodroski, J. G. (1998) Nature 393, 705.

Xiao, Q., Gregoriadis, G. and Ferguson, M. (1989) Biochem. Soc. Trans. 17, 695.

Yasuda, T., Dancey, G. F. and Kinsky, S. C. (1977) Proc. Natl. Acad. Sci. USA 74, 1234.

Yiannaki, F. F., Tzioufas, G., Bachmann, M., Hantoumi, J., Tsikaris, V., Sakarellos-Daitsiotis, M., Sakarellos, C. and Moutsopoulos,H. M. (1998) Clin. Exp. Immunol. 112, 152.

Youinou, P., Semana, G., Muller, S., Piette, J. C., Guillevin, L., Jouquan, J., Salmon, D., Salmon, J., Genetet, B. and Bach, J. F. (1997) Human Immunol. 52, 12.

Young, C. R. and Atassi, M. Z. (1982) Immunol. Commun. 11, 9.

Young, C. R. and Atassi, M. Z. (1985) Immun. Invest. 14, 1.

Young, C. R., Schmitz, H. E. and Atassi, M. Z. (1983) Mol. Immunol. *20*, 567.

Young, J. D., Benjamini, E., Shimizu, VI. and Leung, C. Y. (1966) Biochemistry *5*, 1481.

Young, J. D., Benjamini, B., Stewart, J. M. and Leung, C. Y. (1967) Biochemistry *6*, 1455.

Young, J. D. and Leung, C. Y. (1970) Biochemistry *9*, 2755.

Young, R. A. and Davis, R. W. (1983b) Science *22*, 778.

Young, R. A. and Davis, R. W. (1983a) Proc. Natl. Acad. Sci. USA *80*, 1194.

Zalipsky, S., Puntambekar, B., Boulikas, P., Engbers, C. M. and Woodle, M. C. (1995) Bioconjugate Chem. *6*, 705.

Zavala, F., Masuda, A., Graves, P. M., Nussenzweig, V. and Nussenzweig, R. (1985) J. Immunol. *135*, 2790.

Zeder-Lutz, G., Altschuh, D., Denery-Papini, S., Briand, J.-P., Tribbick, G. and Van Regenmortel, M. H. V. (1993a) J. Mol. Recogn. *6*, 71.

Zeder-Lutz, G., Altschuh, D., Geysen, M., Trifilieff, F., Sommermeyer, G. and Van Regenmortel, M. H. V. (1993b) Mol. Immunol. *30*, 145.

Zeder-Lutz, G., Wenger, R., Van Regenmortel, M. H. V. and Altschuh, D. (1993c) FEBS Lett. *326*, 153.

Zegers, N. D. and Boersma, W. J. A. (1995:) In: Immunological Recognition of Peptides in Medicine and Biology (Zegers, N. D., Boersma, W. J. A. and Claassen, F., eds.). CRC Press, Boca Raton, p. 105.

Zegers, N. D., Gerritse, K., Deen, C., Boersma, W. J. A. and Claassen, F. (1990) J. Immunol. Meth. *130*, 195.

Zegers, N. D., Van Holten, C., Claassen, E. and Boersma, W. J. A. (1993) Eur. J. Immunol. *23*, 630.

Zeppezauer, M., Hoffmann, R., Schönberger, A., Rawer, S., Rapp, W. and Bayer, F. (1993:) Z. Naturforsch. *48b*, 1801.

Zhang, J. and Raus, J. (1995) In: T Cell Vaccination and Autoimmune Disease (Zhang, J. and Ratis, J., eds.). Springer-Verlag, Heidelberg, p. 135.

Zhang, L. and Tam, J. P. (1996) Anal. Biochem. *233*, 87.

Ziegler, V., Laquel, P., Guilley, H., Richards, K. and Jonard, G. (1985) Gene *36*, 271.

Zimmerman, J M., Eliezer, N. and Simha, R. J. (1968) Theor. Biol. *21*, 170.

Zimmermann, D. and Van Regenmortel, M. H. V. (1989) Arch. Virol. *106*, 15.

Zollinger, W. D., Brandt, B., Moran, F. B. and Ray, J. (1986) J. Microbiol. *52*, 225.

Zvi, A., Kustanovich, I., Feigelson, D., Levy, R., Eisenstein, M., Matsushita, S., Richalet-Secordel, P., Van Regenmortel, M. H. V. and Anglister, J. (1995) Eur. J. Biochem. *229*, 178.

Zwick, M. B., Shen, J. and Scott, J. K. (1998) Curr. Opinion Biotech. *9*, 427.

Subject Index

375

Printed and bound by CPI Group (UK) Ltd, Croydon, CR0 4YY

08/10/2024

01042186-0001